LEECHES TO LASERS

To Anne, variously wife, daughter-in-law, sister-in-law, mother, and grandmother to, and much loved by, her family which is pictured within.

leeches to lasers

Sketches of a Medical Family

Richard Moore

F R C G P

Morrigan

First published 2002 by

Morrigan
Killala, County Mayo,
Ireland

© 2002 Richard Moore

ISBN 0 907677 33 9

Editorial Services by Gillian Brennan
Cover and book design by Identikit
Typeset by Carole Lynch
Printed by Betaprint

A catalogue record for this book is available
from the British Library.

contents

acknowledgements

Although I had long envisaged the possibility of sketching the outline of my family's record in medical practice, without generous help and support it would not have been written. John Horder and Irvine Loudon encouraged me to begin the task, and when doubts assailed me, they and David Haslam kindly commented on early drafts with suggestions for improvement, and encouraged me to persist.

Many people helped me with access to historical documents and other resources, and with ideas. In Dublin the Mercer Library was a rich source of Irish material, and I am grateful to the Librarian, Beatrice Doran, and the Archivist, Mary O'Doherty, and their ever-helpful staff. The interest shown by Professor J. B. Lyons fired my enthusiasm, as did the advice of John Fleetwood, and Malachy Powell kindly allowed me access to the records of the Apothecaries' Hall of Dublin. Robert Mills, Librarian of the Royal College of Physicians of Ireland kindly supplied both published material and extracts from the minutes of the College. Mary Reynolds of Longford County Library, and Luke Baxter and colleagues in the Longford Historical Society, inspired an image of past times in Ballymahon. I am grateful to Margaret Lennon Wynne for details of the connections between the Lennons and Moores.

In England, Marshall Barr let me roam in the treasure house of the Old Library of the Reading Pathological Society for documents and illustrations. The Wellcome History of Medicine Library supplied other illustrations, and the Shropshire County Library provided the picture of Butcher Row, where my own surgery once was. Many others have been kind and supportive with ideas, material and encouragement, especially the family members who contributed their thoughts to the final chapter. When I believed the task was nearly complete, Gillian Brennan's editorial wisdom guided me in pruning and re-modelling the text into a more coherent form.

I am grateful to all these people, and if there are others whom I have failed to mention the omission is due to my fallibility, not their lack of contribution. Without such support the task would have been much more daunting, and I thank them all.

Richard Moore
May 2002

An EPIGRAM,

shewing who are Docters of
Physick, and who not.

Doctors or *Teachers* they of *Physick* are
(Whether by Pen they do it, or in Chair
With lively Voyce) that teach the way to know
Mans Nature, *Health,* and *Sickness;* and do show
Diseases, *Cause,* and *Cure.* But they who spend
Their Life in *Visits,* and whose Labors end
In taking *Fees,* and giving *Paper-scrowls*
FACTORS of *Physick* are; and none but *Owls*
Do count such *Doctors,* that *no Latin* know,
From whence that *Name* did to our Language flow.

W. R. *Doctor* and *Factor*
    Of Physick.

From The Practice of Physick, by Lazarus Riverius
(Physician to the King of France),
translated by Nicholas Culpeper, Abdiah Cole and
William Rowland, and printed in London by
Peter and Edward Cole in 1661.

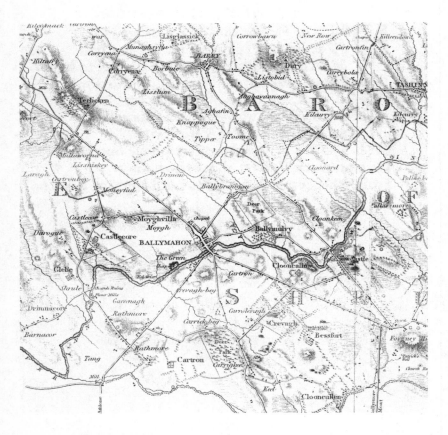

The town of Ballymahon, and neighbouring parish of Shruel, or Shrule, County Longford in Ireland, Circa 1813. Edgeworth 1813.

CHAPTER ONE

The Family

The omens were not good for William Moore, when in 1740 he decided to set up business as apothecary in Ballymahon. He would sell medicines, wigs, and perfumes to those who came to his shop, and be the medical attendant of the sick. The middle years of the eighteenth century in the midlands of Ireland were unusually cold, with failing crops and frequent famine[1], but this ill wind blew some good to William, at least, for his business prospered well enough to sustain him, his wife, and their four children. The inheritance he passed on through his oldest son has long endured, although his own prosperity was cut short when he met an untimely death. In the two hundred and sixty years since he opened his shop, no fewer than twenty-two of his descendants have joined the medical profession in one way or another.

Each generation must choose the way it earns its keep, which is often by continuing an inheritance or family business, or being drawn into a profession by the kind of magnetism that attracts daughters and sons to follow their parents. In medicine it is not unusual for there to be doctors in two, three or even four successive generations, and several in the same one. Notable among these are the five generations of the Monro family in the eighteenth and nineteenth centuries who held the office of Physician to the Bethlem Hospital in London, among them the celebrated and eclectic Dr Thomas Monro whose famous 'Academy' nurtured Turner, Girtin and many other famous English artists [2]. The Maurice family have worked in the same practice in Marlborough in Wiltshire for six generations[3]. Dr Neil Arnott, famous for his contribution to early awareness of Public Health issues in London, as well as for being the guardian of the captive Napoleon Bonaparte's health, was one of seven generations whose latest member is in general practice in England today[4]. The Bebb-Williams family from Wales has seventeen members in four generations who all qualified at The Royal London Hospital[5]. Spreading so many medical members over several generations might seem easy compared with the achievements of Monsieur Asclar, a remarkably fecund nineteenth century Frenchman. His seventeen sons were doctors, and his five daughters became *sages femmes*, the contemporary French term for midwives.[6]

The achievements of these people are admirable, yet the Moore family which is sketched in this book, can claim to go a little further. Since William's time eight successive generations in a direct line from father to son and now to daughter have practised medicine as apothecary, physician, naval medical officer, general practitioner, and gynaecologist. Scions of the family also entered the profession, making twenty-two doctors in all so far. They have seen the rise and fall of new ideas, witnessed success, conflict and failure, and have participated in the extraordinary progress from therapeutic impotence to a state where it seems as though there is a cure for all ills. In their time medicine has evolved from a constant struggle of hope over expectation into a science whose predictable results would have counted as miracles in years gone by. In the Moore family what began as the apothecary's trade has become a medical tradition. If ancestors can thus influence their descendants, do family traditions become embedded in genes? How much of what we do in life do we choose for ourselves, and how much depends on what we inherit? If we inherit character, as we surely do, do we also inherit an inclination to a particular kind of occupation? If so this tendency is strong in the Moore family.

———

William's grandfather Christopher was a farmer in Tashinny, near Ballymahon in County Longford, who thought the rent of his land at one shilling and sixpence an acre was too high, and gave it up; and his father was Daniel Moore of Kilmanogue, Co Westmeath, an Excise Officer.

Why William chose to be an apothecary rather than follow his father into the Customs and Excise is unknown, but whatever the reason it was a turning point for his descendants. Ballymahon was a self-sufficient village when William began his business there, an economic and social microcosm remote from developments elsewhere in Britain and Europe which we now look back on as the Enlightenment. In Ireland, self-governing but subject to the London Parliament, Jonathan Swift had recently published *Gulliver's Travels*, and was achieving fame as Dean of St Patrick's Cathedral. In London the Hanoverian George II ruled the United Kingdom, and in Europe culture and science were thriving in the peace that followed the War of Spanish Succession, Bach and Handel were middle aged, Gainsborough a mere boy and Turner unborn. If anyone thought of America it was as 'The British Colonies'. The Industrial Revolution, soon to change the world for ever, was just beginning.

Medical practice was primitive, although some great minds were beginning to reject the thousand year-old dogmas of Galen and his classical predecessors. The new Medical School in Edinburgh, founded in 1726, had introduced bedside clinical teaching to Britain, but elsewhere there was little organised teaching, and there were few hospitals. Surgeons were still associated more with barbers than physicians, and surgery not yet formed into a coherent discipline. Physicians, that is Doctors of Medicine from the ancient universities, practised only among those who could pay their fees. Others patronised apothecaries who offered medicines and applications for sale, or turned to priests and old wives for healing. The field was open to quacks and charlatans in a gullible society in which injury, malnutrition and epidemic disease were common. In this open market the apothecaries, in contrast to the quacks, were one strand of a developing system of medical care who studied medical remedies and chemistry, and belonged to organisations with published rules of conduct. It would be more than a hundred years after William Moore's time before these strands of the medical profession were united by the creation of the General Medical Council, and a common education for all doctors was made compulsory.

When William opened his apothecary's shop in Ballymahon, medical science was virtually non-existent. Classification of disease and diagnosis was elementary, and of the numerous and complex treatments very few were effective. Cinchona, derived from the bark of a Peruvian tree, was useful for fever; colchicine from the autumn crocus worked quite well against gout; and pain could be relieved with opium from the seeds of oriental poppies. These medicines and their derivatives have survived to this day, but in William's time Withering had not yet described the use of digitalis nor had Lind done his classic experiment to find a cure for scurvy, that killer of seamen. Inoculation against smallpox had been practised since the early eighteenth century, using fluid from the blisters of smallpox cases, but it was a dangerous procedure until Jenner made it safe in 1796 by using cowpox matter instead. Surgical operations were primitive, though to their credit surgeons saved the lives of many soldiers and sailors wounded in battle. Illness was to be feared, for neither were its causes and courses understood nor were there the means to help, yet people could not and would not give up in the face of disease.

That was the setting in which the first member of the Moore family to practise medicine began work. In the subsequent 260 years each generation of his descendants has witnessed, and often contributed, to the development of ideas, organisations and methods which have brought the science and art of medicine to their present state. Not all the bright ideas were successful, or even, in our latter-day view, sensible. Some have been revolutionary and extraordinarily beneficial; others have been transient, useless, and sometimes disastrous.

William was born in 1721. Of his education and early life nothing is known, nor how he came to be interested in the apothecary's trade or what his training for it was. Qualification was not then required in the sense of the passing of an examination, except to practise in Dublin and London where the Colleges of Physicians had the right to grant licences. He probably served an apprenticeship with a Master apothecary, possibly in Kilmanogue or Ballymahon. While not aspiring to the social or professional status of a physician, he undoubtedly mixed with the gentry of the county, and would have seen nothing incongruous in simultaneously being a shopkeeper, a medical man and a gentleman. Among the gentry he met the Lennon family who were landowners, and in about 1745 married one of them. This marriage was short-lived because the young Mrs Moore's life was prematurely ended, perhaps by the all-too-common death in childbirth for no children survived. William was not a widower for long. He married another member of the Lennon family, Martha, second daughter of Charles ('Big Charley') Lennon who lived at Walshstown in the neighbouring County Westmeath. They had four children; Daniel, born in 1750 and destined to follow his father into the apothecary's trade, and John, Judith and young Martha. All was well while the children were young, but in 1758 William died at the age of thirty-seven. Of Martha Moore née Lennon we know nothing further, and little more of the fate of the children except that family came to the rescue for Daniel at least, who was apprenticed to his uncle John Clarke, an apothecary with a business in Capel Street, Dublin.

Daniel was only eight years old when his father died. When he was twelve or thirteen he was apprenticed to his uncle. Apprenticeship at that time began early, and by the age of nineteen Daniel had completed his time both as an apothecary and a surgeon, and was in business with John Clarke. Until the late eighteenth century when the Colleges of Surgeons were founded the only training for surgery was through apprenticeship, and the profession was still considered to be a somewhat menial one. Opportunities for a young surgeon were limited and probably less attractive than that of apothecary. So, after a few years assisting his uncle, and also working in another established business, Daniel set up on his own in 1780 in premises at No 10 Grafton Street. Ten years later he moved to a new shop and home at No 8 South Anne Street. Dublin was growing fast, a capital city and the seat of government, and with the rising prosperity of its merchant and professional citizens the demand for medical services was growing. But there was a darker side to its prosperity in the thousands of people who had migrated to towns and cities from the impoverished countryside among whom there were many who were destitute. Their plight deteriorated as the city declined in fortune when many of the richer people left Ireland for England after the Act of Union in 1801.

Daniel thrived in this expanding city, and was one of the leaders of a movement to improve the status and competence of the apothecary through the foundation of the Dublin Apothecaries' Hall. His portrait was commissioned by the Hall when he was Governor in 1806, and in his mid-fifties. It shows a dignified, seemingly quite small man, with a firm mouth and an aquiline nose, and cheeks that are well coloured but not rubicund. His grey-green eyes look studiously at some distant object, but ready to turn his attention to the viewer. A long forehead is edged by receding hair, white and without a periwig, its powder falling on the collar of his long, brass-buttoned and double-breasted tail coat. These features must have been well portrayed by the unknown artist, for they are replicated in the photographic portraits of at least four subsequent generations, and seem to reappear daily as the author, his great-great-great grandson, sees himself in the mirror. Though determination and purpose seem to be among Daniel's characteristics, there are signs of a gentle, warm and kindly nature, too

Daniel married Hannah, daughter of John Semple of Abbey Street, Dublin. They had ten children, but, as was so common at that time, four died before the age of three, and of those who survived to adulthood four more were dead by the age of forty-two. John William, born in 1782, was the oldest survivor, and in due course joined his father in the apothecary's business in South Anne Street. His brother William, eight years younger, went further by graduating MD, and moved to London to work as a physician at the Westminster Dispensary. Where he obtained his degree, and whether he did so by examination or purchase is unclear. In 1815 William married Eleanor Jane Ross, daughter of John Ross of Balkail, Wigtonshire, which suggests he may have spent time in Scotland, perhaps studying there for his degree and meeting his bride while he did so. Alas, neither of these medical sons lived long. William died in 1817 aged twenty-seven having married only two years before, and leaving a widow and two young children. John died seven years later. Perhaps they were casualties of exposure to highly infectious diseases in the pursuit of their profession. The longest lived of Daniel's children was Charles, born in 1787, who died at the age of 71. He was not a doctor, and nothing is known of his personal life, nor of the subsequent lives of his sisters. After the death of his first wife Hannah, Daniel married Alicia, another member of the Lennon family of Westmeath and the widow of a Captain Poitier.

John William left no records or writings, and there is no portrait that can be positively identified as his. He must have served his apprenticeship, probably with his father in the family business, for he was a member of the Apothecaries' Hall, and like his father was elected its Governor in 1811. Although his father's position in the Hall may have been of help in establishing his place there, to be elected to the office of Governor at the age of twenty-nine suggests that he had qualities which justified that position at such a young age. His son William Daniel recorded that he was a friend of both John Wollaston and Sir Humphrey Davy, who is known to have visited his laboratory in South Anne Street when in Dublin for the British Association meeting there. The study of chemistry was, of course, a particular interest of his colleagues in the Apothecaries' Hall.

John married Mary, daughter of John Stewart of Stormanstown, but she died childless in 1810. He later married Marianne, daughter of Nathaniel Low, Chief Cashier of the Bank of Ireland, with whom he had six children. They were William Daniel (b1813), Robert (b1816) and Charles (b1820) who all graduated in medicine, Hannah and Margaret, and another son who died at the age of two years. John's early death in 1824 was a severe blow to the security of the family. Daniel was then aged 74, and his grandson William Daniel was too young to take on any of the business, though before long he began learning the trade as apprentice. There were also the other four surviving children ranging from Robert at eight to Margaret at two years of age. Despite the difficulties, both business and family survived. Daniel supported them until his three grandsons graduated in medicine, and he lived to see the birth of his first great grandson, another John.

The oldest grandson William Daniel was articled to his grandfather soon after his 13th birthday in May 1826, and was later apprenticed in surgery to Dr Charles Johnson, a surgeon and Professor of Midwifery at the Royal College of Surgeons in Ireland[7]. He passed the final examination of the Apothecaries' Hall in 1833, and although he then started studying for an Arts degree at Trinity College, he interrupted his studies to take his medical education further by going to Edinburgh and becoming, in 1834, a Licentiate of the Royal College of Surgeons there. He returned to Trinity in 1840 and graduated as both a bachelor of Arts and of Medicine.

William Daniel ran the business in South Anne Street and lived there until 1868. During those years the dual functions of the apothecary as medical practitioner and pharmacist were beginning to diverge. He chose the former, and, by giving up the shop and home in South Anne Street in favour of a house in Fitzwilliam Square, he established himself firmly in the medical sphere. As a general practitioner he was interested in the advances of science and the implications which new discoveries had for medicine, but coming from a family with pharmaceutical interests he also remained an enthusiastic chemist. Through his study of Arts he had also developed a flair for languages, having a command of German, Dutch and Norwegian amongst others, as well as Latin then essential for entry to the profession of medicine and for membership of the Apothecaries' Hall. He often translated articles published in European journals for reproduction in the Dublin Quarterly Journal of Medical Science, and translated several books. He was said to have been 'a principal channel by which European literature was brought to Britain'. He published several papers describing his own experiments and made a number of original observations. He was thoughtful and perceptive, but like most writing of the period, his style is somewhat discursive. Nevertheless he was a thinker who was not afraid to challenge other men's assumptions.

In education he was active both as a student, proceeding to MD Dublin in 1860, and as an Examiner in Arts at the Apothecaries' Hall and in Materia Medica and Medical Jurisprudence at Queen's University. He was admitted MD *ad eundem* of both Oxford and Cambridge Universities. When the Medical Bill of 1858 which created the General Medical Council was being debated he argued strongly in favour of it through his role as the President of the Association of General Practitioners in Ireland. Despite his preference for medicine he never lost his concern for pharmacy. Amongst his contributions to that profession he was adviser to the Branch Medical Council (Ireland) on the progress of pharmacy, and he wrote a History of Pharmacy in Ireland.

Two portraits of William Daniel, an oil painting and a photograph, show him as middle height, wearing a frock coat and generous bow tie under a winged collar, as the fashion of the day required. His high forehead and receding hair are like his grandfather Daniel's, offset by large sideburns. His nose is long, in the photograph not so aquiline as Daniel's though in the oil painting the artist has emphasised this feature, and the mouth, too, is wider and softer. A wistful smile plays across his lips. One can imagine him being persuasive and determined, yet kind and interested in anyone under his care.

William Daniel's younger brother Robert studied at the Royal College of Surgeons in Ireland, becoming a member and later a Fellow.

He soon became interested in dentistry, and was involved in founding the Dublin Dental Hospital. Robert married late in life, so his son George was not born until 1870. He, too, graduated at the RCSI and followed a career in dental surgery, and also married late. His son Ian, who was born in 1920, later studied medicine at Trinity College Dublin, qualified in 1944, and after some hospital experience in England became Chief Medical Officer at the Guiness's brewery in Dublin. He is still active in medicine today though retired from the brewery. George's daughter Diana married a surgeon, Brandon Stephens, and their son Richard is now on the staff of the St James's Hospital in Dublin, specialising in endoscopic surgery.

The third medical member of William Daniel's generation was the youngest brother Charles (b1820) who also graduated at both the Apothecaries' Hall and the RCSI, where he later became a Fellow. His career began as a medical officer with Peninsular and Oriental Steam Packet Company, which took him on voyages to the Mediterranean and Middle Eastern countries. He was shocked by the crowded and insanitary conditions in towns like Suez, where he first encountered cholera. Though the cause of cholera was still unknown he was convinced the epidemics then common in the region were connected with the absence of proper drainage and the lack of clean water. After his return to Ireland he described an outbreak of cholera in a village near Dublin, and was ashamed that the sanitary conditions there were as bad as, or even worse than those he had seen in Egypt, a country which he considered to be much more primitive. Motivated by these experiences, he became a vigorous campaigner for improvements in the sanitation of the rapidly growing Irish towns. For a short time he was Medical Officer at Middletown Dispensary in Ulster, then returned to Dublin as Physician to the Cork St Fever Hospital, and finally became a general practitioner and medical officer of health to the South Dublin Union. He was a Governor of the Apothecaries' Hall in 1888 and 1889, and later repre-sented the Hall on the General Medical Council.

The brothers William Daniel, Robert and Charles lived in a period of extraordinary developments in medicine. In their youth the art of diagnosis was little understood, and even if a disease could be clearly iden-tified, treatment of it was at best unpredictable and at worst poisonous.

During their lifetime, despite these imperfections, the foundations of modern medicine were being laid. Among the many discoveries were anaesthesia and antisepsis which permitted safe surgery, the microscope which opened up the sciences of pathology and bacteriology, and the stethoscope which allowed increased understanding of heart and chest diseases. The youngest of the three brothers, Charles, lived into the twentieth century. During their lifetimes medical science moved from a state of ignorance, at least as far as physiology and biochemistry were concerned though anatomy was already well understood, to the beginnings of a well-informed discipline. The causes of many diseases were explained by the discovery of bacteria, anaesthesia and antisepsis made surgery feasible and bearable, and investigation by the stethoscope and other instruments, even X-rays, became everyday practicalities.

Returning to William Daniel's family, the next generation was to see even greater progress in medicine as the causes of disease became better understood, and methods were found to prevent and cure it. This generation's first member was another John, born in 1845, the oldest of William Daniel's two sons and six daughters, and the only one to follow the family tradition of medicine. His brother, another Charles, was ordained and became Vicar of Louth in County Meath, and of the girls three were married and three remained single; a career in medicine, or indeed anything, was not then thought to be a sensible way to use their talents and energies. When the family moved to 40 Fitzwilliam Square William Daniel was one of the first doctors to live there, leading a trend in which Fitzwilliam Square became a preferred residence for many well-respected doctors, second only to its near neighbour, Merrion Square[8]. John took over the lease when his father died, and lived there for the next 65 years.

Although his forebears had been in medical practice by now for four generations, the second John's original intention may not have been a career in medicine, for his studies at Trinity College Dublin were in classics. He was elected Classics Scholar in 1865, retaining an interest in Latin and Greek languages and literature throughout his life, and it was only after graduation in the Arts that he read medicine and surgery, which was quite usual at the time. He graduated MB in 1869, proceeded MD in 1871 and in 1873 was elected Fellow of the King's and Queen's (later the

Royal) College of Physicians of Ireland. His clinical studies were made at the Meath Hospital under William Stokes, one of the great teachers of the Dublin medical schools, whose name is remembered in 'Stokes Adams attacks' and 'Cheyne Stokes breathing'. After graduation he became his house physician. When Stokes retired in 1875, John Moore was chosen to succeed him, and remained on the staff of the Meath Hospital until 1933[9]. Between them William Stokes and John Moore held that position for 107 years[10]. His appointment was not without controversy, however. The *Medical Press and Circular* protested that it "was shadowed by the fact of its being an uncontested 'walkover'", and "must be unqualifiedly condemned as constituting a bad precedent"[11]. His subsequent career showed that in fact the choice had been a wise one, however it had been made. Despite the protestation of the *Medical Press* the system of appointment by patronage continued, and was still in use at the Meath more than 80 years later, when a more open and competitive method was introduced[12].

As well as the medical care of individual patients, which had been the main concern of most doctors until then, Stokes and his young colleague shared an interest in the effect of the dreadful living conditions and defective sanitation on the health of the populations of the crowded cities and towns like Dublin. The first Public Health Act in the United Kingdom had been passed in 1848, applying only in England and Wales[13], and the discipline of public health, then called 'political' or 'State' medicine, was gaining recognition at that time. Largely at Stokes's suggestion Dublin University instituted a Diploma in State Medicine, (later renamed the Diploma in Public Health), and John was persuaded to sit the examination along with three young colleagues. They were all successful and thus became the first four doctors to hold a diploma in that field[14].

As well as being on the staff of the Meath Hospital, he was Physician to the Cork Street Fever Hospital, which at that time was an important resource in meeting the huge demand created by the epidemics of infectious disease that ravaged the overcrowded citizens of Dublin. Fevers remained a serious problem and were an important interest throughout his career. Although busy enough with these appointments and his developing private practice, he also contributed papers to the medical press, particularly the Dublin Journal of Medical Science. After a short time as assistant to its editor, Sir William Wilde, he became editor

himself in 1874, continuing in that post for forty seven years and publishing ninety-four volumes.

John rapidly rose to prominence in Dublin. He was elected President
of the Royal College of Physicians of Ireland (RCPI) in 1894, and held
the office of Professor of Medicine in the Royal College of Surgeons of
Ireland from 1889 to 1916. He was a member of several important
committees, including the representative of the RCPI on the Irish Branch
of the General Medical Council, and from 1905 on the main Council in
London. He was chairman of its Public Health Committee from 1910
until 1932, when, having reached the age of eighty-eight, he felt it
necessary to resign from the GMC which he had served for 37 years. In
announcing his retirement the then President of the Council, Sir Norman
Walker, paid him this compliment:

> *Sir John Moore replaced Sir Donald Macalister as 'Father of the Council',*
> *and occupied a position on the Council all his own. His unfailing old-world*
> *courtesy endeared him to us all'.*

In fact, his predecessor Sir Donald had served even longer as 'father of the
GMC', for forty-four years from 1887-1931 including seventeen as
President[15].

Several photographs of John exist, mostly taken in later life. He
had a full beard as was fashionable at the time, which, with the familial
recession of the hair and long nose and cheek-bones, gave him a dignified and authoritative appearance. One famous photograph, familiar to
older doctors in Dublin today, shows him approaching the steps of the
main entrance of the Meath Hospital from the rain-moistened courtyard.
He appears an elderly, stooped and rather shrunken man, carrying an
umbrella, elf-like with his long white beard, and perhaps a little breath-
less from his walk to the hospital. Other, younger pictures are more
vigorous, suggesting a tall and handsome man and, like his father's and
great-grandfather's portraits, they show a kind but determined character.
The author's recollection of him is one of a *very* old man, for ninety
seemed impossibly ancient to a six year old. His smiling kindly face was
framed by a silvery beard, above which his eyes were bright and pene-
trating. As research for this book has revealed more of my grandfather's

true nature, and as old age creeps up on me too, the memory of this aus-
tere enigma has mellowed into one of deep and reverent affection. My
older brother, also called John, remembers that when he was discovered
ripping leaves off a tree, he was reprimanded and made to understand that
the tree would suffer damage from such needless injury. The advice was
wise and kindly given. One of my own memories of him is of a picnic in
the Wicklow Mountains, and an attempt to retrieve a half-penny lost on
the summit of the Sugarloaf. As the party climbed towards the peak,
among the scattered white boulders that give the mountain its name, my
ninety year-old grandfather and I were side-by-side on a narrow path
between the rocks that led to the last few yards of ascent. I stepped aside,
or tried an easier route, allowing the revered old man reach the summit
first, an event which was later used to bear testimony to the superiority
of his aged vigour over my youthful fatigue. Certainly, from John's own
writings and the descriptions of him by others, his kindness was remarkable, as was the esteem in which he was held by those who knew him,
which was acknowledged by his knighthood in 1900.

After his father's death early in 1871, the newly qualified John
became head of the family at the age of 26, and his brother and six sisters
lived in the house at Fitzwilliam Square. Like his great-grandfather
Daniel, John therefore had to provide for the young family until in the
fullness of time they grew up and moved away. One of the sisters,
Catherine, married Henry Le Fanu of the Madras Civil Service, and two
of their sons, Hugh (b1874) and Cecil (b1877), emulating their uncle
John rather than their father in choice of profession, qualified at
Aberdeen. They joined the West African Medical Service, spending most
of their working lives in the Gold Coast. Cecil was the first to go there
in 1903, followed by his older brother Hugh in 1907. On retirement
Cecil returned to England to be Consulting Physician to the Colonial
Office at Liverpool in the School of Tropical Medicine. After his death
in 1936, he was succeeded at Liverpool by his brother, who remained a
Lecturer in the School throughout the second World War[16]. Though
Cecil's son Richard chose a non-medical career in the British Council,
his grandson James qualified at Cambridge and is now a general practitioner in the south of England, and a writer and commentator on
medical affairs.

In 1875 John was married too. His bride was Ellie, daughter of Dr John Ridley of Moore Hall. Ellie died soon after childbirth in 1878, quite possibly of puerperal fever brought home by her husband from his work in the fever hospital. There were two daughters from this marriage, and four grandchildren, of whom the two boys died young and for the girls medicine was still not generally accepted as a suitable career. He married again, this time to Louisa, daughter of Edmund Armstrong, barrister-at-law, of nearby Leeson Street. They had three sons, William, Arthur, and Maurice, and a daughter Nora. All thrived and were a happy and successful family until the shadow of war fell across Europe.

When the First World War began all three sons joined the Services; William, a librarian, and Arthur, a barrister like his maternal grandfather, joined the 4th Battalion, The London Regiment. Arthur was awarded the Military Cross in 1915 for leading his platoon in a heroic stand against a German counter-attack following the British assault on Thiepval in the battle at Neuve Chappelle. He was promoted to command the Battalion's 'A' Company, and on 1st July 1916 led his men into action again in the first assault of the Battle of the Somme. 'A' Company reached a point six yards short of the enemy wire, with the result that from this courageous but futile attack only 18 men returned. Among those who fell was their captain, Arthur Moore. Already twice wounded, he was last seen 'still going ahead, revolver in hand'[17]. William's army service was just as tragic, for wounded and shell-shocked, he died soon after the end of the war.

The loss of his sons was a deep sorrow to John Moore. His friendship with William Osler, the great physician and teacher with whom he had a common interest in medical education, grew closer through the shared grief of losing sons in the fighting, like so many parents of their generation. Osler wrote

> *I am grieved to hear you have lost the boy. How terribly the profession has suffered in this war! Our boy is in the thick of it in France in the R.F.A.*
> *Ever yours, Wm. Osler*

John recalled how the correspondence continued. Letters from Osler said '"Dear Moore", then "My dear Moore", and then at last, under the date September 14th 1917, came this touching note:

Thanks, dear Moore, for your kind message of sympathy in our sorrow. You
know how hard it is — but one must bear these blows bravely.
             Sincerely yours, Wm.Osler"[18]

By some gift of Providence it was Maurice, born in 1886, the youngest of
the three sons and the one who chose to be a doctor, who survived the
massacre of the War to end Wars. Having graduated MB, BChir, BAO at
Trinity College in 1909, he joined his father at the Meath Hospital as
house physician, and while there took his MD. He spent some time in
practice in Enniskillen, and was contemplating a career in general practice
when he volunteered for the Navy. He was appointed 'Surgeon in His
Majesty's Fleet' on November 14th 1914, and by his commission he was

... authorised and required from time to time to repair on board and dis-
charge the duty of Surgeon in any Ship or Vessel to which [he] may here-
after be duly appointed......

At first he was appointed to the Royal Marine Barracks in Plymouth,
until in September 1916 he joined HMS Hussar, a small ship patrolling
the Mediterranean. His diary records his journey to Malta, travelling by
train from London, via a cross-channel ferry to Calais. The train to Paris
took him within a few miles of the front line where the Battle of the
Somme was raging, and in which his brother had been killed, but he
makes no mention of it. On reaching Paris he stayed to enjoy a sight-
seeing tour of the city. Then, via Rome and Taranto, he reached Malta, to
find his ship was not there. After a seemingly relaxed and sociable time in
Valetta while awaiting her arrival, Hussar returned, he joined her and
they sailed to patrol the Aegean Sea. The only hints in his diary that this
was anything other than a peaceful summertime exploration of the Eastern
Mediterranean are one mention of 'a hostile aircraft' and another of a sight
of Gallipoli, the scene of ignominious Allied defeat the previous year.

    After the war Maurice remained in the Navy, because opportunities
for practice in his native Ireland were few. The Admiralty encouraged
their medical officers to study for postgraduate qualifications, amongst
them the Diploma in Public Health (DPH). By chance, this was the subject of correspondence between the Medical Director General of the

Navy and the GMC, whose Public Health Committee was chaired by none other than John Moore. The Navy ran a course for Medical Officers at the Royal Naval Medical School, Greenwich, but as it was shorter than the six months required by rules of the examination, the GMC said it was inadequate and would not recognise it for the diploma. The Admiralty insisted that there were too few medical officers to allow longer periods of study unless they took the course 'at their own expense', the logic of which is puzzling as they would still be unavailable for duty. Eventually the GMC approved the Greenwich course if taken in conjunction with other studies elsewhere[19], so Maurice availed himself of this provision to spend nine months at Corpus Christi College, Cambridge, obtaining his diploma on 3d May 1922. The Certificate declares in charmingly archaic phrasing

> **KNOW ALL MEN** *by these presents that*
> *Maurice Sydney Moore*
> *Has been duly examined by the Examiners in that behalf appointed by the CHANCELLOR MASTERS and SCHOLARS of* **THE UNIVERSITY OF CAMBRIDGE** *and having approved himself to KNOWLEDGE and SKILL in SANITARY SCIENCE to wit the examiners by his CHEMISTRY AND PHYSICS ..... [and] is CERTIFIED to be well qualified ... to fulfil the Duties of* **MEDICAL OFFICER OF HEALTH**
>
> **E.L.Pearce**   **Vice-Chancellor**
> *J.I.Keynes*   *Registrary of the University*

The award of the Diploma must have been a proud moment for both Maurice and his father. Born in 1886, the year in which the GMC first allowed registration of post-graduate qualifications in addition to original medical degrees, he achieved the DPH in 1922 when his father was the Chairman of the GMC's Public Health Committee which supervised the quality of the education and examination for it. As John was one of the first four doctors ever to take a specialist examination in Public Health, he had cause for quiet satisfaction that Maurice was following where he had led, though by nature neither would have shown more than the mildest exuberance.

This postgraduate qualification set the pattern for Maurice's promotion through the ranks of the Royal Naval Medical Service. After service in HMS Temeraire, he was appointed Naval Medical Officer of Health in Malta in 1926 and again in 1930, and Principal Medical Officer (PMO) of the battle-cruiser HMS Renown from 1935 to 1937. As the storm clouds of the Second World War were gathering he was promoted to Surgeon Captain and sent to Malta once more, this time as PMO of HM Hospital Ship Maine. When Italy entered the war and threatened the isolated island of Malta, Maine was moved to Alexandria. The North African campaign followed, with the siege of Tobruk and battle of Alamein, as well as the naval battle at Cape Matapan, and the hospital was fully occupied with the injured from this fighting. News was scanty and slow to reach the family, who were alarmed when the popular illustrated paper *Picture Post* published a photograph of the unmistakable shape and markings of HMHS Maine, obscured by a plume of smoke as a bomb exploded alongside her. Although at home we were proud to see one of our own involved in action it was a worrying time. After days of anxious waiting the news came that, though there had been casualties, Maurice was safe. He had been spared the fate of his brothers.

On return to Britain, he became a Naval MOH again, first at Rosyth and then at Royal Naval Hospital Haslar, his last appointment before retiring from the Navy in 1948. He worked in general practice for a time, largely to fund the medical education of his two sons, John and Richard, who must for ever be grateful to him for this, for it was a heavy burden to re-enter the clinical field amid the uncertainties and disorganisation of post-war general practice and the new National Health Service. By his decision to stay in the Navy in 1918, his family continued to live in England when Ireland became independent, though his love for his Irish homeland was unmistakable. Thus his children and grandchildren are English.

Maurice's two sons are a third John (b1926), and Richard (b1930) who is the author of this book. Their decisions to become doctors thus brought a seventh consecutive generation of the family to the practice of medicine. John graduated at Oxford in 1951, and Richard at Cambridge in 1954, both eventually becoming general practitioners. By then it was a matter of some pride, or perhaps conceit, that there had already been six generations of doctors, and the glow of Sir John's distinguished career still shone over the two young Moores as, in the mid 1940s, they contemplated their futures. No pressure was imposed on us to study medicine, but neither were alternatives constructively explored; rather there was a silent expectation that we would follow the family trend, and according to the aspirations of our Scottish mother, would have distinguished careers. Sixty years ago career options for middle class boys were fewer than now, guidance was minimal if it existed at all, and the professions were held in higher esteem than commerce, or so it seemed to us. In a war-torn world the study of medicine allowed deferment from conscription into military service, too. Perhaps subconsciously influenced by the fate of our uncles in the First World War, medicine seemed a sensible choice. The scientific discoveries of the earlier ages were beginning to bear fruit with unprecedented advances in methods of diagnosis and treatment that changed the nature of a doctors' work, and we were both able to find fulfilment in our careers. But who knows whether we would have fared better or worse in some other field?

John and Richard have now retired, their professional lives as much things of the past as those of William, Daniel and their nineteenth century descendants. The tradition continues, still, into an eighth generation through two of Richard's three children who chose to be doctors. With such a family history it seemed important not to impose any expectation on the next generation, yet James (b1956) had declared by the age of thirteen that he wanted to be a doctor, and Jane (b1963) did so when not much older. Whether they would have made the same choices had their parents been bakers or candlestick-makers is debatable, and they might have prospered more or less in another occupation.

After hospital experience and some travel and work overseas James completed the postgraduate training which has been made compulsory for general practice, and is now a principal in a partnership in Cornwall. At the time of writing he is Chairman of the Tamar Faculty of the Royal College of General Practitioners. Jane, too, travelled abroad including a year spent in a rural hospital in South Africa. She is a Member of the Royal College of Obstetricians and Gynaecologists, and after a period of research at Oxford graduated MSc. They have both made promising starts to their careers and enjoy the challenges of their profession. It also makes heavy demands, not least of which is the pace at which changes occur in knowledge, diagnosis, therapy, and in the structure and organisation of the profession. The earlier generations of the family saw radical changes as medicine became a science rather than a craft, and its practice became the application of increasingly certain knowledge in a caring and conscientious way. Change can be stressful, and our forbears may have found the progress of their own time as hard as later generations have done. It is certainly stressful now, for modern doctors see change happen almost day by day, not just within medicine itself, but also in the political and social pressure for involvement and accountability. No sooner has one change been accepted and absorbed than another is on its way. Even the fundamental nature of the doctor's role has changed, from one that was often paternalistic if ineffective, to one in which doctors not only seek to preserve health and cure disease, but sometimes seem to challenge the very nature of human life. As treatments become increasingly complex, so does accountability. Whereas earlier generations were not required to prove themselves again after their initial examinations except through their practice and reputations, today's generation is facing the challenge of continuous scrutiny and formal re-evaluation of their professional competence. Doctors now live in the public eye as never before, and if the public is not pleased, they face the prospect of litigation by aggrieved patients seeking redress.

If they could see their medical descendants of today, the earlier doctors in the family might wonder at this change in the public's perception, as well as at the clinical advances and challenges since their own times. The epidemics they battled with are gone, and many of the infectious diseases they saw are preventable. Smallpox, an epidemic killer a hundred years ago, has been eradicated. Maternal mortality, 8 or 9 per thousand when Ellie Moore died in 1878, is now nearer 1 per *hundred* thousand. Men can expect to live for 75 years and women for 80, twice as long as a hundred and fifty years ago. Despite these benefits we have cancer, heart attacks, the diseases of old age, contraception, in-vitro fertilisation, and AIDS, all of which were previously unknown, rare or impossible. Scientific advances have given us chemotherapy, radiotherapy, CT scans and microbiology, which our forebears might have dreamed of but could not experience.

Medicine has always changed and always will, because it is subject to pressure from the ideas of contemporary society whether expressed through individuals, ethical groups, the churches or the state. There are always new and seemingly insuperable challenges, but the resources available will never be enough to meet every need. So it was in the days of William and Daniel. So it was when Sir John reached the peak of his profession, when his grandsons John and Richard entered general practice nearly half a century ago, and still is for James and Jane in practice now. If, in retrospect, our forebears seem naïve or ignorant, they could only do what was possible in their own time. Problems that once seemed insuperable have been solved. Doctors have sought and found better treatments, but have also complained of their lot and demanded better. Sometimes their assumptions were false and their conclusions wrong, but out of those imperfections has come progress.

In the 260 years since William Moore set up his shop in Ballymahon, he and his descendants have practised their profession in many ways, adapting to change, often promoting progress, sometimes opposing it. The following chapters sketch some of the significant events of those years, as experienced and recorded by members of the Moore family, or seen through their eyes and those of their contemporaries. How much longer the family will observe the medical scene from within remains to be seen.

The armorial bearings of Sir John Moore.
Azure, on a chief dancetté or, a fleam between two mullets gules.
Crest.
Out of a ducal crest coronet gold, charged with a fleam* gules, a Moor's
head in profile proper, wreathed about the temples or and azure.
Motto.
"Fortis cadere, cedere non potest"
(A brave man may fall but cannot yield)

*Fleam: a lancet for opening a vein: OED

The Royal Gift of Healing

Charles II touching a patient for the king's evil (scrofula) surrounded by courtiers, clergy and general public, from an engraving by R.White, 1684. (Wellcome Library, London)

CHAPTER TWO

William at Ballymahon

This parish [Shruel] generally affords an opportunity to a medical practitioner to accumulate a fortune provided he adds the vending of medicines to the practice of physic[1].

William Shaw Mason, 1819

T he parish of Shruel was one of several in the area served by William Moore's shop in Ballymahon in County Longford, though this was a little before William Shaw Mason's survey. By the eighteenth century standards Longford was probably quite a healthy place, though everywhere diseases such as malaria, small-pox, plague and typhus were common and beyond anyone's power to cure. Many less life-threatening conditions such as gout, rheumatism, whooping cough and measles were also prevalent, and much of the population was under-nourished. Diagnosis was based on superficial inspection, if that, and to us who are used to remedies that really work, the methods of treatment then available seem to have been hopelessly ineffective.

Because many of the remedies for illness were derived from plants, Medicine, or to use the earlier term of 'Physic', was taught in the universities as a province of botany, and concepts of disease were still those based on the theory of the 'four humours' that had been current for 1500 years since Galen's time. If medicine, and even more so surgery, were elementary, the public were equally gullible and ignorant. Seventeenth century kings of England and France had purported to cure tuberculosis, then known as 'struma', by touching the sufferers. At one time the popular belief was that the "great concourse of strumous persons to White-Hall, and the success they find in it" was sufficient evidence for its effectiveness as a cure[2]. In 1726 a Mrs Toft of Godalmin was alleged to have given birth to a litter of rabbits, an obstetric oddity which was 'confirmed' by some of the most eminent medical men of the day, and even interested the royal household until it was exposed as a hoax[3]. Not everyone accepted such unconvincing stories or admired the doctors despite their ineffectiveness, for the poet Dryden sceptically recalled the "happy days before doctors learned to kill people"[4]. A little later the Parisian physician Corvisart (1755-1821) remarked that medicine is "not the art of curing disease", leaving unanswered the question of what it is[5]. This scepticism and a desire for a more objective enquiry into the physical world led to the scientific discoveries of the Enlightenment and a rational approach to medical practice.

The mid-eighteenth century was a time of change, therefore, and William was a witness, albeit remotely, to the dawn of medical science in what became known as the Enlightenment. In distant Ballymahon the traditional ideas may have continued, but changes were on the way, at least in clearer and more accurate descriptions of disease. Richard Morton (1637-1698) had written about tuberculosis rather more objectively than his contemporaries, and differentiated it from the wasting caused by jaundice, gout and fevers. Scarlet fever, which would have been a common problem for William, had been accurately described by Sennert. He wrote, 'the entire body appears red and as if on fire' and likened it correctly to erysipelas[6]. Thomas Sydenham (1624-89) observed scarlet fever in more detail and described some of its sequelae, and wrote about epidemic diseases such as influenza. His great contribution to medicine was his emphasis on accurate observation rather than prejudice or assumption, though it seems that the physicians who attended Mrs Toft in her multiple confinement had not learned that lesson. Recognising both the potential dangers and the ineffectiveness of the medicines of his day, Sydenham said:-

I have consulted my patients' safety and my own reputation most effectually by doing nothing at all.[7]

This was hardly fair to himself, for he advocated the use of the newly introduced Jesuit's Bark, derived from a South American tree and now known to contain quinine, and thereby not only relieved the sufferers of his own time but led the way for the modern use of quinine in the treatment of malaria. An example of this therapeutic caution is that his most potent remedies for the devastating and often fatal scarlet fever were a powder consisting of hartshorn, cochineal and white sugar, and a julep (a stimulant drink) of cherry water and lemon juice. He also advised a blister to the neck – and 'syrup of poppies to be taken every night as a paregoric', which was an opium medicine flavoured with camphor and aniseed[8].

Even these astute observers were working in the dark, since their knowledge of anatomy and physiology was still slight, but Galen's long shadow was fading. William Harvey had described the circulation of the blood in 1628, though it was not until 1723, when William Moore was two years old, that Stephen Hales showed that blood is under pressure as it circulates. An instrument to measure that pressure easily in everyday clinical situations was not developed for another 175 years. Most of the treatments used by eighteenth century doctors were never objectively tested. There were exceptions, however, such as William Withering studies of digitalis which led in 1785 to his *Account of the Foxglove and Some of its Medical Uses*. In France, Pierre Louis challenged the use of blood-letting as a cure for pneumonia, showing that it made no difference to the outcome whether it was done early or late, or how much was taken. These men were early exponents of the use of statistics in medical research.

Despite these developments in more populous places, William Moore in his apothecary's shop in Ballymahon during the 1740s and 50s could only trust the conventional methods of treatment. Bloodletting, emetics and purges were clearly doing something, for the intention was still to remove the supposedly offensive matter from the body: the more that was sweated, vomited, purged or bled the better. The addition of chemicals such as antimony, arsenic and mercury which produced vomiting, sweating and salivation were also believed to be effective – at least in producing dramatic effects, if not cures. Indeed the relief of 'plethora', which was observed in inflammation as an obvious congestion of the tissues by blood and the benefit sometimes to be had by bleeding, seemed proof that bloodletting was a sovereign remedy. It was a first-line treatment for many conditions, rationally or not, until someone pointed out that by bleeding patients they were all-too often 'cured to death'. In 1714 the poet Matthew Prior had remarked that:-

Cur'd yesterday of my Disease, I died last night of my Physician[9]

How William came by such medical knowledge as he had is uncertain. Had he been wealthy or well educated he might have gone to Dublin University, or Oxford or Cambridge, where an Arts degree would have enabled him to proceed to Doctor of Medicine by studying Physic. There he would have studied botany and the medicines that could be made from plants, though not how to prepare or administer them because that was the function of the apothecary. Nor would he have learned much about diseases or their causes and cures, which were largely unknown. If he had preferred to study clinical medicine he might have gone to the new Medical School in Edinburgh, or to Europe where language would not have been a problem because teaching was done in the common language of Latin. Certainly neither Dublin nor London had anything else to offer him. But he was the son of an excise man from the County Westmeath, so his more humble destiny was to be apprenticed to an apothecary. If he had gone to Dublin his Master would have belonged to the Worshipful Company of Barbers, Surgeons, Apothecaries and Periwig Makers. As a trade organisation the Company's main purpose was to protect the interests of its members, so it had no system of educating or examining candidates for entry to the craft, nor of continuing education for them as we might expect from such a body today. The task of overseeing the education of its future members was developed by its successor in the field, the august Apothecaries' Hall of Ireland, founded at the end of the eighteenth century by a group of ambitious men, including William's son Daniel. In any case the Barbers, Surgeons, Apothecaries and Periwig makers were a Company of the City of Dublin, and had no authority or even any presence in Westmeath. After serving his time as apprentice, much of which would have been spent running errands and cleaning the shop, he set up on his own or, possibly, as an assistant to an apothecary already working in Ballymahon.

In the mid-eighteenth century the lack of knowledge, or even of a definition of a 'medical man' let alone a job description, meant that the business of the apothecary was a mixture of things. By 1810, however, it could be said by Jenkins in *Observations on the Present State of the Trade of Medicine* that:-

> *The apothecary of this country is qualified by education to attend the bedside of the sick, and, being better acquainted with pharmacy than the physicians of English Universities .... is often the most successful practitioner.*[10]

Jenkins also mentioned that though the physicians were no cleverer it was usually they who claimed both the credit and the fees.

Before apothecaries became independent traders, the ingredients of medicines were largely vegetable and were therefore stocked by grocers along with spices, sugars, flavourings and colourings. The public view of the apothecary may have been scathing or sceptical, at least in the view of some, for accounts of apothecaries in the literature are not complimentary. Shakespeare described the one who supplied Romeo with his suicidal draught as:-

> *'a caitiff wretch [whom] sharp misery had worn ... to the bones'*★

whose shop was:-

> *'full of empty boxes, green earthen pots, bladders and musty seeds ......* *thinly scattered to make up a show'*[11].

If, as Jenkins claimed, the apothecaries were often the most successful practitioners, they stood a long way below the physicians in the medical hierarchy. In one picture in Hogarth's *Marriage a la Mode,* a diminutive apothecary has been in consultation with a well-heeled physician about a patient[12]. The apothecary talks to a servant about some mundane matter, while the physician pockets his fee and goes on his way. The increasing demand for skilfully prepared medicines stimulated a retail trade in them which called for special knowledge and skills, though the physicians retained their prerogative of knowing how and when to use them.

★ Caitiff: base, despicable, cowardly

In seventeenth century England, James I had been persuaded that the apothecaries' claim to be specialists justified their separation from the Company of Grocers, and granted their incorporation as The Society of the Art and Mystery of the Apothecaries of the City of London. Apothecaries also dealt in other goods such as perfumes and perukes or periwigs, but their main business was to stock the vegetable and mineral ingredients of medicines, and to prepare them. Therefore, although in London the Apothecaries were now incorporated as a City company, that was conditional on their shops being supervised by the Royal College of Physicians. The physicians saw themselves as the powerful nobility of medicine, a status granted through their possession of doctorates from the Universities of Oxford and Cambridge. They were well aware that when ordinary folk were unwell many of them went straight to the apothecary for a cure, and in by-passing the physician by-passed his fee as well. It was therefore in the interest of preserving professional income and status that the physicians demanded to be seen as guardians of the medical standards. But for all their eminence, the authority of the Royal College of Physicians of London only extended to the City and seven miles around it, so their influence was limited. Similarly in Ireland the Worshipful Company of Barbers, Surgeons, Apothecaries and Periwig Makers controlled the trade under the supervision of the College of Physicians, but only in the City of Dublin.

The demand for the services of a periwig maker from the few gentry in Ballymahon and its neighbourhood in the 1740s must have been small. Had William set up shop in Bath, he might have prospered in that trade and forsaken the medical part of the business, but Ballymahon was not Bath. Although there were modestly grand houses in County Longford, they would not have sustained many periwigmakers. Indeed in his early years William must have found it hard, for the winters were very cold, and it was a period when famine was severe in Ireland[13,14]. Disease accompanied the famine, and it has been estimated that deaths from disease or starvation amounted to no less than 810,000 people out of the population at that time of two and a half million – one person in three[15]. In Ballymahon the situation improved in the next decades, and writing a little later, in 1818, Rev. John Graham could say that the farmers in that area:-

[though] not wealthy, lived comfortably on a diet of bacon, fowl, eggs pota-toes oatmeal and milk[16].

The diet of the lower classes was, however:-

*very indifferent, consisting chiefly of potatoes with butter milk or salt. ....
There are few parts of Ireland .... in which persons of a moderate income
can live cheaper or better than in this parish.*

The general appearance of the inhabitants was:-

*... prepossessing, generally of middle size, with manly open countenances,
[but the] lowest order of females generally prefer walking barefoot, and carry
their shoes in their hands or aprons on the way to market, or to mass, till
they come within a few yards of the place where they think it necessary to
change their dress ... [which is often] ... a well or a brook which served the
double purpose of reflecting their appearance and washing their feet.*

Not much scope for perukes in that society, perhaps, but by the standards
of the time Ballymahon was quite bustling with trade. It was connected
to the Shannon by the navigable River Inny, and so could easily move
goods to and from other towns. It had a mill, and much trade was done
in linen and wool, as well as groceries, hardware, grain and foodstuffs,
including wine and porter. There were two distilleries and 'several' malt-
houses. Leather and nails were manufactured, and it had its quota of
'taylors, hatters, hosiers, blacksmiths, carpenters .... and other artizans', –
including William Moore, Apothecary.

When farmers and traders prospered they kept healthy too, and may
have had little call for the apothecary. The 'lowest orders', while more
likely to suffer from the effects of poor nutrition and rotten housing, would
have found it hard to meet an apothecary's fees even if they needed his
help. But there must have been enough to keep William busy, for there
were some thousands of people living in the surrounding parishes
who might fall ill and need medicine, or be injured in the mills or nail
factories. There were frequent epidemics of fever, a group of undefined
illnesses with high mortality not peculiar to Ireland but unusually

common there, and like the rest of the world in the eighteenth century, expectation of life was low. Official records of births and deaths do not exist for County Longford at that period, but some idea can be gained from a study of gravestones erected between 1681 and 1839 in a nearby churchyard at Moydow, where some of William's erstwhile patients or customers may have been buried[17]. On many of these stones the ages at death are recorded, among them those of 102 males and 76 females. The average age was 50.8 years for men and 50.5 for women, figures which are high for the time when a baby could be expected to live for little more than forty years (in Britain as a whole in 1841 expectation of life at birth was 41 for males and 43 for female[18]). This suggests that Ballymahon and its neighbouring villages were relatively healthy places. But there are big variations within these figures; eleven children died before their first birthdays (seven boys and four girls), and probably many more who were not recorded because they died at birth; nine of the men and ten of the women died before they were twenty-five, and a further twenty-two people before they were forty. Childbirth was a risky process and some of these deaths may have been due to that. Whether William attended at childbirth is uncertain, for at that time it was largely the province of women, but he would certainly have been concerned with the deaths and morbidity that followed it. He would also have been busy looking after people suffering from the fevers and infections which took their toll of both sexes.

For those who survived these hazards a long life was possible. Nearly one in five of the people buried at Moydow lived beyond seventy years, twenty-two men and ten women. Two women and eight men reached more than eighty, a proportion reversed in more recent times. These figure illustrate just how far improvements in health have come since William's day, and how different is the medicine practised by his professional successors. It is hard to imagine what it must have been like to know that one in four boys and one in three girls would not see their fortieth birthday.

The fevers and epidemics were not the only problems, of course. Without Health and Safety legislation to protect them workers in the mills might fall through trap doors or be injured by machinery; farmers had no tractors, but could be hurt by animals, or die of tetanus; builders could fall and break bones; scurvy and other deficiencies would lead to ulcers and infections; rheumatism and arthritis would need medication, and gout was common and severe. Many of these ills would have been treated by 'folk' remedies, or with materials kept in the medicine cupboards of the houses of the gentry, which an apothecary worth his salt would be keen to keep stocked.

Some remedies were simple and available from the kitchen garden, such as the application of cabbage leaves to ulcers and infected swellings. Burns were treated with one part of beeswax to three of mutton fat heated together, and applied on linen bandages; or with poultices of bran, flax seed and turpentine. Romeo's apothecary might have recognised a preparation from oil of bream, a flat fish from the nearby lakes which was kept until it was rotten and then squeezed to express the oil. An ointment made by mixing "well mingled droppings of ancient ganders and goats with the lard of ancient hens" was said to be good in scrofula[19], another name for struma or tuberculosis, especially if no king was available to touch the sufferer. A handful of garlic, boiled in two quarts of spring water and reduced to one pint, with added honey, would '*infallibly* cure cough, asthma, and shortness of breath'. Earache could be relieved by pricking a snail on a thorn and then dropping the froth that came from it into the ear, or by blowing tobacco smoke into the ear through a funnel. Gout was treated by applying a raw lean beefsteak to the afflicted part every twelve hours, or rosemary leaves wrapped in linen. For coughs and chest diseases a cupful of linseed oil with honey was taken daily, which 'as an electuary [was] a great pulmonic'[20]. As in Galen's time, it was still widely believed that "for every illness the Lord may choose to afflict his people, he has also provided a herb to cure it"[21].

That belief was understandable because for centuries it has been known that many plant and animal preparations have poisonous or beneficial effects, and several effective and useful drugs in use today were originally derived from plants. Unfortunately it was not always recognised which were the poisonous and which the beneficial effects. Among others, the following were known to produce effects though not always curative ones, so much so that some were even used for the ruthless purposes as murder, suicide or for poisoning the tips of arrows.

Poisons:-	*Hemlock, Mandrake, Strychnine, Ergot, Curare, Henbane,*
Medicines:-	*Opium, cinchona (quinine), coca, rhubarb, deadly nightshade (atropine), Jalap (Ipomoea), Aconite, Foxglove, Male Fern, Guaiacum, Sassafras,*
Folk remedies:-	*Dandelion, nettles etc.*
Minerals:-	*Antimony, mercury and arsenic.*

In William's time ingredients for the medicines made in the houses of the gentry needed specific materials such as Sarsaparilla (a carminative to cure flatulence), Hippoic powder, Salt of Hartshorn, Camphor (for rheumatism and lumbago, also 'anaphrodisiac'), Calomel (a form of mercury), Magnesium, and both Cream and Salt of Tartar (for constipation). The apothecary was the best person to supply these, for it was important to ensure pure ingredients and accurate dosage. Remedies made from these and similar ingredients were used to treat many common complaints like chilblains, toothache, sore throats, rheumatism and gout, as well as more serious conditions like typhus and fevers, hydrophobia, scrofula, and eye problems. Many of these conditions are familiar to us now, and some still defy cure. The confidence placed in the remedies in William's time may seem somewhat ill-founded in the light of the precise indications and effectiveness of medicines we now demand, but if you have no other remedy you must believe in what you have. Even now we don't have remedies for everything. Remarks attached to the recipes for medicines such as 'this never fails' and 'it is rarely one has to apply this remedy more than twice' testify to the great expectation placed upon them[22]. Hope of relief, and the expectation that a chosen medicine will be effective are important ingredients of any cure. Speedy cures for headaches, hangovers and anything from corns to constipation are still advertised daily in the press and on television. We desire relief from pain just as our forebears did.

William probably also prepared the recipes of more traditional medicines from previous centuries. He might well have offered some recommended by Robert Boyle at the end of the seventeenth[23], such as:-

For convulsions:-	*Take earthworms, wash them well in White wine to cleanse them but so that they may not*

	die..... dry the worms... and reduce to a powder. To one ounce of which add a pretty number of Grains of Ambergris both to perfume the powder... and to make the medicine more efficacious. The dose is from one Dram to a Dram and a half.
For the Goute:-	*The head of a Young Kitte, being burnt to ashes and the quantity of A Dragme taken every morning in a little water, is an admirable remedy.*
For Whooping cough:-	*Take some house Mice. Flaw them and dry them in an oven, then make them into a fine powder and Lett the party take as much of the powder as will Lye on a broad shilling, in Beere or possett, first in The Morning and Last att Night.*

Note the lack of precision in the measurements: one ounce of the powdered earthworms to a 'pretty number of Grains' of Ambergris; 'as much powder as will lie on a broad shilling'. Did William spend his time collecting earthworms, and washing them in wine ready to dispense as an anticonvulsant, and breed mice to be flawed or prepare them only on demand? (How does one flaw a mouse?★) Perhaps he preferred the prescriptions of more learned physicians, such as Thomas Sydenham's for Ague:-

> *Take of the conserve of Roman Wormwood, of Rosemary-flowers, and of Venice Treacle, each one ounce; of the conserve of the yellow Peel of Oranges, of candied Angelica and of Nutmegs candied, each half an ounce; make an Electuary, with sufficient quantity of Syrup of Gillyflowers; let them take the quantity of a Nutmeg twice a Day, and drink a small Draught of Canary after it, wherein Cowslip flowers have been infused cold.*[24]

Being several days journey from Dublin or other sources of supply William would have needed to stock a sizeable quantity of the regular

---

★ flaw = obsolete form of 'flay'

ingredients. This was a business from which he intended to make money, or at least earn a living. He would surely wish to do better than that 'caitiff wretch' who was Romeo's apothecary.

Although the names of the ordinary folk of Ballymahon have long been forgotten, one name is well remembered, that of Oliver Goldsmith who was the son of the vicar of Pallas, the neighbouring parish. He was born in 1728, just seven years younger than William. After his father died he and his mother moved into Ballymahon, where the young Oliver would go on errands and amuse himself in other, prankish ways. One such errand, quoted by Rev John Graham, was the purchase of some groceries from Sarah Shore in 1756. Their account already stood at £0 15s 5d, to which was added 3d for a quarter pound of sugar and 7d for an ounce of green tea. Did Oliver also call at William's shop, perhaps to fetch laudanum to help his mother sleep when she grieved for her dead husband? Oliver suffered from smallpox as a boy, and though he recovered from the dreadful and often fatal disease, he was left with a badly scarred face. It is tempting to think that William attended him, and perhaps, as they talked, the eager young apothecary put the idea of becoming a doctor into the boy's head. If so, Oliver pursued it with inconsistent effort and dubious success, for he is less famous for his medical achievements than his literary ones.

William must have done quite well in his business, and in social status would have considered himself a gentleman as well as a tradesman. A poetic comment[25] in Gilborne's Medical Review in 1775 advised apothecaries not to identify themselves with the more questionable surgeons, who were themselves struggling for recognition as an independent profession:-

Keep clean your shops in eminent degree
From all annoyance, dust and cobwebs free
Make up your medicines with the nicest care
But to dispense them cautiously forbear.
Mind your own bus'ness, study where and when,
And ne'er forget that you are gentlemen.

In William's time the apothecary and the surgeon were developing their own identities, distinct from each other but with overlapping roles in the same field. The relationship between them, particularly in the prescribing and dispensing of medicines, became the subject of many acrimonious disputes in years to come. But William took no part in these conflicts, for he died in 1758 aged only thirty-seven, leaving a widow and four children. It fell to his son Daniel and the next generation of apothecaries to fight these battles.

Design for a general chemical laboratory, (as might have existed at the Apothecaries' Hall) from an etching by A.W.Warren 1822. (Wellcome Library, London).

CHAPTER THREE

Daniel Moore,
Master Apothecary

To preserve health and improve pharmacy
Motto on the Seal of the Apothecaries' Hall, Dublin[1]

After William's death the eight year old Daniel moved to Dublin to live with his uncle John Clarke, an eminent chemist and apothecary with a business in Capel Street. Within a few years he was apprenticed to his uncle to learn the apothecary's trade, and then began a further apprenticeship in surgery with a Mr Whiteway, surgeon to Steeven's (*sic*) Hospital. Despite this experience he was unable to practise surgery, because the College of Surgeons did not yet exist as a licensing authority and without a university degree he could not obtain a licence from the College of Physicians. On completion of his apprenticeships he was appointed apothecary to the Foundling Hospital, where his duties were akin to a present-day house surgeon, that is, he had day-to-day responsibility for the patients between the visits of the surgeons or physicians, for the admission of new patients, and for preparing medicines. After he left the hospital he went into partnership with Messrs Lee and Bardin, who had premises in Suffolk Street in central Dublin. When Mr Bardin died the partnership dissolved, providing Daniel with the opportunity to set up on his own. By 1790, when he moved to the shop in South Anne Street, he had become a prominent figure in his line of business, and was involved in three important areas. One was the confirmation of the role of apothecaries as an independent and self-regulating part of the medical organisation, through the foundation of the Apothecaries' Hall of Dublin; the second was the relationship of apothecaries with other medical men; and the third was the establishment of his own business, in which his son and grandson were to play their parts in due course.

At that time the fast-growing City of Dublin was governed by a city council, and was the seat of the Irish Parliament. About 180,000 people lived there, in houses spreading out from the old settlement around the castle and the commercial waterside area. Many citizens were prosperous, but there were also many migrants from the depressed countryside who were miserably destitute. To meet the medical needs of this growing population in 1780 there were forty-eight physicians and sixty-six surgeons, and of the latter eighteen also practised midwifery. By 1791 the number of physicians had increased to sixty-four, but of these less than half were fellows or licentiates of the King's and Queen's College of Physicians in Dublin, the remainder having no license to practise from the college. The surgeons then numbered seventy eight, nearly all of them fellows or members of the newly founded Royal College of Surgeons in Ireland, the others being licentiates only. There were also fifty-five apothecaries in 1780, including Daniel Moore and his uncle John Clarke, who offered medical care to the population both by attendance on the sick in their homes, and by the sale of medicines from apothecaries' shops. This number remained constant for the next fifty years despite the growth in the population, and in 1829 was still only fifty-four[2]. The growth in physicians and surgeons was the shaping of things to come, for as the nature of the future medical profession became clearer it was the trained surgeons and physicians who treated patients, while apothecaries developed the role of dispensers of medicine rather than attendance on the sick

The new Georgian streets, straight and wide, were linked to the older parts of the city through College Green and Grafton Street. These still showed the twisting course of their medieval origins before opening out into the spacious amenity of St Stephens Green, laid out 'for the ornament and pleasure of the cittie'[3]. Daniel's decision to move from Capel Street, north of the river and therefore distant from the new developments of government, hospitals and the houses of the well-to-do, to the more central Grafton Street, was sensible. It placed him at the centre of affairs, at least geographically and as far as the apothecary's trade was concerned, and helped him to play a central role in the foundation of

Apothecaries' Hall of Ireland, in which he was one of the original twelve directors, and was three times its most senior officer, the Governor.

By the middle of the eighteenth century the association between the various trades within the Company of Barbers, Surgeons, Apothecaries and Periwig Makers was beginning to break down. In 1745 some of its members formed the Guild of St Luke, a new society whose purpose was to promote the interests of apothecaries to the City Council, without being involved in the concerns of the wig-makers and others in the former Company. On completing his apprenticeship Daniel became a member of this Guild, and before long was taking a prominent part in its affairs. The surgeons in the Company also claimed, in what now seems like a masterly understatement, that the union with the Barbers 'was inconvenient in many respects, and did not tend to the progress of surgical knowledge'[4]. In 1781 they, too, broke away to be incorporated into the Royal College of Surgeons in Ireland. This was to become an organisation which, like the Royal College of Surgeons in London, promoted the interests of the rising specialty of surgery, but unlike its London counterpart was a complete undergraduate medical school, which it still is. Furthermore, like the new Hall for the apothecaries ten years later, the new College was a national body with responsibilities throughout Ireland, not a municipal one with authority limited to Dublin[5].

This separation of the disciplines was more revolutionary at the time than it seems two centuries later, and was achieved by a subtle deception. The surgeons and apothecaries in the old Barbers' Company began to resent their status as 'mere assistants to physicians', under the control and supervision of the College of Physicians. In the opinion of those 'assistants', physicians knew very little about the practicalities of surgery and pharmacy. The Barbers' Company therefore invited the President, Bursars and Fellows of the King's and Queen's College of Physicians who numbered no more than fourteen, to accept the Freedom of the Company. They were admitted with due ceremony at Full Hall, that is to say, a general meeting. The Physicians thus became members of the Company, but retained their responsibilities to examine the surgeons and apothecaries in their various disciplines and skills. The examination rules were framed in such a way that, if no one from the College of Physicians attended when the examinations were held, those surgeons or apothecaries who *were* there were empowered to conduct the examination on their behalf. When no physicians appeared in the examinations, which were entirely oral, the surgeons examined the candidates themselves and so demonstrated that they were indeed capable of determining their own professional standards independently of the physicians[6]

The formation of the Guild of St Luke and the foundation of their own college by the surgeons created a three-way division of the fledgling medical profession into apothecaries, surgeons and physicians. Each of them now had the right to teach and examine their own candidates and to protect their own interests. Unfortunately their members guarded their own areas of operation jealously, which led to fragmentation of the disciplines and frequent bitter disputes, both in Ireland and England. It took nearly a century to resolve this fragmentation, eventually achieved by the establishment under the Medical Act of 1858 of the General Council for Medical Education and the institution of a common educational curriculum for all those who wished to be registered with the Council as medical practitioners.

The Guild of St Luke, ostensibly an organisation to protect the interests of the apothecaries, was also a vigorous political force. The City Companies were the means by which various trades argued for their rights, and would-be politicians among them could gain prominence. The full membership, or 'Freedom', of a Company or Guild enabled an individual to climb the political ladder in order to present the Company's pleas in high places. One such politician was Charles Lucas, who played an important part in establishing the status of apothecaries. He looked with disfavour on the supposed superiority of physicians, and especially on their College which had been founded by William and Mary and had the full title of The King's and Queen's College of Physicians in Ireland. He was determined to challenge them, both personally and through their college, and in particular to expose the inadequacy of their supervision of apothecaries' shops. When the College's members visited his own shop to examine its stock and facilities, he doubted whether they would really know what was what among the large variety of medicines and ingredients on the shelves. He showed them a bottle labelled as a preparation of rhubarb, one of the favourite remedies of the time, which they accepted as of good quality. It was actually a mixture of toast and turmeric, a dye extracted from ginger root[7]. He took pleasure in claiming that by accepting the adulterated preparation as a pure one they revealed the depth of their ignorance of things pharmaceutical.

More importantly, Lucas sought improvement by political means. He was elected in 1741 to represent the apothecaries and surgeons on the Common Council of the City of Dublin, where he was a vigorous contender against the Aldermen, who, in his view,

> obscured the Council of this unfortunate city and brought it to the verge of destruction[8].

Lucas's continued allegations about the impropriety of the Council, which he published in a series of abusive pamphlets, led him into trouble. His support for his fellow apothecaries earned him election as Master of the Guild, but outside the Guild he made many enemies by his allegations of corruption, for instance that Aldermen were appropriating city assets for their own use. He was brought before the Bar of the Irish House of Commons, convicted, and ordered to be imprisoned. Although he failed to secure favours from the jailer, who, unlike the aldermen, seems to have been curiously incorruptible, he managed to escape from prison, and fled to London. There, free from Irish jurisdiction, he continued to be politically provocative. From London he went to Paris and took the opportunity to further his education, and then to Leyden where he graduated MD. Determined to pursue his desired reforms in Ireland, he appealed to George III and succeeded in having his conviction quashed. He was thus free to return to Dublin.

The Guild of St Luke was also a mutual protection system. It levied fines on 'foreigners', that is to say, outsiders and non-members who attempted to set up business in Dublin without joining the Guild. Such persons would be expected to become members unless they could produce a certificate that they were 'free of the city', that is, had permission to trade from the council. If this could not be shown a fine of £1 10s 0d was imposed. This seems a small sum, equivalent perhaps to the fees earned by administering an enema to a patient on three occasions. Fines were also imposed on others who had no pretensions to be apothecaries, but who were allegedly making or selling medicines. One such was a distiller who manufactured Compound Bryony Water, which was a 'very untoothsome composition but admirably suited to the intention of an hysterick', and because it was 'very forcing upon the uterus' it was a useful obstetric stimulant. Its protean properties also made it 'good against convulsions in children, and of service in any nervous complaint in either sex'[9] This offender also made Hot Cinnamon Water, which consisted of one pound of cinnamon in a gallon of French brandy, of which William Daniel says "Hot it certainly must have been"[10]. Offenders were fined 5s 5d a quarter so long as they persisted, but in this case the apothecaries failed to suppress the distillers' activities.

The Guild also sought to regulate the standard and quality of goods sold. For instance, one of the more effective medicines was derived from the bark of a tree native to Peru, which was used to treat fevers, including malaria, then common in Ireland and England. It was called Jesuit's Bark because it was originally imported into Europe by Jesuit missionaries returning from South America, and being difficult to obtain was costly and therefore potentially profitable. But it was also easily imitated, so in 1756 it was felt necessary to call a meeting of all members of the Guild to warn them about fake commodities and substandard goods. 'The Master and Commonality assembled in Special Summons' to receive information that:-

Very large quantities of a Bark imported from North America have been late-ly sold in London as Jesuit's Bark ..... that tho' it has the appearance it has not the taste or qualities of Jesuits or Peruvian Bark.

Ordered that an Advertisement be published, giving Notice to all Apothecaries Druggists and other public dispencers of medicines to caution them against buying any Peruvian Bark without tasting and carefully examining it.

Ordered that said advertisement be published twice a week for a month in the Dublin Gazette, in Pires Occurrences, Faulkners Dublin Journal and the Universal Advertiser[11].

It is interesting to note that, though the 'druggists', who were unlicenced sellers of medicines without the training or licences of apothecaries, were not permitted to sell remedies like Jesuit's Bark, they were still cautioned to ensure they had the real thing. Quality assurance was a problem, so it was proposed that a central depot be opened where apothecaries could obtain supplies of material of known purity, but as this would have been costly they proposed to seek help from the government. Unfortunately, even the cost of applying for assistance was more than they could afford, and the Master had to report that:-

> *The expences of apposing to the heads of a Bill for preventing Fraud and Abuses in the vending, preparing and administering Drugs and Medicines in the House of Commons amounted to £85 9s 3d... the money available was £44 18s 7½d, therefore £40 10s 7½d was needed.*
>
> *Every Apothecary and Druggist in the City of Dublin to pay half a guinea to defray the Sd expences*[12]

The druggists were included in this appeal for funds, yet before long they were being ostracised as an unworthy and dangerous rival to regular medical men, but they were impossible to regulate because they had no controlling organisation. More importantly, as well as allegedly offering substandard or dangerous goods, they posed a commercial threat to the apothecaries. There were other conscientious and educated people, however, who sought to put the sale of medicines without simultaneous attendance on the sick on a proper footing. The Guild received notice of the formation of the new Pharmaceutical Society, which

> *...brought to voice many affecting grievances under which the profession of apothecary laboured.*

This early warning of the formation of an organisation which was to rival the unity of apothecaries was later to erupt into schism within Apothecaries Hall, and to involve Daniel.

In the view of Charles Lucas, whose political interest was wider than his concern for the medical profession, the Guild of St Luke should be more than a trade association. He was determined to improve the condition of the many people in Ireland who were struggling in deep poverty. Thousands of destitute people had congregated in Dublin and other towns, and were suffering malnutrition and illness as a result of poverty and overcrowding. Lucas believed this should be prevented, and that it could be if appropriate steps were taken. As it was people who needed medicine could not get it, because even if they could pay for it there was no one to supply it. He therefore envisaged a scheme whereby men could be trained to prepare and sell medicines, and after suitable examination would be licensed to do so. They would then distribute themselves to all parts of the country to make at least some sort of medical care available to those in need.

At that time the duty of a 'medical man' was simply to 'give advice' about which medicine was needed for a person who was ill. Diagnostic skills, that is to say the classification and identification of the causes of illness, were poorly developed, the more important task being to provide a remedy that would promise relief from the affliction. The apothecaries, who were able both to identify the problem and supply the correct treatment were thus the right people to fulfil Lucas's dreams, as well as meeting the medical needs of the public as a whole. Surgeons had other skills, such as the treatment of wounds and injuries, much needed in time of war, but were not associated in the public mind with illness. The apothecary derived his income from selling medicines and therefore did not need to charge for 'advice', that is to say for attendance and diagnosis, any more than a tailor would charge for advising on the choice of cloth for a suit or for taking measurements, however wise that advice might be. This distinction between the surgeons and physicians who charged fees for advice but supplied no medicine, and the apothecaries who charged for the medicine but not for advice, remained a bone of contention between the different sections of the profession throughout the nineteenth century. It still has echoes in the professional attitudes of today.

It was generally accepted that the apothecary was the doctor of the people, a principle established by the famous Rose case one hundred years earlier. Rose was an apothecary who had been challenged by the Royal College of Physicians of London. They alleged that he had treated patients without the guidance of a licensed physician, which in their view was a flagrant breach of the rules. Rose's victory in the courts established that it was legitimate for apothecaries to attend the sick[13], and by the end of the eighteenth century Irish law even permitted authorities to employ and pay them as medical officers of jails. Lucas envisaged the apothecary as the person to provide medical care to the sick poor. His proposals included an organisation with powers to examine entrants to the profession, oversee their training by apprenticeship, and supervise the standards of the shops where medicines were stocked, prepared and sold[14]. This remarkable scheme was conceived well before the foundation of public dispensaries to treat the sick poor, and 130 years before any system of national health insurance. Unfortunately the proposals, which included the appointment of apothecaries as medical officers to some hospitals and asylums, were only partially implemented, but the important part was the concept of a professional body to set and regulate standards and this was realised by the foundation of the Apothecaries' Hall in 1791, though Lucas did not live to see it.

Daniel Moore was to play a major part in bringing the new Hall into being. The Guild of St Luke was ruled by a Master and two Wardens, and on its 'Election Day', 19th October 1789, Mr Dalton and Mr Moore were elected Wardens. The first steps towards the new organisation were taken when it was resolved:-

...that the establishment of an Apothecaries' Hall in this City on a plan similar to that instituted by the Corporation of Apothecaries in London would be highly advantageous to the Publick ..... a plan was then agreed to appoint a committee to review the London Plan.

The committee consisted of the Master and ten others, including Daniel, under the chairmanship of his uncle John Clarke. At a meeting on 16th January 1790 it was unanimously agreed:-

That the establishment of an Apothecaries' Hall in this City would be a great National benefit.

That to make such an Institution permanent and respectable, it is absolutely necessary to take in the aid of every branch of medicine.

That physicians, surgeons, apothecaries, druggists and chymists, following their respective professions in this Kingdom, be considered eligible to subscribe.

In an effort to secure their support, subscriptions were invited from other members of the fledgling medical profession. A communication from

John Clarke was accordingly addressed to R. S. Obré, Esq., President of the Royal College of Surgeons in Ireland, with whom 'informal conversations of an amicable nature had been held'[15].

> *'Sir,*
>
> *In consequence of the very flattering attention so politely expressed by your Secretary to our Chairman, we, the Committee appointed by the general meeting of the Apothecaries and Druggists in this City, have the honor of laying before you the Resolutions agreed on by them, for forming an Apothecaries' Hall in Dublin, on an enlarged plan. Should the sentiments of this very respectable College coincide with these Resolutions, we shall immediately proceed to form the general plan, which we hope will deserve their concurrence and support.*
>
> *We have the honor to be &c,*
>
> *John Clarke, Chairman'*

The surgeons were favourably impressed with these proposals. At a special meeting at which a deputation from the apothecaries was received it was resolved unanimously:-

> *That, as the said Resolutions appear to us well calculated to serve the public essentially, they deserve our entire concurrence, and shall have our warmest support.*

In fact the College went further, by allowing their lecture theatre in Mercer Street to be used for the apothecaries' first meeting after the incorporation of their new Hall until they could obtain a building of their own[16].

This co-operation was nothing new, as the apothecaries had long been proposing a union of the profession – "it is absolutely necessary to take in the aid of every branch of medicine" they said. Unfortunately, within thirty years the sentiment of warm friendship expressed by the surgeons vanished when the college's members began to realise that the apothecaries' activities were competitive and unwelcome. One reason for this was the great need for surgeons in the army during the Napoleonic wars. Licentiates of the Hall were accepted into the army as surgeons, though strictly speaking a licence from the Hall did not permit surgery, which the

College saw as improper competition for their own licentiates. However, in the demand for surgeons to replace those who were killed in battle, this nice distinction seems to have been overlooked. The controversy continued to smoulder for fifty years as each fought to maintain its own domain.

So, by an Act of Parliament in 1791 the Guild of St Luke metamorphosed into the Apothecaries' Hall of Dublin. The Act extended the new body's remit beyond Dublin to include the whole of Ireland, whereas the authority of the Guild had been limited to the city. The Guild actually remained in existence for a while, and Daniel was elected Master of it in 1791 even though it had been absorbed into the Hall which took over its functions. The Bill presented to Parliament had been supported by the promises of sixty apothecaries to subscribe one hundred pounds each, which was necessary for the purchase of a building in Cecilia Street. This appears to have been inadequate as they needed to borrow a further £2,000 a few years later. Before long, however, their investments in the Hall which operated as a joint-stock company were bearing fruit in the form of dividends of up to fifty per cent. With this increased prosperity they were able to move to much more imposing premises on the corner of Clare Street and Merrion Square, the latter being the preferred place of residence for the medical elite of the time. Daniel was one of the sixty subscribers, and a member of the foundation Court of Directors. The first Governor was Henry Hunt, who remained in office for the first six years, after which Daniel was elected in his place. He was re-elected in 1806 and 1816, and briefly again in 1829 after an almost catastrophic internal crisis. The Moore family's involvement with the Apothecaries' Hall continued down the generations with Daniel's son John, his grandson William Daniel, and his great-nephew Charles who were all sometime Governors, and his great-grandson John who was Examiner in Arts.

The original purpose of the Apothecaries' Hall was to regulate the businesses of apothecaries throughout the country, unlike its counterpart in London whose responsibilities at this time ran only within that city. The Act says this was necessary because :-

...not only many but great inconveniences have arisen from the want of an Hall amply supplied with Medicines of the purest quality, prepared under the inspection of persons well skilled in the art and mystery of such preparations,

but also frequent frauds have been imposed and practised on many of His Majesty's subjects …. by persons pretending to the art and mystery of the apothecary, to the injury of the fair trader, the disappointment of the physician and the imminent hazard of the lives of His Majesty's faithful subjects throughout the realm.

The new Hall met these obligations in a variety of ways. It was a joint-stock company which bought and sold medicines of proven purity on a wholesale basis and for profit to the shareholders, although in the beginning this was only for the trade in ingredients rather than compounded medicines. An educational standard for entry to apprenticeship was set by examining apprentices before permitting them to start with their Masters. It also examined apprentices in practical matters on completion of their seven years experience, who were thereby licensed to practise independently as 'Masters'. In the thirty five years following its foundation no fewer than 1289 apprentices obtained the licence of the new Hall, an average of nearly 37 a year, and there were a further 491 who qualified as Assistants rather than Masters. Another important function was the maintenance of standards by inspecting the premises of apothecaries anywhere and everywhere in the country, and prosecuting those who infringed the law by selling medicines without being qualified to do so. This was aimed at the untrained druggists, and at those physicians and surgeons who were neither licentiates of the Hall nor graduates of a school such as Edinburgh which included pharmacy in its teaching and examinations. Despite this worthy objective only ten prosecutions were made in the first year of the Hall's existence. It was a tall order to expect people with businesses in Dublin to supervise shops all over the country before the age of good transport and communication. Proper roads, railways, and the General Post Office were yet to come.

As Governor from time to time and a director for many years, Daniel was a diligent member of the Hall. The minute books record his regular attendances at meetings of the directors and at the examination of candidates. All went well at first, needing little more than attention to the trading accounts and business. Sales of medicines and their ingredients from the Hall's shop in 1796 varied from £300 to £600 a month, much of the goods being bought in London[17]. There were sometimes difficulties with staff discipline, such as when it was necessary to order Messrs Henry and Bierne, the shopkeepers, to:-

breakfast and dine at such times that attendance shall be given in the shop during the hours of business by one of them.

On another occasion, in order to keep the books straight and avoid any suspicion of irregularity, Daniel had to instruct the apothecary in charge:-

...to Balance the Cash Receipts of the Day on the evening or on closing the shop each night in the presence of the then attending subscriber who shall annex his name to the amount thereof.
  Daniel Moore, Governor

There was also difficulty in settling accounts for goods imported from London because of unfavourable exchange rates between Irish and English currency.

Other aspects of the Hall seem to have had a more sociable nature, for at a Grand Council attended by thirty members it was decided that:-

....the Wine Room be kept open until nine o'clock in the evening in the summer half of the year.

The smooth running of the Hall was no easy matter, though, for these were troubled times. In Europe the French Revolution had wrought havoc in the established social order, and its influence reached Ireland where it encouraged dissent among those wanting to change the way their country was governed. Though Ireland had its own Parliament, its decisions were always subject to the approval of the London government. Those who considered themselves truly Irish, whether Catholic or Protestant, ancient Irish, Anglo-Norman, or descended from later immigrants, longed to assert their own Irish identity independent of English rule. Secret societies collectively known as 'Defenderism' existed to further the cause of Catholic emancipation. The United Irishmen, founded in Belfast in 1791 in the same year as the Apothecaries' Hall, had turned from a radical debating society into an increasingly militant force, and their leader Wolfe Tone had fled to France. The growing unrest finally erupted into violence, when under Tone's influence a French naval force reached Bantry Bay. Though this episode came to nothing the threat of war remained, and in 1798 the French again attempted invasion. Martial law was imposed, and discovery of plans for insurrection led to violent and bloody engagements, such as those at Wexford and Vinegar Hill at Enniscorthy[18].

In such troubled times new ventures such as the Hall, and small businesses such as the Moore family's shop, were at risk. As well as the political instability which threatened trade, there was a call to defend the country against armed rebellion and the very real threat of a French invasion. A general call to arms in defence of the nation was made, but the members of the Hall were reluctant to comply with it because of the adverse effect it would have on their businesses. It fell to Daniel, as Governor in 1798, to join with his fellow directors in writing to the Lord Lieutenant, the London government's authority in Dublin, pleading exemption from military duty, saying:-

My Lord,

Our professional Duties prevent us from making those exertions under arms at this eventful period which we wish to render to our most gracious King and Country. Permit us, my Lord, again to offer our services to Government in our professional capacity to serve as medical assistants to his Majesty's troops should it be necessary. At the same time we declare that should the standard of rebellion raise its head in this city we will join with the civil powers at the first appearance of disturbance or act in any other manner which your Excellency shall be pleased to Direct....

Signed by the Governor and Directors 23rd May 1798

The Lord Lieutenant's reply from Dublin Castle a week later thanked them for their 'spirited efforts' and said the Lord Lieutenant 'would not hesitate to avail himself of their offer if necessary'[19].

Yet it is an ill wind that blows no good. Though Dublin was spared, the continuing military activity offered an opportunity for trade which the shareholders of the Hall eagerly seized. With thousands of soldiers in the country liable to wounds and the many illnesses and fevers of camp life, there was a great need for good quality medicines. Who better to supply the large quantities needed than the loyal apothecaries? Hesitant to follow the military in person, they were more than willing to supply the necessary goods. But though the goods were supplied the Army authorities refused to pay for them, alleging that the apothecaries had taken the opportunity of unrest to maximise their profits by some creative accounting. The Hall denied the charge and demanded that their bills be met, its dignity offended by this scurrilous allegation. Eventually the army's Director of Hospitals agreed not to enquire too closely into the accounts, provided the apothecaries promised that they were not using the fluctuations in price due to the troublesome times to overcharge.

Daniel was re-elected Governor in 1806, by which time Ireland was again being governed from London under the Act of Union, which had abolished the Irish parliament. The Act was effective from 1801, and though it brought the laws in Ireland closer to those in England, Wales and Scotland, there remained many differences concerning the practice of medicine. Ireland was no longer threatened by invasion or insurrection, though the war against Napoleon continued on the continent until the battle of Waterloo nine years later. When the threat of war receded it was possible to return to consideration of matters of a more scientific and medical nature. Because medicines were becoming more potent, and their poisonous properties realised, accuracy of measurement was increasingly important. The Court of Directors, presided over by Daniel, met on 14 November 1806 to be addressed by Dr Perceval, who:-

Presented an ounce weight Troy adjusted to a standard certified by Sir Isaac Newton when Master of the Mint, ... Also a measure of eight ounces, or half an English Wine Pint made to contain Grains 3655 of Distilled Water at the temperature of 60 and another of one ounce, one sixteenth of an English Wine Pint, with its subdivisions made to contain Grains 457 of Distilled Water at the same temperature. These were adjusted with Sir Isaac Newton's Weight on the supposition that the English Wine Gallon contains 231 cubic inches and that the cubic inch of Distilled Water weighs Grs 253.37.

The result agrees with the calculations of the accurate Dr Lewis, author of the New Dispensatory,

$$231[vol] \times 253.37 \ [weight] = 58482/16 = 3655.$$

Signed   Daniel Moore Governor[20]

Clearly apothecaries had to be competent in arithmetic, and might have found the modern metric system rather simpler than the one they adopted in 1806. Despite this apparently very precise method of measurement, doses of medicines continued to be prescribed in such variable volumes as 'a wineglass-full', 'a dessertspoon-full' or a 'teaspoon-full' even until the author's early days in practice in the 1960s.

By the first few years of the nineteenth century the term 'general practitioner' was in common use in both Ireland and England to describe a person who, like physicians, attends a patient in illness, and may both prescribe and dispense the necessary medicines; and when necessary also employs some of the practical techniques of a surgeon. Such people were neither 'pure surgeons' trained in the manual skills of surgery but not pharmacy, nor physicians who diagnosed and prescribed but did not dispense. Most of these new medical practitioners were apothecaries who learned the skills of surgeons and physicians by observation and experience rather than by formal training. To meet the needs of young apothecaries whose work was developing in this way, the Apothecaries' Hall began training its apprentices accordingly. Surgeons, whose discipline was being clarified and established by the new Royal Colleges which guarded their new specialty against their rivals, argued that general practitioners should be properly trained as surgeons, and therefore by surgeons. Similarly physicians, keen to defend their own field, would not allow anyone to practise physic without their licence. Apothecaries were not usually eligible for such a licence and the Hall was not authorised to grant them, and even those people who were listed as physicians in the Dublin Directory often did not claim to have one. Yet here was the Apothecaries' Hall purporting to train people as general medical practitioners without benefit of education by the surgeons or physicians.

Another view prevailed which opposed the activities of the Hall from another direction. This was that the prime role of apothecaries was to stock and prepare medicines for sale in their shops, and that those who wished to be 'medical men' should confine themselves to caring for the sick and leave the preparation of medicines to the pharmacists. Dr Michael Donovan, a prominent member of the Hall, declared that general practitioners should not be pharmacists and should therefore stop selling medicines. In his view, and that of a growing number of his colleagues, pharmacy was a complex science that needed a knowledge of chemistry, and could not be combined with the clinical work of general practice. This was contrary to the policy of the Hall, and if followed would put them in conflict with the surgeons. Because the apothecaries' incomes were derived from the sale of medicines, not from the 'giving of advice', they were not permitted to charge for the diagnostic or advisory part of their service.

As an eminent chemist, Donovan had established the *Journal of Chemistry and Pharmacy*, and was said to have a 'violent and ungovernable temperament'[21]. Among his researches was an investigation of the medical effects of marijhuana, carried out on unsuspecting fever patients in a Calcutta hospital. He was a leading member of the recently formed Pharmaceutical Society, whose policy was that attendance on the sick and the dispensing of medicines were separate functions and should not be performed by the same person. Nevertheless the Hall welcomed his talents, elected him a Director in 1828, and put him in charge of the laboratory with instructions to draft the rules for using it. He was elected Governor in 1829, but by placing such a controversial figure in high office the Hall laid an explosive charge which all but destroyed it.

At that time many people outside and far from Dublin who called themselves apothecaries were preparing and selling medicines directly to the public. These people, it was alleged, possessed neither medical nor pharmaceutical skills, and traded in other goods, including perfumes, oils and poisons. This was serious because apothecaries were specifically prevented from selling oils and colours, especially arsenic, in the same premises as medicines. These 'irregular' traders also prepared their own medicines, or 'nostrums', so called from the Latin *nostrum*, meaning 'ours', or 'of our own making'. These preparations might contain anything the inventor fancied, whether or not it had a recognised medical effect. In the view of the Hall these 'quack' medicines were dangerous and should not be allowed. The directors resolved that:-

> ... *any attempt to amalgamate the profession of an apothecary with the business of Merchant, Druggist, Grocery, Perfumery, Oilman etc, notwithstanding the deservedly high respectability of these different avocations, must be quite inconsistent and impolitic and derogatory to the character of a medical man and dangerous to the public health.*[22]

Prosecution of offenders had been carried out since the early years of the Hall, and by the 1820s were running at about sixty a year, but following this resolution there was something of a witch hunt. A committee of three was formed to inspect every shop and every medical hall, that is all the sellers of nostrums. One of the three was the young physician Robert Graves, representing the College of Physicians, who had recently returned to Dublin from studies in Europe, and was on the brink of a famous career as a teacher. The duty of the committee was to visit the shops and decide:-

> as to the certificates of the owner, ...and in every case of any degree of
> irregularity to make correct observations thereon, in order to report to the
> Court [of Directors]

It was this new enthusiasm for eliminating the improper sale of medicines that prompted the sudden rise in prosecutions, which in 1829 exceeded six hundred. The directors took the matter further to enquire whether any legislation could prevent grocers selling medicines without endangering the Act of Incorporation of the Hall. Two of the three directors who sought a legal opinion on this point were Michael Donovan and Daniel Moore[23], but the opinion given did not result in any further legislation. Meanwhile, the mood amongst apothecaries in other parts of Ireland, of whom there were some 1,500, was restless and angry at what they saw as the autocratic domination of the Hall, and the interference of the Directors in their legitimate business. A meeting was called to remonstrate and seek redress, which took place at the Rotunda Hospital, because the directors had refused permission for it to be held at the Hall. The meeting was heated, many members and shareholders of the Hall threatening to sell their shares, which would have caused their value to collapse. The leader of these dissenters was Dr Michael Donovan, protagonist for the movement to separate pharmacy from medical practice, who was attacking the very body of which he was the Governor. He had no choice but to resign. He wrote to the Secretary of the Hall:-

12 D'Olier St,
December 5th 1829

Sir,

The proceedings of the Company of Apothecaries' Hall for some time
past .... have induced me to resign the honour of being Governor, and of
course, of being a Director.

I have the honour to be, Sir,
Your faithful servant
M. Donovan

It was Daniel Moore who took the place of the disgraced Donovan, at
the age of 79 and the only surviving founder-director of the Hall, and,
perhaps, as the grand old man of the profession, the only one who could
restore tranquillity[24]. This was a turning point in the history of the Hall,
for the disciplines of medicine and pharmacy were destined to go their
separate ways. Subsequent events have followed Donovan's view that
pharmacy deserves to regulate itself independently from supervision by
another profession. The Hall was left with its medical activities, but as the
universities and medical schools developed in the subsequent years the
Hall even surrendered such educational role as it had.

In June 1841 Daniel was guest of honour at a dinner at the Hall to
commemorate its fiftieth anniversary. He was an old man of 89, the sole
survivor of the Hall's founders. In that half century he had lived through
war and insurrection, had prospered in business despite the political and
social upheavals, and had seen the beginnings of remarkable developments
in medicine. Not least among these events was the struggle for domi-
nance among the various members of the fledgling medical profession,
another contest in which Daniel was destined to play his part.

BREATHING A VEIN.

An ill man being bled by his doctor, from an etching after J. Sneyd 1804.
(Wellcome Library, London.)

CHAPTER FOUR

A Fragmented Profession

It is said that King George III was once approached by Lord Melville who nervously beseeched His Majesty to create a certain apothecary a baronet. Noticing his lordship's trembling hesitation the King exclaimed "Of course, it shall be done! I thought you would ask me to make him a Physician, *but that would be more difficult". Then, with a touching expression of confidence in his physicians, or perhaps a realistic awareness of their lack of curative skills, he remarked "They may make as many baronets as they please, but I shall die by the College!"* [1]

Twiss's Life of Lord Chancellor Eldon

When Daniel Moore and his colleagues founded the Apothecaries' Hall as the eighteenth century gave way to the nineteenth, the medical profession was a loose association of men with different but complementary functions, rather than a distinct and united entity. The physicians were learned in 'physic', that is to say the selection and prescription of medicines appropriate for the perceived problem; the surgeons used 'hands-on' treatments of injuries, abscesses, and ulcers like bleeding, cupping or the application of plaisters or splints; and the apothecaries prepared and dispensed medicines and applications to the prescription of a physician or a surgeon, and also performed some of the others' functions on their own initiative. Professor J B Lyons, writing at the end of the twentieth century has said that the "apothecaries stood at the lowest level of a rigid hierarchy", while the physicians who considered themselves to be the medical elite "appear to us to reflect a measure of complacency permitting a self-satisfied regard while they energetically purged cupped and bled their patients"[2]. The members of the Apothecaries' Hall resolved to improve the status of the apothecary by broadening his education to include those subjects studied by the physicians and surgeons. Daniel, his son William and grandson William Daniel were all involved in these developments, which were not received with favour by their rivals in the other disciplines. Indeed they were the cause of considerable strife.

The United Kingdom, formed by the Acts of Union between England and Scotland in 1704, and between Ireland, England, Wales and Scotland in 1800, was by no means united in its legislation regarding the medical profession. In Dublin, as we have seen, the qualification of the Apothecaries' Hall gave a licence to practise as an apothecary in any part of Ireland, but the Dublin licence was not recognised in England because the 1791 Act which created the Hall predated the Union of 1800. In any case it did not provide qualifications in surgery and physic alone. In London it was necessary to have a licence from the Royal College of Physicians of London to practise as a physician, but it gave no right to act as a surgeon, to dispense medicine, or to practise more than seven miles outside the city. Members of the Royal College of Surgeons could not be physicians, nor dispense medicines. Therefore, as supplying medicines was part and parcel of the work of the general practitioner many students also took the examination of the Company of Apothecaries to obtain a licence to do so. Graduates of Edinburgh, where the course included pharmacy, were no better situated because they had to have the licences of the college governing the area where they wanted to practise, and such licences were reluctantly given. Nor was it feasible to study in one place, say Dublin, and take examinations at another such as London, because London authorities would not recognise the certificates of attendance at lectures of other schools. Someone who had qualified in Dublin but not in London would have to undertake further attendance at London schools before obtaining a licence to practise there. This rule was easily flouted by purchasing certificates of attendance without actually attending any lectures, a convenient and time-saving way of meeting the formalities. In the rest of England the situation was even more confused: because the London Colleges' licences only applied to that city no license was needed to practise in a country district or town, so however well qualified a 'proper' doctor might be, in the eyes of the law and regulatory bodies he was indistinguishable from any charlatan, impostor or quack. Even more confusingly, it was possible to buy the degree of MD from certain universities, and even from the Archbishop of Canterbury, without any formal education at all in either medicine, surgery or pharmacy.

The number of Fellows of the College of Physicians of London was strictly limited to maintain their status, and only Doctors in Medicine from Oxford or Cambridge were eligible for fellowship, and for them Latin and Greek were as important as medical knowledge. One Dr Pearson, a determined applicant for the honour and prestige that election to fellowship would bring him:-

> ... had reached his 80th year, [and] being informed in 1828, that he would
> at length be admitted to an examination as a preliminary to admission into
> the college, bravely set about preparing himself for the ordeal by getting up
> his Greek, and died reading Aretaeus![3]

In Ireland the licences of the College of Surgeons and the Apothecaries' Hall were valid throughout Ireland, but were not recognised in England. Legislation protected licensed apothecaries against competition from irregular sellers of medicines, including surgeons unless they were licensed by the Hall. Such a licence required a seven year apprenticeship in pharmacy as well as training in surgery. Conversely, the College of Surgeons objected if apothecaries who sold medicines from their shops pretended to the skills of the surgeon without their apprenticeship. This controversy was a bone of contention between the surgeons and apothecaries for much of the nineteenth century, revolving around whether or not a medical practitioner 'kept shop', that is whether he dispensed medicines prescribed by others as well as for his own patients. According to convention, apothecaries who kept shop were not permitted to charge for any 'advice' given, by which was meant attendance and diagnosis, and therefore set a price for the medicines they sold which would cover all their costs. They could, and did, prescribe as many medicines as they wished in order to increase their income to what they considered appropriate and justifiable. As late as the 1850s this was still happening[4]. When Mr Dalley, merchant of Ludgate Hill, was attended by his apothecary Mr Parrett, prescriptions for the fourth day of his illness amounted to:-

Another pearl jalap	6s 10d	Another hypnotic draught	2s 0d
A cordial bolus	2s 0d	A cordial draught	1s 8d
A cordial pearl emulsion	4s 6d	Another pearl jalap	6s 8d
Another cordial jalap	3s 8d	Another bolus	2s 4d
Another draught	1s 8d	A pearl julap	4s 6d
A cordial draught	2s 6d	An anodyne mixture	4s 6d
A glass of cordial spirits	2s 0d	Another mucilage	3s 4d
A cooling mixture	3s 6d	A blistering plaster to the neck	2s 6d
Two more of the same to		Plaster to dress the	
the arms	3s 0d	blisters	0s 6d
Spirit of Hartshorn	0s 6d	Another apozem	3s 6d

The total for only one day's treatment was £3 4s 2d, and assuming his illness lasted a week, at this rate Mr Dalley would have paid his apothecary about £20, which is probably more than he paid his housemaid in a whole year. Surgeons, however, charged only for visiting the patient and for the service given, and envied their rivals who could improve their incomes by the simple expedient of prescribing and supplying more medicine.

In England it was even less clear who was permitted to call himself a regular medical practitioner. Even those who had undergone expensive courses of study were unable to make an appropriate living in the face of competition from quacks and charlatans with no pretension to a medical education at all. The Apothecaries' Act of 1815 'for better regulating the Practice of Apothecaries throughout England and Wales' attempted to put this right by making the Master, Apothecaries and Assistants of the London Company of Apothecaries (the 'Hall') responsible for examinations and granting certificates to successful candidates[5], which was a licence to prepare, dispense and sell medicines. Because membership of the London College of Surgeons, like the Irish, did not grant such a license, many students intending to enter the new field of 'general practice' took both the College's and the Hall's examinations despite the further study and expense. Students undertaking this system of education still received no recognised education or examination in 'physic'. Worse still, the wording of the Act gave the impression that it was not an offence to do the things that surgeons and apothecaries do without a licence, such as treating symptoms of pain or fever; the offence merely lay in *claiming* to be licenced. This did nothing to protect genuine medical practitioners from the competition, so long as any irregular and improper competitor did not claim to be licenced.

The confusion that this fragmentation produced is well illustrated by the case of Mr Ryan. He was a member of the London College of Surgeons and after seven years' apprenticeship in pharmacy at Dublin had the licence of the Apothecaries' Hall, for which he may have been examined by Daniel or John William Moore. When he started a new practice in Farningham in Kent in the 1820s with qualifications in both surgery and pharmacy from competent authorities within the United Kingdom, he believed he could practise anywhere in either Ireland, England, Wales or Scotland. Unfortunately for him, the London Apothecaries' Hall discovered he had no London license and refused to recognise the Dublin one. They charged him with practising without their certificate and prosecuted him successfully. The Lancet pointed out that the prosecution did not allege incompetence:-

> ....*indeed, he has cured all his patients (with the exception of one, whom he saw but twice) and that, too, in many instances where other practitioners had failed to afford relief.*[6]

Here was a man who had proper license from one part of the kingdom being penalised for infringing the rules of licensing authority in another of the same kingdom, even though he was perfectly competent. He was ruined.

In 1830 an apothecary called Handey sued a patient named Henson for non-payment of fees for attendance and medicine. Handey said he followed the principle of:-

> *not sending in large quantities of useless medicines, but of attending when necessary and charging for his professional talents and visits*[7].

Henson claimed that apothecaries should not charge for 'advice', and refused to pay for Handey's visits on the grounds that he could not prove that he had actually visited, and therefore also refused to pay for the medicine. Handey said he had visited fifteen times and claimed fees of £7 0s 6d, and had only issued twenty-one prescriptions, so was hardly 'sending in large quantities of useless medicines'. In the Court of the King's Bench the jury took only one minute to find in Handey's favour. From then on apothecaries were free to charge for their knowledge and skills in medicine, as well as for goods supplied in their capacity as pharmacists.

On the other hand those who had no licence of any kind were free from the law so long as they did not claim to be licensed, or to practise medicine 'for gain'. In the case of Apothecaries' Company v Baldwin, the Company's prosecution was unsuccessful because they could not prove that Baldwin had actually sent in a bill for medicines or that he had acted 'for gain'. Using that case as a precedent, a "Dr" Coffin and his Botanic College, a group 'made up of tailors, cobblers and bakers' wives' were acquitted of practising without a licence[8]. The Botanic College believed that:-

Heat is life, and life is heat, and it causes all the operations of the body', and that 'the fire in the stomach makes water boil there, which heats the lungs......and that steam thus generated sets the limbs in motion.

This was the age of the newly invented steam engine, after all. A Society was formed to distribute 'Botanic' medicines among the poor, including an 'Anti-Cholera Powder' consisting of spices, Cayenne pepper, and *Lobelia inflata,* all warming substances which would keep the fires burning. The dose to ensure an adequate supply of fuel for the fires was a teaspoonful every half-hour. This wonderful remedy was purchased at *wholesale* prices by the benevolent and generous Society, who distributed 339 packets of the powder gratuitously to the poor of Whitechapel. Unfortunately, when one George Burt took the powder he was 'so ungrateful as to die'. The Apothecaries' Company brought a prosecution, but lost because the 'Society' bought the powder at wholesale prices from 'Dr Coffin' and supplied it without further charge, that is to say *'not for gain'*[9]. No attempt was made to prosecute the mysterious 'Dr' Coffin who made the powder and sold it to the naïve and gullible members of the 'Society' at the 'wholesale' price, which presumably included his own profit margin. It seemed to *The Lancet* that the Apothecaries Act was not only stupid and powerless, but had defined the difference between a medical practitioner and a charlatan as whether the person in question purported to cure illness *for gain.*

The crux of the matter was that there was no defined form of education for medical practitioners, nor a generally applicable way of distinguishing those of proven ability from untrained pretenders and mountebanks. To obtain a licence to practise candidates had to be examined by one or more of numerous bodies whose authority varied in different parts of the nation, and even then their licence was not universally recognised. In Ireland the Apothecaries' Hall of Dublin, including members of the Moore family, set about tackling the first of these issues, and proposed a scheme to tackle the second. In England the remedy took a rather different route. Neither was successful, and both were controversial.

The first step taken by the Dublin Apothecaries' Hall was intended to improve the public esteem of the profession of apothecary. Those who had their licence of the Hall and were entitled to run their own businesses had long been known as 'Masters', as they had been in the old trades' guilds, but in the nineteenth century the more progressive members of the Hall thought this term was below their dignity. It was 'Dr' Moore, but whether this was Daniel or John William is uncertain, who seconded a motion:-

That the appellation 'Master Apothecary' is degrading to the profession, and that the word 'Licentiate' be the term used for the future.[10]

In this way the apothecaries came into line with their surgeon and physician colleagues who already used the term 'licentiate' to describe a person who had passed the college's examination, but who was below the status of fellow and not a doctor of a university. At the same time the idea was gaining ground that it was not enough merely to supervise apprenticeships and hold examinations as empowered by the 1791 Act: students needed to be taught. The Hall had offered a limited amount of teaching since 1792 when it founded a school in Mary Street to celebrate its first anniversary, but the curriculum was limited. In 1815, when Daniel was Governor-elect and John William was a director, a series of lectures in Chemistry, Pharmacy and Materia Medica were instituted, given at first by some of the directors, but later enhanced and given by eminent teachers from outside[11]. There were several 'private' schools run by surgeons in Dublin, as in London, giving instruction in anatomy and surgery with opportunities for dissection, which were a lucrative side-line and useful in the competition for public notice. The Royal College of Surgeons in Ireland had been a medical school since 1790, when they had "established a school for the younger part of the profession"[12], which provided additional income for the College, and for the surgeons individually. The apothecaries' decision to engage in teaching was therefore a threat to the proprietors of established schools who were quick to challenge its legitimacy. In defence the directors sought a legal opinion, which confirmed that they were entitled to found a school if they so wished. Not to be outdone, and to maintain its own position in the face of competition from the existing private and corporate schools, the King's and Queen's College of Physicians in Ireland also set up a school and held examinations. It was not a success, and *The Lancet* poured scorn on its lack of achievement. It commented on the exodus of Irishmen to Edinburgh to obtain a diploma there:-

We dare say that…. the College of Surgeons in Edinburgh, not to include the University of that City, has pocketed more Irish cash in its seven pound diplomas than the College of Physicians, since the promulgation of their ill-fated regulation, have by their sixty-guinea licences.[13]

It also rebuked the Irish College of Physicians for not allowing surgeons or apothecaries to attend patients within the city of Dublin or seven miles around it, which was "sufficient to account for the merited contempt with which the regulations were received". In practice, most medical attention was given by apothecaries, or by surgeons with a pharmacy licence, that is to say by the 'general practitioners'; or put another way, the new general practitioners were surgeons-cum-pharmacists, and had no pretension to be physicians. Opportunities to practise as a pure physician were thus strictly limited, and demand for a physician's licence was small. The infant school of the physicians failed to thrive, and soon died. The custom of going to Edinburgh continued, with the approval of *The Lancet*, because the Irish College of Surgeons would only grant a licence in surgery to those who had done a surgical apprenticeship, and not everyone wished to do that[14]. One of those who went to Edinburgh was William Daniel Moore.

The apothecaries were keen to fill the void left by the physicians' failure, believing that the future of their profession could be assured only by teaching new entrants according to a full and well-designed curriculum. The existing lectures were developed into a full-scale programme which eventually led to the formation of a new School of Medicine. Dr Michael Donovan was appointed professor of Chemistry, Pharmacy and Materia Medica in 1820, and being a very able teacher was a strong attraction. His association with the school was short-lived, however, for within seven years he had resigned his Governorship in the dispute about the roles of the pharmacist and general practitioner. With or without him success bred success, and in 1832 the School of Medicine was formally constituted. A lecture theatre to hold 150 people was built, and within five years a completely new building was opened with two theatres, dissecting rooms, and three laboratories[15].

The school was staffed by professors chosen from the most eminent men of the day. Between 1836 and 1854 it was very popular, having at times 100 students, ten or fifteen more than either Trinity College or the College of Surgeons[16]. It was not the first medical school in Dublin, for the school of the Royal College of Surgeons was already in existence. In England the London Hospital Medical College, England's first complete medical school[17], had been founded in 1785, and the Edinburgh school had been in existence even longer. It is arguable, however, that the School of the Dublin Apothecaries' Hall was the first to offer a comprehensive education specifically for students intending to be general practitioners. It was to be another 130 years before the importance of including general practice in the undergraduate curriculum of all medical students was recognised by the appointment of the world's first professor of general practice at Edinburgh University[18].

The regulations regarding certificates and degrees imposed on the teachers at the new school were more strict than was usual at the time, when rules were lax and often ignored. The Court of Examiners would not recognise any teacher who lectured on more than one subject, and all teachers had to be properly equipped and supported. For instance, chemistry teachers had to have a laboratory and apparatus, and for materia

medica and anatomy they needed to have a museum of appropriate specimens. For medicine they had to be Fellows or Licentiates of the College
of Physicians or an MD of Oxford, Cambridge, Dublin, Edinburgh or
Glasgow, and in anatomy a member of the London or Dublin College of
Surgeons[19]. Teaching which consisted of theory only without any practical
experience was considered inadequate, so in 1834 attendance at hospitals
became compulsory[20]. In 1838 it was William Daniel Moore, now in a
position of authority in the Hall, who jointly signed the regulations for
the Court of Examiners with the Governor-to-be, C. H. Leet[21]. The subjects to be examined included:-

*Translating and explaining the Pharmacopoeia and extemporaneous pre-
scriptions*

Practical Pharmacy   *Materia Medica and Botany*

Chemistry and Physics

Anatomy and Physiology   *Practice of Medicine*

   *One part of the examination to be viva-voce, the other to be practical
demonstration and experiment.*

   *Notes of the examination to be kept by the Chair, and in the result of
insufficient answering in the first four sections, examination to be discontinued.*

   G.H.Leet   *W.D.Moore*

The school was evidently such a success that a very innovative proposal
was made by the Hall, that:-

*"A Board should be formed, composed of all branches of the profession,
and empowered to grant degrees for General Practice ... [to replace] the
twenty-three different authorities which can now licence a man to practice (sic)
medicine"[22]*

If this far-sighted scheme had been implemented the school of the
Apothecaries' Hall would have been the first medical school in the world
to grant degrees on the completion of a course of training specifically for
general practice, though the kind of practice envisaged was very different
from the concept of the primary care physician of today. Unfortunately,
the profession was so divided by sectional disputes and protectionism that

it was unable to grasp the significance of the proposal. The initiative for creating a united profession passed from the apothecaries to the surgeons.

The College of Surgeons was not pleased to have this cuckoo of a school in its nest. Both the college and the proprietors of the private schools felt threatened by such a large and successful rival. To protect itself, in 1838 the College of Surgeons refused to acknowledge the lectures given by the Hall's teachers even if they were members of the College, or to accept their certificates of attendance at lectures at the Hall, or indeed at lectures given by '*any* apothecary who kept open shop'. The College's educational policy was being corrupted by the stigma of 'trade', or more realistically by envy of the apothecaries' freedom to make money by selling medicines, which the 'pure' surgeons could not do. The College's ruling effectively prevented candidates for the surgical examinations studying at the Hall and therefore made them ineligible for a pharmacy diploma, or, if they studied at the Hall, excluded them from the College's examination in surgery so that they were only eligible for a diploma in pharmacy. The Hall retaliated by refusing to acknowledge the College's lectures "until the College's resolution be rescinded"[23], which did not happen for another four years[24]. Worse was to come for the apothecaries when the College of Surgeons instituted its own Court of Pharmacy to examine its pupils in chemistry and materia medica, thereby challenging the apothecaries' monopoly. The granting of diplomas in pharmacy by the College of Surgeons as well as the Hall would have undermined the value of the apothecaries' licence, for students would have preferred a single diploma in surgery-with-pharmacy like the Edinburgh one.

The surgeons were also angry because appointments to infirmaries, gaols and fever hospitals were being given to apothecaries who could supply both medical and non-medical goods to the institutions[25]. To the surgeons it appeared that the apothecaries' commercial success was interfering with the professional opportunities of the surgeons. The taint of trade and shop-keeping was anathema to them, and the cordial relations which had existed when the Hall was founded now turned to jealousy and outrage. The surgeons attempted to break the deadlock in 1838 by petitioning parliament, jointly with the physicians, to restore their right to public appointments. Their "terrible indictment against the apothecaries" alleged that the apothecary was:-

*an imperfectly educated person who had usurped the place of the physician
and the surgeon, and had not properly performed the functions legally
assigned to him.*[26]

The apothecaries responded vigorously, saying that the allegations were

mischievous and dangerous, and altogether unwarranted and untrue.

Although the College was in dispute with the Hall, the antagonism was
not reflected in the medical practitioners as a whole, many of whom held
the double qualification of 'College and Hall'. The controversy was irrel-
evant to them, unless of course, they kept shop. Also, outside Dublin and
bigger towns, populations were too small to support both pure medical
practitioners and pure pharmacists, so it was economically sensible for
medical men to dispense their own medicines if qualified to do so.
Disputes about education and qualification were an esoteric distraction
for many practitioners who were in considerable trouble financially.
Incomes were being depressed by changes in the Poor Laws and consequent reduction in salaries of infirmary medical officers. The profession
was overpopulated and poorly organised, with no central body to speak
for it. Fees were low and bills were often unpaid.

Most practitioners had some connection with the College of
Surgeons which became the one body round which they were prepared
to rally, and at a meeting held on 17th January 1839 it was determined
that action should be taken, in the following words:-

*That it is greatly to be desired, that measures should be adopted to
make this College the centre of union for the practitioners of Ireland; and that
every regularly educated medical man should, as far as possible, be associated
in it.*[27]

This resolution was in the spirit of the Hall's proposal in the previous year
for a "Board composed of all branches of the profession", but the locus
of the movement had now gone to the College of Surgeons. Local
medical associations throughout Ireland sent delegates to a meeting at the
College, which they believed was the only central organisation able to

bring pressure to bear on government. On 22 April 1839 a series of resolutions was passed, designed to provoke the College into action to unite
the profession through legislation[28]. Among others, the principles of a
policy for union were set out by Mr H Maunsell, a friend and supporter
of the apothecaries:-

I   *That the College are willing and anxious to adopt such steps as
    may be considered practicable and expedient, having their object the
    incorporation of the whole body of Practitioners in Ireland into a firm
    and powerful union*

II *That in effecting such a measure ..... only those can be properly
    considered as medical Practitioners who pursue the healing art as a pro-
    fession, and that consequently, persons following the business of Retail
    Druggists ought not to be admissible into the proposed union*
    And

VI *..... this union of the profession should include both Physicians and
    Surgeons with equal privilege.*

Mr Carmichael, who had a vested interest as the proprietor of a private
school of anatomy, proposed the following:-

VII *That in order to carry this into effect .... the College seeing the utility
    of a union of all the Physicians and Surgeons of Ireland,* not engaged
    in the practice of Pharmacy *[added emphasis] willingly consents to
    become the centre of such a Union....*

The scene was thus set for the profession to unite, excluding those
who kept a shop for the sale of medicines or dispensed them on the prescription of another practitioner. Those in favour of union were careful
not to reject licenced apothecaries who were not 'in trade'. This was to
be a *professional* union; it was keeping a shop that was unprofessional, not
merely being an apothecary. A 'Meeting of the Physicians and Surgeons
of Ireland' was held on 29th May 1839 to agree the resolutions to be put
to the College of Surgeons, among which the more important were:-

Moved by professor Porter, seconded by Sir James Murray;
  Resolved – That we, the Physicians and Surgeons of Ireland, having expended large sums of money and much time and labour in the acquisition of professional knowledge, and many of us being engaged in the performance of important duties to the public, feel that it is not unreasonable for us to expect from the Government and the legislature, protection equal to that afforded to the members of the other liberal professions.

Moved by Dr Macartney; seconded by Professor Hargrave;
  Resolved – That it is the opinion of this meeting that the cause of all these evils is to be traced to the existence of divisions and separate interests among members of the medical profession; and that their effectual remedy is to be sought for in a permanent union.

The status of shop-keeping apothecaries was to be protected, even though they were to be excluded from the newly-defined 'medical profession', for they were necessary to the public to supply their medicines, for which they must be suitably, that is, scientifically, qualified:-

Moved by Surgeon White, seconded by Dr Kingsley
  Resolved – That it is our firm conviction that the interests of the public, and of the medical profession, require that encouragement should be given to a class of scientific apothecaries, whose time and attention would be exclusively devoted to the preparation and compounding of medicines, and who would thus have an opportunity of raising the profession of pharmacy from its present degraded position in Ireland to a level with that which it occupies in France and Germany; and we think that encouragement would be best afforded by the establishment of a college of pharmacy....[29]

These and others resolutions were adopted as College policy, though some members of the Council found themselves unable to agree because their interests lay in the developing role of the College as the meeting place of a distinct specialty of operative surgery, not of general practitioners. The proposals were sent to the Lord Lieutenant, who said they should receive his most 'careful attention', but that is the last that was heard of them; perhaps the dissenters within the College also had the ear of the

Lord Lieutenant. Nearly fifty years later, in 1886, the College's official historian Sir Charles Cameron wrote:-

> *It is to be regretted that this attempt to unite medical practitioners into one body, and to have such examinations for the student as would, if he passed them, qualify him to practice in any department of the healing art, ended in failure. The College, undoubtedly, were not to blame for this unfortunate result.*[30]

The physicians observed this professional insurrection with detached superiority. The surgeons had invited them to participate in the formation of a united profession by writing to the King and Queen's College of Physicians. The Fellows of that college, who now numbered twenty, sought the views of the other sixty honorary fellows and licentiates in practice in the whole of Ireland. Their conclusion and reply was dismissive:-

> *That this College ..... is of the opinion that no beneficial results either as to the more effectual cultivation of medical science, or as to the general welfare of the profession at large, can follow from the proposed union;*
> *That this College being satisfied of the inexpediency and impracticability of the proposed union cannot be a party to any Congress of the profession convened "for the purpose of determining the best means" of carrying such a union into effect.*[31]

Maybe the physicians, too, had enough influence in high places to ensure that the Lord Lieutenant did nothing. Their response was no surprise to the *Dublin Medical Press*, who viewed the College of Physicians with some scorn:-

> *This college is a limited corporation operating under an obsolete charter..... It has no power to grant degrees, and has no real connection with the university, although its members endeavour to lead members to suppose that it has. ......*
> *On the other hand there are two hundred and fifty physicians, members or licentiates of the College of Surgeons and a thousand more unconnected with that body, and in Dublin nearly fifty physicians who have no connection with*

the King and Queen's College. How utterly absurd, therefore, are their pre-
tensions to be considered the College of Physicians of Ireland.[32]

The Colleges were not the only ones to threaten both the future of the
traditional apothecary and the successful progress of Hall's new school.
Mr Travers Blackley, a member of the College of Surgeons, wrote to the
Dublin Medical Press in support of a unified profession, but was scathing
about the apothecaries' school:-

> *Let no petty feelings of jealousy towards each other actuate our motives, let*
> *us recollect that we are embarked (both physicians and surgeons) in the same*
> *ship, that we have common cause against the apothecaries, and that a*
> *mortal blow struck against either of our bodies, would be a prelude to the*
> *destruction of the other ...... Above all let me impress upon the junior*
> *members of the profession, that it is to them we must look for regeneration,*
> *for the seniors are for the most part bound hand and foot to the Apothecaries,*
> *and dare not appear openly to oppose them.....*[33]

Did Travers Blackley have the 89 year old Daniel in mind as binding his
colleagues hand and foot? Surely he could not have so described the
young and progressive William Daniel who had qualified as a surgeon at
Edinburgh, and favoured a school for general practitioners. Blackley's
solution to the problem was a 'Medico-Chirurgical Society' to include
'every lawfully qualified physician or surgeon' but not apothecaries, who
should confine themselves to the 'legitimate duties of their laboratories'.
He conceded that they might be honorary members if they promised not
to engage in medical practice.

A writer calling himself "Verax" took a different view of the cause
of the troubles, that:-

> *the medical profession, like that of law or divinity, is at present overstocked.*

He attributed this excess of doctors both to the many medical men who
had returned from the army and navy after the Napoleonic wars, and to
the large number of new entrants to the profession which he implicitly
blamed on the apothecaries new educational and professional ambitions.[34]

The practice of medicine has fallen into other hands than those which heretofore held it. ..... For the apothecary who was formerly confined to his counter, (or, if he ventured beyond its precincts, it was merely for the purpose of prescribing for slight biliary derangements, or the minor complaints of children,) at present boldly undertakes the treatment of every disease to which the human body is subject, and of every accident to which it is liable. Now allow me to ask, is it prudent or wise in the public to trust their health and lives to a body of men decidedly unfitted for the charge ?

He argued that the apothecaries were not properly educated, because they had not attended "year after year" in the dissecting rooms and hospital wards. He admitted that they had founded their comprehensive new school, but objected to the practice of medicine and pharmacy by the same person:-

It is true, the apothecaries have established a school in which lectures are delivered on anatomy, and surgery, medicine, &c, &c, in order to fit the rising generation of apothecaries for the situation of general practitioner, ... which they themselves never enjoyed. But it is against the principle of permitting the pharmacopolist to engage in the practice of medicine and surgery I contend.

The *Medical Press* was scathing about the social aspirations of some members of the profession:-

The unhappy cause is to be found in one of the original sins of Ireland – the love of gentility. The apothecary's wife is not satisfied with her husband being only an apothecary, and never rests until her lord issues forth to Glasgow, or St Andrew's, comes back an M.D., and forthwith establishes his gentility upon a brass door-plate 18 inches in length.[35]

It must be confessed that it is not clear how Daniel, Master Apothecary but not a graduate of any university, obtained his M.D. By this time his first wife Hannah had died, and he had married his second cousin Alicia, great niece of Big Charlie Lennon. It is doubtful that either of these ladies had such an influence, for Daniel remained in the modest house in South Anne Street for nearly fifty years, and it was his grandson William Daniel who placed his 'brass door-plate' outside more elegant premises in Fitzwilliam Square.

Not everyone shared the view of the *Press* and Travers Blackley. Another writer styling himself BETA argued at length that the real problem was professional rivalry and envy rather than whether a person was physician, surgeon or shop-keeper.

> *I verily believe that there is not a more envious, jealous, disunited body of men than the members of the medical profession. This is a great evil, and I fear it is an evil which is on the increase. It is quite a curiosity in country districts to see two medical men good friends or acting harmoniously together. .....*
>
> *In the name of common sense, why should a medical man who keeps a shop be excluded from the benefits of such an association [as medical union]? If he be already qualified to practise his profession, the mere circumstance of his keeping a shop for the sale of medicines should not – indeed, cannot – disqualify him for practice. ..... Other grounds of exclusion should be sought for – bad character, gross ignorance, unprofessional or ungentlemanly conduct .... [these] would afford valid reason for exclusion; but to deny a man because he keeps a shop! One might as reasonably object to his keeping a cow.*[36]

BETA argued for education of the public to enable them to discriminate between properly qualified men and charlatans, which would be greatly helped if the professionals would only talk English rather than doggerel Latin and explain themselves to their patients in ways they could understand. A pretence at education was no substitute for a real one.

Support for the apothecaries against this onslaught came from Mr H. Maunsell, the correspondence secretary of the College of Surgeons and proposer of many of the resolutions of the April meeting, who took up their cause in the interest of unity:-

> *It is only very lately that the public have heard of such bickerings between persons who ought to avoid all differences with one another, and unite to improve the condition of the profession on which they all, in their several departments, depend for the maintenance of their station in society. Why should the rival jealousies of one corporation with another, enlist the bitter enmities of men who are embarked in the same vessel, though some have been so fortunate to get cabin passage while the less fortunate must remain on deck.*[37]

At this point Dr Michael Donovan, the sometime professor of pharmacy in the apothecaries' school who had rebelliously resigned his Governorship of the Hall ten years previously, threw his weight into the contest. Writing to the same Mr Maunsell, he invited the College to support his proposals to separate pharmacy from medicine at the general congress on 29th May 1839, and thereby:-

> ... assist the apothecaries of Ireland in obtaining from the legislature the incorporation of a college of pharmacy on the conditions:-
>   I   That all existing apothecaries shall be protected in the exercise of their profession, as at present practised by them
>   II That the diploma of the college of pharmacy shall not authorise any person to practise medicine or surgery.[38]

That seemed mild enough, and protected the present practitioners while proposing change for the future, but within days he published a ferocious attack on the Hall. His objective was to establish a new discipline, which in the light of history seems obvious but was revolutionary and contentious then, and likely to destroy the livelihoods of many of his colleagues. He was determined to establish the skilled and properly regulated profession of pharmacy, dependent on proficiency in chemistry, and distinct from the practice of medicine. In a verbose letter to the *Dublin Medical Press* he said:-

> .... Pharmacy, as a profession does not exist in Ireland, ... for there are almost no apothecaries; those who are classed under that name are general practitioners whose time is entirely occupied in treatment of disease.
>   The surgeons and apothecaries have waged a fierce war.... The physicians agreed with neither party and seemed a little suspicious of both. The Governor and company of apothecaries' hall had enforced a course of education which was contrary to law, and had erected a school of medicine in opposition to the schools established by those bodies that had a legal right to dictate a course of studies. .....
>   The apothecaries [ie pharmacists not practising medicine] are now a disunited, unprotected race, ... without house or home to assemble, ... They have no library, no museum, no lecture room.... They are slaves from

morning to night – Sunday and Monday – their slavery begins at sixteen years old and terminates with their lives.[39]

A few months later he attacked the Hall again, challenging the legitimacy of its school:-

In 1791, a bungling act of the Irish Parliament incorporated our Apothecaries' hall, with power to do everything or nothing, as the Governor and the company might think fit to interpret the law. At first they preferred the latter course, and of late they choose the former. The consequence is that our profession consists of men who have complied with the act, and of those who have set it at defiance. ..... We have amongst us a body without power, and power without a body, just as the wind blows in Mary-street [the then premises of the Hall].[40]

Donovan's intention was to establish pharmacy, but his achievement was to damage the Hall and its school. The apothecaries had tried to unite the profession of general practice by appropriate education, but without the support of the rest of the medical profession or legal authority it was not possible for their school to continue.

The damage was done. The school of the apothecaries flourished for a few years yet, but competition from other institutions gradually reduced the number of students. The most important of these was Trinity College, where William Daniel was soon to be one of the first to obtain the degree of Bachelor of Medicine, and where several members of his family in the next three generations would follow. Having signed the order regulating the examinations in 1838, he took the full burden of the animosity when he was elected Governor in 1842 and with his fellow directors tried to keep the school alive. Yet within ten years the student numbers had dwindled to less than forty, and in 1854 the school ceased to exist as a separate entity. The new Catholic University of Ireland purchased its premises in Cecilia Street, and absorbed its functions into its own Medical Faculty[41,42]. The Hall remained an examining body granting licences to practise until 1971, when even this function was withdrawn. It is surprising that it lasted so long, for attempts to deny its right to do so were made in 1858 when the General Medical Council was formed. The idea of a school for general practitioners had been a good one, but before its time. General practice, then as now the specialty of at least half of all medical graduates, needed a proper educational base, and the apothecaries had tried to provide it.

In the schism that followed, pharmacy became the retail, research and manufacturing processes we now take for granted. William Daniel, at one time both pharmacist and general practitioner, took the medical route and eventually closed his shop. The foundation of the Apothecaries Hall and its Medical School in Dublin, and the Apothecaries Act of 1815 in England, were steps in the process of unification of the medical profession. The Medical Act of 1858, which created the General Medical Council (GMC) and introduced a common education for all members of the medical profession, completed it. Three generations of the Moore family were closely involved in the developments, Daniel by his part in founding the Hall, John William in his promotion of the medical school, and William Daniel as Governor of the Hall and later as Chairman of the General Practitioners Association of Ireland and would-be Registrar of the Irish Branch of the GMC.

In the context of this story, however, one curious enigma remains: William Daniel obtained his surgical diploma in Edinburgh before the battle between College and Hall began, possibly because he chose not do the necessary surgical apprenticeship. When his brothers Robert and Charles began their studies in the late 1830s the dispute was at its height, yet they qualified at both College and Hall and were later admitted to Fellowship of the College. Perhaps the dispute was not so bitter after all, or was at an institutional rather than a personal level. Official animosity echoed down the years, however, for in 1875:-

> *The Council [of the College] having learned that one of the Fellows pos-sessed a share in the Apothecaries Hall, obtained an opinion from Mr Litton Q.C., that it was in the power of the Council to withdraw his Fellowship diploma, if they thought proper.*[43]

Was this unnamed Fellow Charles Frederick Moore, Governor of the Hall in 1888 an 1889, and their representative on the General Medical Council in the 1890s? If so, he remained a Fellow until his death in 1904, a member of a profession united at last!

UNIVERSITY OF DUBLIN.
TRINITY COLLEGE.

EXAMINATION FOR MEDICAL DEGREES.
TRINITY, 1865.

PHYSIOLOGY AND PHYSIOLOGICAL ANATOMY.—Professor McDOWEL.

1. Classify and describe the papillæ of the tongue.
2. Give an account of the excretory apparatus of the skin.
3. Describe the microscopical anatomy of the retina.
4. The minute structure of the human lung.
5. Enumerate the functions of the sympathetic nervous system, and give illustrations of each.

SURGERY.—Dr. R. W. SMITH.

1. Injuries most likely to cause glucohæmia?
2. Affection of the eye resulting from glucohæmia; its peculiarities when so produced?
3. Supposed advantages of amylene over chloroform as an anæsthetic agent?
4. Laryngeal affections of a nervous character met with in adult life?
5. Diseases resulting from continued presence of a foreign body in the air passages?
6. Signs indicating that a foreign body has entered the windpipe?
7. Surgical affections in which carbonic acid is used as a local application?
8. Abscesses best adapted for being opened with caustic potass?
9. Treatment of fracture of the olecranon?
10. Symptoms of luxation of the head of the femur into the perineum?

MEDICINE.—DR. STOKES.

1. Compare hepatalgia and hepatitis as to their symptoms, history, results, treatment.
2. Tumour, calor, rubor, dolor, are enumerated as characteristics of inflammation; which of them is most often found absent in local disease?
3. Is there any state of the tongue in fever indicative of an important local disease?
4. Indicate the immediate and remote dangers of purgation in the early state of fever?
5. A patient with extensive organic cardiac disease may become suddenly amaurotic; explain how this occurs.
6. State the causes of exophthalmus.
7. Is any special local disease necessarily connected with a discoloration of the skin?
8. Enumerate the causes of paralysis of the vocal cords.
9. State Virchow's views as to the so-called tubercular infiltration.
10. At what period in a case of permanent patency of the aortic valves are the characteristic phenomena, except the regurgitant murmur, absent?

CHAPTER FIVE

A New Kind of Doctor

In no branch of science is an extensive observation of facts more
necessary to the deduction of general principles than in medicine[1]
William Daniel Moore

The early years of the nineteenth century were a time of enormous change, with the industrial revolution in full swing and rapid developments occurring in transport and communication. In medical affairs the physicians, surgeons and apothecaries were active both politically and scientifically in forming the profession that we recognise today. But as scientific and medical knowledge advanced, the place of the apothecary in relation to the rest of the medical profession, even though it was still being established, was already under threat.

In its own microcosm of medical practice the Moore family was creating and evolving too, as the scene changed around them. When Daniel was a young man looking to the future apothecaries were struggling to improve their status beyond being 'mere assistants to physicians', but by the time his grandson William Daniel was in charge of the shop the apothecary's trade had reached the height of its prosperity, and was already dying.

Daniel had been brought up by his uncle John Clarke in the Capel Street shop to be a businessman, so he was no stranger to commerce, or to approaching government for support in the furtherance of commercial enterprises. The Capel Street business must have been something of a manufacturing pharmacy, for in 1775 Clarke had perfected a method of producing a pure form of magnesia alba, and produced over six metric tons of it. Magnesia was much in demand as a laxative and poultice material, so it was a particularly profitable product at a time when purging and poulticing were the basis of many treatments. He also made five tons of Rochelle Salt. Anxious to safeguard his interests, he petitioned Parliament for financial support, saying that:-

in consequence of the difficulty in procuring pure chemicals for medicinal use he had, at much expense, brought their manufacture to perfection: in four years he had made 16,000 pounds of magnesia alba, in all respects equal to what had been imported at a guinea a pound. He had reduced the price by so much that even the consumer did not then pay more than one-third that amount for it; and, notwithstanding the heavy duty had established a considerable export trade to Bristol and London; and praying the House to assist him in erecting an "apparatus for preparing sal ammoniac and several other articles, for which large sums were annually sent to Italy and Holland.

The parliamentary committee heard this with approval and concluded that 'he deserved the aid of Parliament[2].

Daniel and Hannah's oldest son John was born in 1782 while they were still in Grafton Street, where the first seven of their ten children were born, though only six of the ten survived to adult life. Eight years later they moved to the house and shop in South Anne Street, which runs between Grafton and Dawson Streets in the very centre of Dublin. This was only a few minutes walk from College Green and the Parliament House, and from the Mansion House, Mercer's and Steevens Hospitals and the houses of many eminent members of Dublin society. By moving there Daniel placed himself well to look for business in both the private houses and the new hospitals then being founded in the city. It was a modest house in a commercial street containing the homes, shops or offices of an architect, a watchmaker, a silk throwster, a tallow chandler, and several other tradesmen, as well as His Danish Majesty's Consul in Ireland. The house still stands, though the restorative sold in the shop now is coffee, not medicines. From there he and the next two generations of the family carried on their business for eighty-four years.

After John's marriage in 1809 his growing family also lived in the house, so when his children were born the household eventually consisted of twelve people in three generations, from one to seventy years of age. In the next generation, when his grandson William Daniel became head of the household, Daniel was an old man, and having lost his first wife Hannah and married Alice, his second, he moved away to a new house in the new and quieter suburb of Ranelagh. A few articles remain from the family home in Anne Street; some of Daniel's books, his portrait and that of his grandson William Daniel and others unidentified, and an early wooden stethoscope. There is also an elegant long case clock, made by Charles Smith of Dublin in 1750, the year that Daniel was born, which has faithfully counted the hours and years of each generation, and still does.

When Daniel began his apprenticeships in the 1760s, the cause and nature of disease were only sketchily known and based upon observations of doubtful accuracy or even frank assumption. In 1775 Professor Stack of Mentz, could write:-

> *Fever takes place when the peculiar miasma acts upon a body, which by its previous diseased state is fitted to receive and cherish this miasma. Thus intermittent fever may be considered as formed from a depraved state of the habit and from an acute miasma ...... [a cure] may be accomplished by purging the body from that impure colluvies* in which it is at first seated.*[3]

Another example of the vagueness of contemporary knowledge comes from one of Daniel's own textbooks, *A System of Rational and Practical Chirurgery wherein all the General Intentions, whether Natural or Artificial, are accounted for and explained.....,* by Richard Boulton, late of Brazen-Nose College in Oxford. London 1713:-

> *The Scab and Itch are too well known to want any description. As to the Cause it chiefly depends on the depraved Disposition of the Serum of the Blood, ... when the Serum is too much impregnated with Vitious Salts, by which means the natural and due Fermentation of the Blood is perverted.*

Neither of these examples provide a detailed explanation of disease, and seem to depend overmuch on the presence of depravity. Other books of Daniel's which still exist include *A Treaty on a Consumption of the Lungs,*

---

* colluvies = a collection of foul matter (OED)

by Edward Barry MD. 1726; *A Mechanical Account of Poisons in Several Essays,* by Richard Mead, MD, FRS. 1708: and perhaps best of all *The Whole Works of that Excellent Practical Physician Dr Thomas Sydenham, wherein ..... are treated of ... the shortest and safest way of curing most Chronical Diseases.* 1734

Daniel entered practice in 1770, so these books were already years out of date when he obtained them. Knowledge advanced more slowly then, and perhaps his patients did not expect the same up-to-date expertise as people do now. But if the medicine he practised was primitive and pragmatic, Daniel was an enthusiastic medical politician, as shown by his membership of the Guild of St Luke and election to Warden of the Guild at the age of thirty-nine, and his subsequent contributions to Apothecaries Hall. This high profile must have been useful in drawing attention to his services, for he was determined to make his way in the medical world of Dublin, and evidently succeeded in doing so, for his obituary records that:-

His business became very extensive, and he was much engaged in medical practice, being the usual attendant of many of the first families in Dublin[4].

His work as a director of Apothecaries Hall took up much of his time, and when his son John qualified as an apothecary in 1804 Daniel could safely leave much of the shop business and medical practice to him. By then he may have been looking forward to reducing his work load, although with his abundant energy he might have preferred to continue working. The choice was not to be, however, because in 1824, when Daniel was aged 74 and John 42, the son and heir suddenly died. To keep the business going and support the six young children Daniel took in a partner. Apothecaries' Hall then became all the more important, for his investment was paying very well just then, with annual dividends of £50 to £80 per hundred pound share of which he had many[5].

The business survived. William Daniel, though too young to help out at first, was soon old enough to begin his medical studies. He became a licentiate of Apothecaries' Hall, Dublin, and then in 1833 qualified at the Royal College of Surgeons in Edinburgh. Although in his youth Daniel had been a surgical apprentice he had no licence to practise that craft, so William Daniel thus became the first of the family to hold a surgical diploma. He joined his grandfather in the shop, Pearson the partner departed, and the business returned fully to family ownership.

The shop was the centre of an apothecary's business, where he kept his stock, prepared medicines for his own patients or to the prescriptions of other doctors, and sold non-prescription medicines to the public. It was also the base for any medical work he did on his own account, and in the Moore's shop there was also a well-equipped chemical laboratory. Beyond the shop an apothecary's activities included attendance on patients to administer the medicines they had dispensed, or to apply antiphlogistic★ treatments such as blisters, plasters, and cupping. Bleeding, too, was an important part of their work, and was done either by cutting into a vein or by the attachment of leeches. Charges were made for visiting patients in their homes for such purposes, according to a scale determined by Apothecaries' Hall, which represented most of the Dublin apothecaries. There were seventy chargeable items on the list, the first five of which were for 'visiting the sick' at various distances. As apothecaries were supposed only to charge for supplying medicines and not for 'advice', it seems curious that there was a list of charges for visiting only. Yet in a time of slow transport it was sensible to charge more for the additional time needed to attend a patient living 6 miles from the shop than for one living nearby. The scale of charges was also published in the local papers such as the Dublin Post and Saunders Newsletter[6], which was an open declaration that apothecaries were visiting and 'giving advice' as well as supplying medicines, a double function for the second part of which, the supply of medicines, the surgeons and physicians could not charge unless they were licenced by Apothecaries' Hall as well as their own colleges. It is understandable that in the unformed state of the medical profession at that time, the surgeons and physicians felt threatened by those whom they considered poorly qualified tradesmen publishing their scale of charges in this way, and thereby advertising the nature of the service they provided.

For attending the sick the charges were:-[7]

★ antiphlogistic; treatment intended to reduce inflammation

1 mile distant from Dublin	5s 5d
[and increasing by the mile to] more than 6 miles	£2 5s 6d
For being called out at night to attend the sick	£1 2s 9d
For sitting up or staying in the house a whole night	£2 5s 9d
For attendance during the operation of emetics	5s 5d

At that time a fee of £1 2s 9d (£1.40) for a night visit was a substantial sum, and for staying up all night to watch over a patient £2 5s 9d (£2.29) must have felt like a well-earned reward. A fee of 5s5d (27p) for waiting beside the patient until an emetic had produced its intended effect of vomiting may have seemed less than adequate.

Treatments were priced according to who did them, whether a Master like Daniel and his sons or a junior assistant, and whether the patient was adult, child or servant. For instance:-

Bleeding, the application of leeches and the administering of a glister [enema]	
By a Master	5 s
By a journeyman or apprentice	2 s 8d
Blistering plaister applied to the arm	
of grown persons	5s 5d
of a child	2s
Plaister to the arm	2s 8½d
Strengthening plaister to the loins [reason unspecified]	2s 8d
Sinapisms [mustard bath] to the feet	3s 3d
Gargles	2s 6d
Juleps and mixtures [various liquid medicines]	6d
Linctuses	2s 4d
Purging electuaries	1s
Blue pill [mercury and chalk]	1d
Calomel pill [mercurous chloride]	2d

Inoculations against smallpox cost two guineas, though whether this was vaccination by Jenner's new method using cowpox, or the older and more dangerous technique with matter from smallpox blisters is not stated. The charge varied 'according to circumstance', but at that price it seems to have been a major undertaking, and a major source of income.

The apothecary was often the first person to be called to a patient, but if the case was difficult a physician or surgeon might also be called in consultation. At other times a physician who had already seen the patient might send for an apothecary to carry out the treatments he had ordered, such as the application of leeches or plaisters. William Daniel records his attendance in 1845 on an 18 year old girl who had a severe attack of swollen tonsils and glands in the neck, which might nowadays be diagnosed as tonsillitis, or possibly infectious mononucleosis (glandular fever)[8]. His treatment was to apply twelve leeches to the neck, but he also called in Dr Robert Graves. The choice of Dr Graves, only one of several able physicians in Dublin, was possibly influenced by Graves' famous description ten years earlier of the association of swelling in the neck, prominence of the eyes and palpitations of the heart, for which his name is still remembered[9]. Graves agreed with the diagnosis and treatment, and when seen two days later:-

> her throat had been much relieved by the leeching; she could speak and swallow better[10].

Then, after a further two days with Graves 'continuing in attendance', the typical rash of scarlet fever appeared "vividly on the hands and feet, representing, as it were, gloves and socks". The swelling subsided, but she developed joint pains for several days, which were treated with carbonate of ammonia with camphor, and syrup of poppies. The legs were:-

> wrapped in flannel wrung out of hot water, and sprinkled with camphor liniment. [The affected joints were] gently rubbed with mercurial ointment mixed with a small portion of extract of belladonna.

With this treatment the young lady made good progress, though today's doctors might not think that such apparently irrational management actually cured the disease. She was last heard of in France, fully recovered and without any of the dreaded heart or joint complications of scarlet fever. Her enlarged tonsils were successfully removed the following year. Perhaps this was done with the benefit of ether, the newly discovered anaesthetic, first used that very year.

Scarlet fever had been relatively mild for some years before the time of this case, but it was becoming much more severe again and was especially serious among the poorest people of Dublin with a fatality rate sometimes as high as 30 percent. Epidemics of great ferocity were occurring, but its cause and mode of transmission were unknown and mysterious. It was about this time that Ignaz Semelweiss in Austria showed that puerperal fever, which we now know is caused by the same germ as scarlet fever, could be carried on the hands of medical attendants. William Daniel, though he may have read of Semmelweiss's ideas, was himself a keen observer and record keeper and made notes about the transmission of scarlet fever. He was especially interested in how long it took for the symptoms to develop after contact with a known sufferer. He recorded these three cases, amongst others:-

1. *On November 2nd 1848 a gentleman aged 20 went down to County Wexford from Dublin three weeks after the disappearance of a rash of scarlet fever. On his arrival he saw two sisters, both of whom took to bed with scarlet fever on November 8th - that is, in six days - incubation = five days*

2. *A boy aged eight sickened with scarlet fever on January 12th 1851. His sister took ill on the 17th and five days later another sister sickened*

3. *Two girls, cousins, slept in the same bed on April 5th and 6th 1855. One of them complained of a sore throat on the night of April 5th, and showed rash of scarlatina on 7th. The other sickened on April 10th – that is, on the fourth day.*[11]

These observations were made 80 years before the classic work of William Pickles in the 1930s on the incubation periods of infectious diseases like measles, mumps and chickenpox[12]. Pickles was less sure about scarlet fever, as he saw it infrequently and by then it had again became less severe. He had probably not read William Daniel's case-reports.

Much of the work of physicians, surgeons and apothecaries of the time was concerned with "fever", a term used to describe any state in which the patient was hot, delirious and prostrated, often with rashes and diarrhoea. We now know that these symptoms are common to several different diseases, of course, but at that time the criteria to differentiate one from another had not been established, so prolonged feverish illnesses were known by many different names. Writing about this in 1837, Dr Henry Kennedy, who had had extensive experience in fever hospitals, remarked:-

> To anyone reflecting on the subject, there is nothing more remarkable in the whole history of medicine, than the fact of the different, I may say, opposite opinions of medical men of equal renown, as to the treatment or cause of disease apparently similar: the varied treatment of puerperal fever or syphilis, will bear me out on this assertion, as also numerous opinions held as to the cause of fever.[13]

Despite this lack of consensus, or maybe because of it, he recommended a wide range of treatments himself, both external or internal. For the latter he variously advised rhubarb, mercury, or Dover's powder which contained Ipecacuanha obtained from the root of the tropical plant *Psychotria ipecacuanha*. He also used 'injections', that is to say enemas, of tepid water, or spirit of turpentine 'with mucilage and a little hyoscyamus', from the flowers of Henbane, *Hyoscyamus niger*. He sensibly stressed the importance of adequate drinking, and said that when it was thought necessary to use wine, which was recommended as a stimulant, it should be given well diluted. External treatment consisted of:-

> ... the repeated application of leeches in small numbers to the ileo-caecal region [abdomen]... but the cupping glass may be frequently applied with great benefit. ..... The application of large blisters will sometimes put a stop to the disease, particularly if they be applied immediately after the leeching; they should not be left on longer than six hours, and are to be covered with silk paper.

Treatment by bleeding, either from a vein or with leeches, was not problem-free. The leech bites would often continue to bleed profusely – unsurprisingly, as we now know that leeches and other biters like mosquitoes secrete substances to make the blood flow readily and stop it clotting. Worse still, bleeding by opening a vein could injure other structures, as in a case reported by Thomas Wall RCSI[14]. A man from Cork had had a vein 'breathed' to bleed him, but unfortunately the lancet had also nicked the neighbouring artery where an aneurism formed. Dr Wall could feel it pulsating, and also heard the sound of it through his stethoscope, which must be one of the earliest records of such a diagnostic sign. The patient, 'though but a poor uneducated peasant, unhesitatingly agreed to be operated upon', which was successfully done. Dr Wall, who had a country practice, commented that 'the peasantry appear to be full, strong, plethoric, and apparently in robust health', but a colleague, Dr Babbington of Donoughmore, was less inclined to take their health for granted and urged caution when bleeding. In the treatment of fever he advised against the:-

copious depletion [by] the very free abstraction of blood, too often had recourse to by village practitioners' *[original emphasis]*[15]

The members of the Moore family were no 'village practitioners', however, for between the 1770s and the 1840s they were close to enthusiastic medical teachers using novel approaches, and kept up with the new developments. Older physicians from the ancient universities may have been slow to give up their cherished beliefs, but elsewhere traditional practice was being replaced by an inquisitive scientific discipline, based on accurate observation of both the living and the dead. The medical school in Edinburgh was educating students by the observation of actual patients in hospital wards, following the method taught in Europe. Many English and Irish men, such as William Daniel, went to study in Scotland, and returned home with fresh ideas and new methods. Post-mortem examinations and demonstrations not only increased the knowledge of anatomy and pathology, but improved understanding of how those diseases could be diagnosed in life. It was an exciting time, as specific conditions were described for the first time, such as William Heberden's work on angina pectoris and heart disease in 1818 and on rheumatism[16]. Auenbrugger in 1760 described how tapping the chest could indicate the state within it[17], and Laennec's invention of the stethoscope in 1816 made it possible to deduce what was happening in the heart as well as the lungs[18]. In therapeutics digitalis extracted from foxglove leaves had been introduced, and pure preparations of quinine had replaced raw Jesuits Bark. Chemistry, not botany, was becoming the basis of therapeutics. But there were some counterproductive ideas too: in Paris, Broussais promoted extensive bleeding as a cure-all, and the medical world followed his lead so enthusiastically that many patients were virtually exsanguinated in the attempt to cure them. The microscope was being increasingly used after a slow start following Leeuwenhoek's description of the 'animalcules' he had seen through his powerful lenses in the early eighteenth century[19] but the recognition of these phenomena as the cause of disease had to wait until the end of the nineteenth.

Changes in the prescribing habits of doctors were revealed by the records of the Moore's shop which had been kept for a period of over sixty years. William Daniel published an analysis of them in 1836, from which it is possible to gather some idea of the business that was carried on there, at least on the retail side[20]. He examined 1200 prescriptions from each of three eighteen-year periods, 1780–98, 1800–17 and 1819–36. This was a remarkable piece of work, for statistical analysis was not commonplace for apothecaries at that time, or indeed for anyone. It was an early example of the scholarly nature for which William Daniel later came to be admired. The first group he analysed was of 'antiphlogistic' preparations, that is medicines intended to reduce inflammations. The rationale of this form of treatment originated in the theory of the four humours, and proposed that illness was due to an excess of one or more of them which should therefore be 'depleted', that is, it should be removed from the body by sweating, purging, vomiting or bleeding. The more that was removed the more certain would be the cure.

Preparations to do this, the 'antiphlogistic' emetics, enemas, blisters and plasters, featured in one in five prescriptions in the 1780 series, but fifty years later they had fallen to one in ten. This presumably reflected a change in the thinking of prescribing physicians away from the theory of the four humours and towards a better understanding of pathology. The overall figures conceal other trends. Whereas in the first series there were two hundred and twenty five prescriptions for emetic or purgative medicines or applications and one for leeches, in the last series nearly half were for leeches – forty-five out of one hundred and thirteen. This was a good time for the living, bloodsucking medicinal leech *Hirudo Sanguinosa* which was prescribed by the million, replacing the dead alligator and musty seeds of the old-fashioned apothecary's shop. An important part of the traditional treatment had been to give a purgative in the form of an electuary (medicine mixed with honey or syrup), followed by enemas if that did not purge well enough. A down-to-earth play upon words comes in *The Merry Wives of Windsor,* when Shakespeare has the host of the Garter Inn lament the possibility of losing the doctor who "gives me the potions and the motions"[21].

Enemas fell from favour as the first line of treatment from one in twenty to one in fifty of the prescriptions, and sympathetic doctors also took pity on their patients by changing from vigorous purgatives like Jalap and Scammony that were 'powerful hyrogogue cathartics producing copious watery evacuations'[22] to gentler preparations that would not gripe, like Rhubarb Root and Senna, the 'Black Draught', which between them occurred in half of all prescriptions. All these medicines were derived from vegetable sources, and although they had been used for centuries they still had their place in the pharmacy despite the introduction of newer ones.

Mineral aperients with fine sounding names like Glaubers Salts, Rochelle Salts and Sal Polychrest went right out of favour, falling from one in nine of all prescriptions to less than one in fifty. Epsom salts had a brief popularity; there were none in the first sample, one in five in the second , but fading away to only one in twelve in the last. A favourite mineral ingredient was antimony, which had been used since ancient times for various purposes. It appeared in one in ten of the prescriptions dispensed in the shop throughout the whole sixty year period. Most commonly it was prescribed as James's Powder, so called after Dr Robert James who included it in his popular Pharmacopoeia of 1747, but also as the bright red pigment Kermes mineral, and as tartar emetic, a name which displays its intended effect. The commercial if not the therapeutic benefits of James's powder are revealed in advertisements often appearing in the *British Medical Journal,* which asked prescribers always to specify *'Pulvis Jacobi vera Newberry's'* to 'avoid disappointment ... by the substitution of common antimonial powder'. It also included the following caveat

*NB. It is a remarkable fact, that James's Powder, prepared from Dr James's original recipe, may **safely** be given in doses of up to **Sixteen** grains, while common Antimonial Powder .... Cannot be administered in doses **exceeding SIX grains without danger.** [original emphasis]*

Dr James and his manufacturing pharmacist Messrs Newberry clearly applied powerful commercial pressure to ensure their proprietary brand was kept in the public view. The rivalry between proprietary and generic forms is not new.

Antimony was said to be an 'emetic, diaphoretic and a powerful depressant'; an all-purpose medicine indeed. It is a metal which can be fashioned in the same way as silver or lead, and in the seventeenth and eighteenth centuries this property was employed to prepare it for medicinal use in a rather more elegant way. Special cups were made in which wine was placed for several hours, after which some of the metal had dissolved into it. The resulting liquid was then drunk by the patient[23]. The dosage cannot have been precise, and consequently the therapeutic results must have varied considerably. Directions that antimony should be prepared by this method do not appear in William Daniel's study, but it was very frequently prescribed in the form of tartar emetic, possibly because it was so much favoured by Robert Graves.

Another mineral constituent of medicine was mercury, which we now regard as a serious poison but was very popular in the late eighteenth and nineteenth centuries. For internal use it was mostly prescribed as mercurous chloride in the form of the powder calomel, or mixed with a little opium as 'Blue Pill', or with chalk as 'Grey Powder'. William Daniel ascribed the popularity of Blue Pill to the famous London surgeon John Abernethy, who strongly recommended it as 'an alterative at bedtime'. Lucas[24] says the powder is a 'favourite way of giving mercury to children with deficient biliary secretion', but this 'deficiency' must have been an assumption before the days of routine liver function tests. It was also said that 'the pill is an excellent remedy in hepatic dyspepsia and syphilis'. Huge amounts of highly toxic mercury were consumed by patients with inevitably poisonous results. One of its toxic effects is profuse salivation, which to nineteenth century doctors was an indication that an adequate dose had been given, but now a dose large enough to produce salivation is also considered large enough to damage the nervous system. Many nineteenth century patients who survived the original fever may have suffered more damage from their treatment than from the illness for which it was given. Sydenham's belief that medicines should be harmless had evidently been forgotten by his nineteenth century successors.

Opium derived from oriental poppy seeds kept its place well in the records of the dispensary, and is the only one of the principal medicines William Daniel mentions in his analysis which is still in everyday use today. In his first series,1780–98, it featured in one prescription in six, and though it went out of favour in the middle years, it had almost regained its place by the 1830s to the extent of one in nine. In the early series it was prescribed as either 'opium' and 'paregoric' (opium extracted in tincture of camphor), but by the end of the study it was nearly always entered as 'opium', with the newer name 'morphia' appearing occasionally.

A similar frequency of use of these medicines in 1833 was recorded by the London surgeon-apothecary Robert Craik[25]. Of 45 prescriptions dispensed in a four week period, 25 contained either mercury or a purgative, including nine instances of Jalap, that 'powerful cholegogue cathartic'. William Daniel speculates on the reasons for their popularity, and for variations in frequency of use, pointing convincingly to recommendations of certain fashionable physicians. He cites Dr Hamilton's textbook of therapeutics, in which the author "directed the medical world to the importance of administering purgative medicines in a great number of diseases".

Another strong influence was the young Dr Robert Graves, who had gone to Paris to further his studies and brought home the most progressive ideas of the time, which he publicised through his lectures and writings in the Dublin Journal of Medical Science and elsewhere. In particular he enthusiastically advocated antimony in the form of tartar emetic. One of his patients was violently agitated and restless, with "a pulse so fast it could scarcely be counted, but exceedingly weak", and Graves confessed to being unsure of the best treatment[26].

What was to be done? The state of his circulation did not admit of our endeavouring to control the cerebral excitement by arteriotomy or even leeches, and [it was considered] a very few leeches would kill him; blisters would be too slow in their action; cold effusion seemed inadmissible. In short the patient seemed beyond the reach of all our resources.

He thought the patient 'would not survive twelve hours' and determined to use tartar emetic as a last resort, despite its known dangers. He ordered a mixture containing:-

> *.... one ounce of syrup of poppies, one of mucilage, and six of water, and eight grains of tartar emetic.*
> *The medicine was administered by Mr Ferguson of Kildare-street, so well known as a skilful and excellent apothecary, who told me afterwards that he was quite surprized at the treatment adopted, and was sure it or any other could not save Mr C.'s life.*

In the end Mr C.'s life was saved, or at least he survived. He took the medicine every few hours, gradually became calmer, and in nine days 'the fever left him'. Antimony prescribed as tartar emetic was not always safe, however, and Graves himself insisted it should be used with great care:–

> *I have had lamentable proofs that I have been misunderstood; and lately was called to see a gentleman in the vicinity of Dublin, who, the practitioner in attendance said, had been treated by my method, whereas the patient was killed, according to his own, by opium given injudiciously during delirium with evident cerebral congestion.*[27]

He justified his own extensive use of it by saying that, if used together, the doses of antimony and opium should be varied according to the responses of the patient, in order to avoid the dreaded and deadly complication of convulsions. His lesson was that if such potent medicines are used they must be of consistent purity, accurately measured and prescribed according to clear indications by an experienced physician.

There is no direct record of John's contribution to the business either clinically or in the shop, though as Governor of the Hall at the age of 29 in 1811 he must have been highly regarded by his colleagues, and his early death was a serious loss. But it meant that William Daniel, though a child when his father died, could apply his youthful enthusiasm to the business when he took it over from his grandfather. He was an able chemist, both as a pharmacist and an analyst, and was keen to receive specimens from colleagues in various parts of Ireland. He used the laboratory at Anne Street to examine and analyse anything that interested him and often published his results. One topic that led to prolonged research was whether and how much human milk could coagulate, because he wanted to know how the nourishment of babies might be affected by diseases in nursing mothers[28]. He measured the specific gravity of the milk, its acidity, the effect of heat and acids, and 'the amount of cream thrown up in a given time', and examined it under the microscope. He compared the colostrum (the first secretions of the breast after birth) with the milk produced a few days later, and compared the results of his experiments on human milk to similar studies of the milk of cows, goats and donkeys. His paper discusses his findings in the light of those of several other contemporary researchers. His research was extensive, but it is not clear that he actually discovered what he was looking for.

The chemical constituents of urine had long been known, but it occurred to him to enquire what was in the urine of new-born infants[29]. With the help of Dr M'Clintock, the Master of the Lying-in Hospital, 'where a large number of infants are yearly born', he was able to obtain urine from babies who died immediately after birth, though he was glad to say that this rarely happened despite the large number of births. He was interested to know if the urine contained sugar, as had been reported, and concluded that it did not. Neither did it contain urea although the other 'usual salts' were present, as in adults.

The chemical constituents of gallstones and urinary stones also interested him, and he was pleased to receive specimens of these from colleagues for analysis. One case was of a young woman who had passed a stone *per rectum* 'the size of a pullet's egg', but although it looked like a gall stone the patient had had no pain or jaundice to suggest that it had come from the gall bladder. He asked himself if it was possible that such stones could be formed in the gut, as well as gall bladder. He analysed it by heating it until it fused, at which point it ignited 'with a bright flame'; by dissolving and re-crystallising in alcohol; and by examination under the microscope, which are the methods used in biochemistry laboratories until very recently. He concluded that the stone was mostly composed of 'cholesterine' (now called cholesterol), and because he knew that 'cholesterine' had been found in many parts of the body, such as blood and various diseased tissues, decided that it *could* have originated in the intestine[30]. He was probably wrong.

A paper of a more clinical nature was *The Spontaneous Cure of a Rectal Tumour in a Child*[31]. The boy had a recurrent rectal prolapse with a small tumour, which was easily replaced by the mother or nurse each day after stool. One day however the tumour came away spontaneously, and the prolapse never recurred. He was at a loss to explain this, but pointed out that direct observation by the doctor was a more reliable way of learning what happened than the hearsay of less critical observers.

Another of his patients was a young woman who had been passing black stools while recovering from fever[32]. This distressed her because she thought that, according to the theory of four humours, she must have been 'labouring under an accumulation of black bile'. William Daniel no longer subscribed to this old idea, of course, and knew that swallowing even small amounts of iron could cause black stools, but not black bile. Having ascertained that she was not taking any iron-containing medicine, he concluded that iron must have been present in something she was eating or drinking. At first he suspected that the water used in the house which came from 'a chalybeate spring' contained iron, but on analysis he showed it to be iron free. He then learned that his patient had been eating jelly made in an iron pot, and tested the jelly for the presence of iron. 'By adding a drop of ferro-cyanate of potash I obtained a blue pre-cipitate and was able to set the patient's mind at rest'.

An experiment with less direct medical significance was *On the Urine of the Crocodile*[33]. In Dublin crocodiles were rare, of course, and the opportunity for the experiment only arose because in 1851 his brother Charles was the medical officer on the P&O Steamer *Ripon*, which had been carrying a crocodile as a gift from the Consul General of Egypt to the Regents Park Zoo. The unfortunate creature was housed in a wooden box, but in its confined space it was overcome at first by heat and then by cold in a sudden storm, and perished before the ship had sailed very far. At that time all doctors were encouraged to 'dissect' if their case proved fatal, that is to carry out a post-mortem examination, so Charles and a colleague travelling on board the *Ripon* did so. They dis-covered 'no lesion in any organ', but having no chemicals to analyse the urine they bottled some to take home. It took a month to reach Dublin, and when it arrived it was 'greenish in colour' with a deposit of sludge at the bottom of the bottle. On removing the cork there was a 'trifling escape of gas'. Various chemical experiments were made and the deposit was examined under the microscope, but no 'animalcules' were found; bacteriology had not yet been sufficiently developed for William Daniel to be aware of the possibilities. He admitted that keeping the sample for thirty days might have obscured the picture, but he concluded that 'the reptile did not appear to have died of disease'. Though this particular experiment was not significant in itself, it is a good example of William Daniel's scientific curiosity.

As well as his own original writings he subscribed to several European medical journals, especially from Scandinavia, Holland, and Germany, and translated articles from them for publication in English. For this contribution to publicising the work of Scandinavian research he was elected to Honorary Fellowships of the Swedish Society of Physicians in 1855, of the Norwegian Medical Society in 1857, and of the Royal Medical Society of Copenhagen in 1861[34]. At home his scientific contributions were recognised by his election in December 1859 to the Royal Irish Academy[35].

When Daniel founded the family business in 1780 medical science was primitive and treatment largely ineffective, though that was not the fault of its practitioners who were already beginning to explain some of its mysteries. Nearly ninety years later, in 1868, William Daniel gave up pharmacy and closed the business. By then medicine had become a science, a long training at university had become necessary, and the profession had been united by the Medical Act of 1858. Daniel had been an apothecary pure and simple, and so had his son John. But his grandsons William Daniel and Charles were general practitioners, a form of medical practice that had come to prominence in their lifetime, and his other grandson Robert had specialised in the new discipline of dentistry. Successive members of the family had played their part in this development, which saw both the rise and the demise of the apothecary as a tradesman keeping shop.

By 1839 Daniel was an old man of 89, though evidently still vigorous, for in that year he moved to the new suburb of Ranelagh for a well deserved retirement, and lived there another eight years. He died in 1847, aged ninety-seven. His obituary in the Dublin Journal of Medical Science says:–

Those who live on the south side of the city may [recall], from the singularity of the equipage, an old-fashioned yellow chaise, drawn by a pair of aged, but still stout, cob horses which lumbered along the Ranelagh road during the fine days of spring and summer for several years past. The occupant was a venerable, grey-bearded old man who always appeared to have come out of the last century for the purpose of contrasting it with the present. And so he had. The best days of Daniel Moore, the father of Irish apothecaries, were past and gone before the nineteenth century.[36]

The shop in Anne Street was taken over by a hatter and clothier, and William Daniel moved to Fitzwilliam Square. He became one of a new kind of medical practitioner, rational, objective, and scientifically well informed. He was both a Doctor of Medicine and a Diplomate in Surgery, and was at last free from the need to sell medicines. Soon there was another generation, for by now his son John was ready to take on the mantle of medical practice within the Moore family.

The Fever Hospital and House of Recovery, Cork Street, Dublin.
(Annual Report of The Fever Hospital, 1882).

CHAPTER SIX

Fevers

In Dublin's fair city, where girls are so pretty
I first set my eyes on sweet Molly Malone
She pushed her wheel barrow,
through streets broad and narrow
Singing cockles and mussels, alive, alive O!
Popular song

At the corner of Grafton and Nassau Streets there stands a statue of Molly Malone with her shellfish-laden wheel barrow. As the crowds bustle past, maybe humming the catchy tune of the popular song, they give little thought to the reality of her fate. She was but one of thousands who died of the fever in the epidemics that swept through Europe in the nineteenth century, especially among the destitute people of Dublin where eight or nine people might be ill in the same overcrowded house in which disease had broken out[1]. If Molly had been treated by the eminent Dr Stokes she would probably have ten leeches applied to her abdomen, a turpentine enema, artificial heat to the extremities, and made to drink eight ounces of wine[2]. But even that bold treatment was of no avail.

As the population of Dublin increased, swelled by migrants from the impoverished countryside, circumstances favoured the spread of disease on a scale only seen before at the time of the Black Death and the Plague. Dublin was not alone in being severely affected by recurrent epidemics, for other towns and country communities throughout Europe were also devastated by outbreaks of deadly disease throughout the nineteenth century. Ireland, though, had a special problem in the widespread occurrence of typhus fever, greater there than anywhere. Such diseases are now preventable, so that today's European doctors have little or no experience of them, but the epidemics of 'fever' must have been as devastating as malaria, AIDS and other new infections which are now taking such a terrible toll in developing countries. For the Moore doctors of the nineteenth century they were commonplace events, and aspects of them were recorded by three members of the family, namely William Daniel and his son John, and Charles. Indeed for John the need to conquer the tragedy of epidemic disease was one of the principal motivations of his professional career.

In the early 1800s, Daniel and John William must have treated patients for fever as these epidemics increased in frequency and severity. The situation could only deteriorate as destitute people crowded into the insanitary houses and courts and Dublin outgrew its water-supply and drainage systems. Apart from the out-patient Dispensaries and the Houses of Industry for the poor and infirm, there was only the small Steevens Hospital to take cases during epidemics until special fever hospitals were founded. The earliest of these was the Hardwicke Fever Hospital in 1801[3], followed in 1804 by the Cork Street Fever Hospital, where both Charles and John were physicians in later years, and for which John wrote the Medical Reports in the 1870s and 80s.[4]

As apothecaries working from their shop, Daniel and John William attended the sick in private houses rather than hospitals, and sold medicines directly to the public. They probably also visited poorer patients in their homes, though the destitute were dependent on the charitable dispensary system of care to avoid the cost of an apothecary. Most of their practice, and the profitable part, is likely to have been in the more prosperous homes, where the common childhood fevers of measles and scarlet fever were frequent, and being less overcrowded the risk of typhus would be lower. Nowadays we think of measles and scarlet fever as mild, and though in the later nineteenth century they were serious problems, Daniel's copy of 'The Whole Works of Dr Thomas Sydenham'[5] does not describe them as dangerous. Sydenham attended the 'five or six children of the most virtuous Countess of Salisbury' for measles without mentioning any expectation of an adverse outcome. He says of scarlet fever:-

I reckon this Disease is nothing else but a moderate effervescence of the blood, occasioned by the Heat of the foregoing Summer, or some other way; and *therefore I do nothing to hinder the Despumation* of the Blood, and the ejecting of the peccant Matter thro' the Pores of the Skin which is easily done by the Blood itself; wherefore I forbear Bleeding and the use of Glisters, by which Forms of Remedies, Revulsion being made, I think the offensive Particles are more mixed with the Blood, and the Motion that is more agreeable to nature is obstructed.*

He advised that the sick person should "keep always within, but not always abed" which suggests that he did not consider the disease to be severe, though he did warn of the danger of convulsions. But his principal caution was aimed at the physician, who should not prescribe:-

... Cordials and other needless Remedies too learnedly, as it commonly appears ... that the disease is presently heightened, and the Sick dies by the Over-officiousness of his Physician.

Sydenham's advice about unwarranted intervention still holds good today, though it may not have pleased Daniel much, as he would have needed to prescribe and dispense at least some medicine to earn his fee.

The severity of scarlet fever, also known as scarlatina, was soon to change from the mildness that Sydenham described, and by the 1840s when William Daniel was in practice it was becoming a dangerous and dreaded condition. In a paper entitled *Observations on the Latent Period of Scarlatina*[6] he describes the ease with which it spread and its variable severity. In one family, for instance, although three older brothers had only mild attacks, the fourth and youngest boy, Clement, was not so fortunate. He was taken ill on 20th June, and by 11th July was dead.

Clement's early death was not unusual, by any means. William Daniel describes nine patients seen by him and others in which the infected throat caused large swellings in the neck and eroded the nearby veins and sometimes the arteries, which then bled profusely and often fatally[7]. One of his own cases was a previously healthy four-year old boy living in

---

* despumation = expulsion of impure matter from the fluids of the body (OED)
peccant = morbid, disease-producing (OED)

Harry Street, off Grafton Street, who had developed scarlatina and just such a swelling. The boy had been treated at the Pitt Street Dispensary, and had had poultices applied to no avail. When the swelling burst William Daniel was sent for urgently, for the Anne Street shop was only 50 yards away. He found the boy:-

> ... *bleeding copiously from a large tumour in the neck; his clothes and the bed on which the boy lay were fearfully drenched with blood; he presented a completely blanched appearance, and was very faint. Measures were taken to prevent a return of the haemorrhage, but it came on again in the course of the night, and was followed by convulsions and death, at 2 A.M., exactly twenty-four hours after the bursting of the abscess.*

At the post-mortem examination the abscess was found to have destroyed the jugular vein, which had bled severely. This event prompted William Daniel to review the European literature in which he found many similar cases. He wisely comments that before opening an abscess in such patients it would be well to consider whether a major blood vessel might be involved. Others reported similar examples, such as Thomas Anstill of Abbey Street Dublin[8]. One of his patients was a seven year-old child who developed a scarlatina rash with sore throat and swollen neck, and died within 30 hours; another, a two-year old boy, was dead forty-eight hours after the rash appeared; and a ten-year old died 26 hours after admission to hospital. Everyone in another household was taken ill. Of the three children, one had only a mild rash; one a rash and sore throat; and one had no sore throat but a severe rash, swollen limbs and fluid in the lungs. The mother had 'tonsillitis', the father 'a bad sore throat', and

> ... *last of all the servant had severe inflammation of the throat and fever, which lasted for ten days.*

This was in 1841, only twelve years after Richard Bright at Guy's Hospital in London had first described the association of such symptoms with disease of the kidneys, which Thomas Anstill was at pains to mention. Such severe disease was common in 1850, but is now rare, though there are occasional cases of necrotising fasciitis caused by the same bacteria – the 'flesh eating bacteria' of the popular press. The fear that this disease must have caused may be compared with the anxiety we now feel about meningitis in its unpredictable suddenness, though this is perhaps one thousand times less common than scarlet fever was then.

The usual treatment was leeches, blisters, mercurial dressings, calomel and opium powders, and 'wine was freely given'. William Daniel treated two sisters who caught scarlatina at the same time[9]. The younger, aged twenty-one months, had a 'copious eruption' but 'passed through the disease favourably'. The older girl, three years of age, was much more ill and had a very sore throat, but the rash was mild. Despite 'James's powder [antimony oxide], carbonate of ammonia every second hour, and cold chicken broth' her throat swelled more and was 'much enlarged on both sides'. Two leeches were applied, and, mindful of the child from Harry Street who bled to death, 'care was taken to stop the bleeding as soon as the leeches fell off'. Blisters were applied, quinine medicine pre-scribed, the throat brushed with silver nitrate, and a turpentine enema was given. She became cold and weak, with a very rapid pulse. The cold was offset with poultices of linseed meal, and scalded bran was applied to the abdomen. As a last resort two glasses of claret-in-water were given. Such multiple medication seems to border on Sydenham's 'over-officiousness of the physician', but the child did recover slowly and completely, apart from an ear infection and lasting deafness. She was also left with partial paralysis of the face, which was treated with more James's powder and blisters.

William Daniel wanted to discover how this common and serious illness was passed from one person to another, because it was obviously very easily spread in crowded places, schools and institutions. In *Observations on the Latent Period of Scarlatina* he quotes other writers who believed that it was actually impossible to prevent it spreading:-

Dr Williams doubts the possibility of checking the dissemination of scarlatina in public schools by isolating the cases, the spread of the miasmata being, he says, more extensive than in most other diseases. Dr Gregory states, that when it invades a school, no precautions avail towards preventing the spread of infection.

But William Daniel was more positive. He did not know that the agent in the 'miasmata' was actually a bacterium which could live in the throats of otherwise healthy people and be dispersed in their breath and on their hands, but realised that it was a material substance, not some abstract evil thing. Scientific logic told him so, though he could not prove it. Accordingly, he wrote:-

> *It has been considered quite practicable to arrest [the spread of the disease], provided due precautions as to washing of hands and strict attention to perfect cleanliness, be observed by* those who are obliged to communicate between the infected and the non-infected; *and it has been recommended to make the attempt, in preference to dispersing the school, as the latter would, probably, convey the disease to the respective homes of those in whom the infection might be latent. [original emphasis]*

No doubt he had in mind the cases like 'Master Clement' who supposedly had the disease conveyed to him by a pinafore that had been stored in the sick-room, though the infection was probably conveyed in the throat of the person who brought the pinafore, not on the pinafore itself. The evidence for such a method of spread was available from his reading of the European literature. *'Observations on the Latent Period of Scarlatina'* was published in 1851, only three years after Ignaz Semmelweiss in Vienna had suggested that puerperal fever (which we now know is also caused by the Streptococcus) could be conveyed to the maternity wards by doctors who had worked in the post-mortem room, and that hand-washing could reduce this spread of infection[10]. Semmelweiss did not publish his ideas himself until after 1851, although his colleagues did[11], and as William Daniel does not mention his name in *Observations* his own conclusions may be independent of Semmelweiss's work which is now so well known.

Charles, William Daniel's younger brother, also wrote about the pathetic state of people living at constant risk of such infection. As a general practitioner and Union medical officer in Dublin, he must have often met such cases as he described to the Dublin Obstetrical Society[12].

> *Last November I was called to an artisan's wife who was lying in an ill-ventilated small back room, adjoining a yard where pigs were kept, in a court*

where many fatal cases of scarlatina occurred a few months before, and who had phlegmasia of both legs, with gradually increasing oedema of the body, face &c, great prostration, and a low febrile state. I could not induce her to remove to hospital, or to a more roomy lodging. After some days she was removed to a room with a fireplace; but this step, and the best nourishment, stimulants, &c, her husband could procure, proved of no avail, as well as what medical treatment was pursued, and she gradually sank in three weeks from the first day I had seen her, leaving her infant a tolerably healthy child. She had been unable to suckle it from the day before I first visited her.

It is now common knowledge that the spread of communicable disease can be minimised by preventing carriers from dispersing their germs throughout the community, but that concept was slow to be accepted in the nineteenth century. When John was appointed Physician to the Cork Street Fever Hospital in the 1870s he became more than ever aware of the danger to life from infectious diseases. He was angry when patients died needlessly, and made many suggestions to minimise the dispersal of infection. This extract is typical:-

Instances are constantly coming under notice of hospital physicians in which scarlatina, small-pox, measles, and fever have spread far and wide, because the first case of the illness, either through wanton neglect or ignorance, was not isolated in due time. Some two years ago several cases of scarlatina were admitted in Cork-street Hospital in this city, from a tenement home in which a child had died of the disease and was waked. No medical practitioner had been called in to see the patient, nor was any report made to the sanitary authority until other children in the house had been attacked. At least two lives were lost in this instance, which is only one out of many which might be adduced.[13]

Scarlatina was "a plague among children in the poorer classes in a city like Dublin", according to John. In a report to the Academy of Medicine in Ireland on the epidemic of 1883 he commented on the appalling death rate among the children, when one child in three under 5 years of age who caught it died, and for 5 to 15 year-olds it was only a little less dangerous[14]. He noticed that most admissions were in the autumn months, especially in 1883 when 60% of the admissions and 75 % of the deaths were in the October to December quarter. The death rate had been even worse in 1879-80, when it reached 36% at one point. In this paper John notes the association between scarlet fever and erysipelas, which we now know are caused by the same organism, but curiously refers to a case of "scarlatinal diphtheria" in a middle aged man. Scarlet fever and diphtheria are now recognised as different diseases with some similar symptoms; they both cause severe sore and swollen throats, and in the case of diphtheria a 'false membrane' forms which can block the airway, but it was impossible to distinguish them accurately before bacteriological tests were available. Indeed the Registrar-General of England and Wales recorded them as the same entity until the twentieth century. Probably two thirds of the cases were scarlet fever[15]. Some of the cases William Daniel and his contemporaries describe are very likely to have been diphtheria, especially those due to swelling within the throat.

John went further than William Daniel in trying to prevent the spread of disease, and advised not only the washing of hands and materials, but actual isolation of infected patients. This, of course, required the identification of cases as they arose, and notification of them to the 'sanitary authorities' – or, as Charles referred to them, 'the sanitary police'[16]. In 1881 this was a radical proposal because it involved the intrusion of officialdom into the freedom of the medical profession, and was far from welcome. But the problem was huge: in 1870 scarlet fever and diphtheria caused the deaths of 31,000 people in England and Wales, and thousands more in Ireland, and puerperal fever, caused by the same germ, more than another thousand[17]. Each year between 1848 and 1872, out of every million people alive, 225 died from cholera and 270 from smallpox, but these numbers were dwarfed by the White Plague of tuberculosis, which killed 2580 in every million every year[18]. The population of the British isles was then about 25 million, so cholera may have killed 140,000, smallpox 170,000 and tuberculosis 1,600,000 people in twenty-five years. John took up the challenge of campaigning for the notification of disease to reduce this appalling loss of life, which is described in another chapter.

In 1879 John was appointed physician to the Cork Street Hospital[19]. In the same year his uncle Charles resigned from the hospital, but retained a lively interest in epidemic disease as a Union medical officer and general practitioner, especially in respect of cholera which he had experienced abroad as a ship's medical officer. The activities at Cork Street are recorded in the Hospital Reports from 1879 to 1888, some of which were written by John. The story they tell was experienced by Charles in earlier years, as much as by John in the 1880s. The hospital had been founded in 1801 by a group of charitable gentlemen who saw the enormous need for 'the relief of the sick poor of Dublin afflicted with fever', and decided to raise money to build a hospital[20]. The ten year-old Apothecaries' Hall, with Daniel and John William among its members, contributed 60 guineas to the first £1300, perhaps with an eye to likely trading opportunities, and not entirely disinterestedly. At first there were only eighty beds, but this was soon increased to 280, which made it a large institution by the standards of the day. New patients could be admitted into a special part of the building, where they would be washed before proceeding to the wards, their clothing being removed and disinfected or destroyed. As they recovered, they would be moved to convalescent wards until they were fit to return home. Not least among the objectives of treatment was a nutritious diet, which the patients had all too often been unable to provide for themselves. It was said that within six years of its opening the Hospital had:-

> ... almost banished typhus, or contagious, or spotted fever from the higher ranks, and greatly reduced its frequency and malignity amongst the poor. The blessings of that great monument of philanthropy are incalculable, [and largely due to] the characteristic industry, the rigid honesty, and the unlimited benevolence of the Quakers.[21]

In the seventy-eight years between its foundation and John's first report the hospital had admitted 207,251 patients, of whom 191,772 had been 'discharged, cured, or relieved'. The overall mortality in that time had been only 7.5 %, remarkably low for diseases from which patients commonly had a one-in-three chance of dying. In his first report of 1879 John recorded the number of cases of each disease that were admitted, compared with the previous year[22] (Table 6.1)

Table 6.1

	1877-8	*1878-99*
Typhus	142 (18%)	134
Enteric fever	60 (8%)	51
Simple fever	173	220
Measles	35 (25%)	42
Pneumonia	16 (12%)	33

(Figures in brackets in 1877–8 indicate death rate)

When John began his time at Cork Street typhus fever was the commonest condition, though smallpox overtook it in epidemic years. 'Simple fever' refers to cases without specific signs in which it was not possible to make an accurate diagnosis in the days before laboratory tests were developed. Besides those admitted to hospital there were many who were ill at home or were admitted to other hospitals, so these figures do not necessarily reflect the overall picture. Now that measles is preventable and pneumonia usually curable, the high mortality from these conditions seems extraordinary. The occurrence of sixty cases of enteric fever now would be considered a major outbreak, although then it was not unusual. Indeed, in Dublin between 1872 and 1891 there was an average of thirteen deaths a month from enteric fever[23].

Because typhus was so common it became a major interest for John. It was a constant threat to the community, especially to the poor and destitute and to anyone living in conditions that lacked even the basic amenities necessary for health, which is why it was known as 'Jail' and 'Trench' fever. It also presented a diagnostic puzzle to the early nineteenth century physicians. Its cause and management was much studied from then until the early twentieth century, because it ravaged populations in distress, especially in Ireland where hundreds of thousands of people died from it. One writer even cynically remarked that in England, if a murderer were to die from typhus in an overcrowded prison, his jailer would be guilty of manslaughter, but in Ireland it was so common that "Irish jailors need not be very apprehensive of punishment for this transgression"[24].

John took as much interest in typhus through his work at the Cork Street and Meath Hospitals as his predecessors had, and devoted a substantial part of his book on Fevers to it. As a former Scholar in Classics at Trinity College, he noted the derivation of its name from the Greek word for 'smoke or vapour', which describes the delirious state of the patient and provides the alternative name of 'Brain Fever'[25]. Because the symptoms are similar it was often confused with what we now call enteric fever, which used to be called 'typhoid', ie 'typhus-like'. Dr H. C. Lombard of Geneva, on leaving Ireland after a long visit, wrote to Dr Graves on the different appearances of the intestine in the Irish form of 'typhus' and in what was called by the same name on the continent, and claiming that they are different diseases[26]. Subsequent careful observation of post-mortem appearances revealed the differences.

Early in the nineteenth century Dr John Cheyne at the Hardwicke Fever Hospital wrote at length about typhus in the *Dublin Hospital Reports*[27]. He published strict and detailed rules for the hospital nurses, which included the duty of instructing patients and visitors about hygiene. New patients were to be washed and dressed in a hospital shirt and night-cap, and the clothes were to be sent without delay to the "woman whose business it is to see them purified". The sheets and shirts were to be changed at stated periods, and no "foul or dirty linen" was to be left in the wards, which was an improvement on the routine of Mercer's Hospital some years earlier where the bed-sheets were to be changed "every month, or oftener if occasion required"[28]. These precautions were insisted upon because it was realised that typhus could be spread by contact in overcrowded households and by close association with people who had the disease. Dr Robert Law described a family where seven members were taken ill.

> First the old grandmother became affected and died; then her daughter-in-law, living in a different part of the city; then her two married daughters, one of whom died; then the husband of this last, and at the same time two children; last of all the grandfather, aged 70, was brought into hospital almost moribund; he, however, recovered.[29]

Other evidence of the contagious nature of typhus was noted by William Stokes, who admitted a woman who "had attended upon and washed the clothes of a person who had died of a peculiarly malignant fever"[30]. It had been noticed at the Hardwicke Hospital that students who did post-mortem examinations on patients who had died of typhus did not get the disease unless they also worked in the wards, so contagion was only from the living[31]. The question 'is typhus contagious?', that is, passed from person to person by touch, had been debated in 1818 by Stokes's father, Dr Whitley Stokes, and was settled by an early example of the use of statistics. Whitley Stokes told his friend Dr Brinkley, Lord Bishop of Cloyne, about eleven people in a family of twelve who had suffered from typhus, although the disease had affected only one in seven of the local population of several thousand. He asked the bishop what was the probability of this happening by chance, if the disease did not spread by contact of one person with another? The reverend doctor calculated that an 'average share' of the disease for a family of twelve would be two cases, and that the probability of eleven occurring in one family was one in 189,600,000; so unlikely as to be impossible[32]. Without microscopes the physicians could not have known that typhus is actually passed from person to person by the body louse, so they blamed 'miasma'. But they were right to remove and 'purify' clothes, and attend to washing and fresh air, and thereby minimise the spread of the disease within the wards.

The size of the problem was huge. In Belfast, for instance, nearly 10,000 cases were admitted to hospital between 1818 and 1835, as well as many who were ill at home[33]. William Mateer's figures from the Belfast Fever Hospital showed that in affected families the average number of cases was 3.9, ranging from one to six, and that in only one affected family in four was the patient the only one in the house. A curious feature of Mateer's writing is that, although he kept meticulous numerical records over a long time and used percentages, he expressed them in fractions, not with a decimal point. For example, he expressed the mortality over an eighteen-year period as 67045/11200 per cent – a precise but rather cumbersome calculation.

Mateer divided the mortality into age bands, and showed that it increased markedly with age, a feature also observed by John later in the century, who quotes figures from the London Fever Hospital. In London the overall mortality from 1848-70 was higher, especially in the elderly. Table 6.2 shows Mateer's Belfast figures, expressed in modern form, compared with the London and Cork Street Fever Hospitals

Table 6.2

Mateer		London Fever		Cork Street	
1818–1835		1848–70		1879	
Age	mortality %	Age	mortality %	Age	mortality %
-	-	-	-	Under 15	4.5
Under 20	2.9	-		15–19	5.2
20–39	8.0	30	36	20–39	20.6
40–59	21	-		40–59	55.5
60+	35	60	67	60+	100
-		80+	100	-	

They all agreed that typhus was most common but least severe in the young, especially the 15–25 age group, and less frequent but more severe in the old. Overall figures cannot illustrate individual cases, but John cites a patient of his own by the name of Owens, who was 104 years old. Despite a severe illness lasting three weeks during which "he was delirious, his body covered with petechiae, and his extremities livid", he recovered and was discharged. Within a week of leaving the hospital he was "in as perfect health as was compatible within his time of life"[34].

Typhus fever presented two other concerns to doctors. One was its association with poverty and destitution so that it was widespread in poor communities and cried out for improvement in their sanitary conditions. Mateer observed that some streets in Belfast harboured the disease more than others, especially where there was:-

> want of cleanliness and bad sewerage, so that decayed animal and vegetable matter accumulate, not being carried off by a current of water in the usual way, and so generate miasmata.

The other danger was that those who tried to help people living in such conditions were themselves at risk, notably those doctors who visited the homes of the poor. In the 1840s William Stokes described the conditions of the rural poor with vivid words.

The poor cottiers live ... not in towns or villages, but in their solitary cabins, on their plots of ground and are thus removed from many of the advantages of social life; their dwellings are hovels, and scattered over the length and breadth of the land; and when an epidemic visits the country it is easy to see that the position of the inmates must be to the last degree unfavourable; their distance from the residence of the physician, or from any other means of assistance, is a cause why disease may continue for days in the family, unknown to any but its members. Want, damp, dirty habits and bad ventilation, all concur to render the disease virulent; and by the time the medical man visits the sick, the hovel, with several of its inmates in malignant typhus, is one focus of concentrated contagion.[35]

While sympathetic to the plight of the "poor cottiers", Stokes and his colleague James Cusack mainly intended to show how much the doctors who went to their aid were at risk of infection themselves from the appalling sanitary conditions. Stokes, as Regius Professor of Physic in the University of Dublin, and Cusack, as President of the Royal College of Surgeons in Ireland, made representations to Government for measures to protect doctors from the risks of infection in their profession, and in the cases of doctors who died, to support their widows and orphans. In one district they found '...nineteen medical men who left sixteen widows and seventy eight children almost unprovided for'.

It has been estimated that between 1818 and 1843, before the famine fever was at its worst, more than 120 of Ireland's 1200 medical practitioners died of typhus[36]. Deaths then increased so sharply that between 1843 and 1846 one third of the deaths of doctors were due to typhus, and in 1847, the worst year of the famine, it was two thirds. In that year 178 doctors, one in fourteen, died of the disease. In the same period the death rate from all causes among doctors rose from 2.2 to 6.7 per hundred. It was not only the doctors who visited the poor who died, for even the Master of the Rotunda Maternity Hospital, Richard Gregory, was a victim in 1830[37]. 'Erinensis', *The Lancet's* provocative correspondent in Dublin, reported in 1826:-

In the commencement of these complaints, they were principally confined to the lower, but of late I perceive that they have broken out in the higher orders of society, some medical men having already become their victims.[38]

Was it typhus that killed John William in 1824, a member of an other-wise long-lived family, and perhaps even his grandfather William in the cold, pestilence and famine of the mid eighteenth century?

In the period 1843-6 which Stokes and Cusack investigated they found that at least 443 doctors had died. One hundred and ninety nine of these deaths (45%) were due to 'fever' and forty to 'Phthisis' (tuberculosis). The other main causes were 'Apoplexy', 'Dropsy' and 'Heart disease'. Some of the heart disease may have been consequent upon scarlet fever which could be caught from patients, so half of all deaths may have been from occupational hazard. Among the rest, there were eleven deaths due to old age and debility, five to suicide, four to drowning, three to falling from a horse, and two to 'intemperance'. Two hundred and eighty deaths, two thirds of the total, were in age groups 26 to 50. Medicine was a high risk profession. A hundred and twenty years later, Donogh Macnamara said in his Doolin Memorial Lecture of 1966:-

If one were to ask for the outstanding quality in a doctor then, surely it would be courage.[39]

For the doctors this was tragic, but for the poor the famine years were cat-astrophic. In Dublin, where William Daniel was, 40,000 people died and he surely must have tried to save some of them. In the rest of Ireland more than a million died[40]. An example from a contemporary medical journal will illus-trate the extent of the calamity as seen by one medical observer[41]. Forty three thousand people lived in the Western District Union of Skibbereen in South West Ireland. In the twelve months to September 1847, over seven thousand of them died – more than one in six. Of those, three thousand died of 'fever', that is, typhus. Another thousand who survived emigrated to England or America. In one year the population had been depleted by one fifth. Dr Daniel Donovan, the Union's Medical Officer, suggested a cure, at least for some – food. When food was distributed to the starving people the number of deaths began to decrease within days. On average in March and April twenty-five people died *per day*. Food distribution began on May 10th, and by the end of July there were only two deaths a day.

What could be done about typhus? John agreed with the prevailing view that it was easier to prevent than cure[42]. He stressed the importance of space ('500 cubic feet per patient'), adequate ventilation ('3,000 cubic feet of fresh air per patient per hour') and cleanliness, good food and good nursing. All the usual medicines were tried,[43] calomel, iron perchloride, washing with vinegar, leeches, cupping, blisters and turpentine enemas, which were mostly ineffective, and to the modern physician almost laughably pointless. Bleeding was still popular, too, as in the case of a man from Skibbereen:-

> ... *advanced in life, who had been bled in the early stage of his illness, [and who] appeared to be rescued from immediate death, by a large bleeding from the jugular vein on the twentieth day, when he was rapidly sinking in the apoplexy of congestive fever.*[44] *[added emphasis]*

When the usual methods failed the most valuable medicine was considered to be wine. Wine was believed to be a stimulant which would counteract the severe debilitation of fever, so there seemed to be good reason for using it. Mateer called it the 'sheet anchor in this disease', but advised great caution:-

> *The plan I have followed for some time past is to keep from its use as long as possible and to begin with it only when the pulse has sunk much, and prostration of strength is very decided. For the most part this happens on the tenth or eleventh day of sickness...*[45]

Cheyne, at the Hardwicke Hospital, also favoured wine, but with reservations[46]. He advocated a good diet consisting of flummery (clotted milk and meal), milk or gruel for the weakest; the addition of stirabout (a porridge of water or milk and oatmeal), bread and gruel as they gained strength, and finally 1½ pounds of bread, ½ pound of beef and 2 pints of milk in convalescence ..... with wine. If it 'caused disgust', patients could have punch or porter instead. Cheyne said that porter:-

> ... *was sometimes preferred to wine by the patients, but it was by no means so generally efficacious, and it was not admissible when the bowels were in a slippery state. ...... in endeavouring to act upon an established principle we must not forget what is due to idiosyncrasies.*

He also had reservations about unlimited supply of 'ardent spirits' in the wards:-

> *The nurses in this country, in general, are excellent: they are kind, handy, and faithful to their trust: but still, if punch were thought necessary, it ought to be administered to the patient by some person of superior trust; more may be ordered than can be taken by the patient, which is often the case with cordials when the patient is dying, and the surplus will be a temptation which a nurse, exhausted by watching, might find difficult to withstand.*

Stokes, too, was a great advocate of wine.

> *By wine, food and other stimulants we support nature, until the struggle is past, so that to use the words of an ancient author....we* 'cure the patient by preventing him from dying'[47].*[original emphasis]*

Stokes promoted the use of the newly introduced stethoscope and was largely instrumental in working out the significance of the sounds that could be heard through it. In his *'Researches on the state of the heart in typhus fever'*[48] he describes how the strength of the heart diminishes as the fever of typhus worsens, and quotes many cases where the patients consumed 20–24 fluid ounces (600–720 ml) of wine per day for ten days or more to stimulate the heart. He was specially proud of one case, an elderly woman who was ill for six weeks, in the course of which she was given:-

> *Wine 292 oz [8.75 litres], Brandy 20 oz [600ml] Porter 7 bottles Ethereal enemata, 2, and Jelly, beef tea, &c, &c. Her recovery was perfect.*
> *Finally, [he said] I would draw the particular attention of my readers to the fact, that in the great majority of these cases the use of wine was followed by the happiest effects.*

Following the received wisdom of Stokes, his teacher and colleague, John was also an advocate of wine. A fourteen-year-old schoolboy, Thomas MacM., had enteric fever but unfortunately also developed typhus while in hospital just as he was recovering from the original illness[49]. He had a parched tongue and was covered with sordes*, and for four days his temperature was 104.8° F (40.5°C). He was deteriorating despite high doses of quinine, which had only a transient effect. John decided that the weakening state of his heart 'necessitated the use of wine'.

I began with marsala, but on the seventh day changed it for eight ounces (240 ml) of port. [Two days later] a rash appeared, and the suffused eyes, dusky countenance, delirium and sordes-loaded lips and tongue fully established the diagnosis of typhus. Some quiet sleep was secured with a mixture of

R	Liquor. Opii sedativ.,	min xii
	Spirit. aether. Oleos.	drams ij
	Tinct. Hyoscyami.	drams ij
	Aequae camphorae,	ad ounces iv
Signa:	sumat unciam tertis horis dum opus sit.	

The heart became weaker, ... the pulse rose to 140, the respirations to 40, and a considerable bronchial complication became developed. Ten ounces (300 ml) of port wine were given daily for three days, and with markedly good effect. The quantity was lessened gradually from the 12th day.

John was clearly very pleased with the successful outcome, not least because it would not do for the boy to die of typhus contracted in hospital while under treatment for another condition. He chose this case, among so many others, to illustrate his confidence in wine as a beneficial medicine. The faith that he and his colleagues placed in wine was enormous, whether it be marsala, claret, port or burgundy. In the absence of any other helpful treatment, let alone cure, such benefits were not to be discarded lightly. Modern port contains up to 20% alcohol by volume, so if it was that strength then Thomas's daily dose of ten ounces was equivalent to about one quarter of a bottle of gin. The modern doctor would consider treatment of patients already toxic from fever with another intoxicant such as wine, or even porter, to be not just useless folly but dangerous malpractice. To John and his contemporaries, however, knowing neither the cause nor the cure, it seemed to work so long as it was used with care. In the absence of knowledge pragmatism may be the best policy.

---

* offensive crusting and scabs

John was sure that early treatment, or better still prevention, were more important than simply admitting the patients to hospital if they were desperate. It made him angry to see patients admitted in a dying state.

Dying on admission, is a grave indictment against those responsible for the removal of the unhappy sick to hospital in their last hours.[50]

A regular feature of John's Medical Reports from Cork Street were tables showing how many patients had died soon after admission. It grieved him that people who had some hope of cure if they were admitted early would probably die if they came too late. An example from his report of 1884 reads

No. in Registry	Duration in Hospital	Disease	Note
403	10 hours	Typhus	Dying on admission
337	24 hours	Typhus	Sent in very bad
581	10 hours	Scarlatina	Sent in dying
808	20 hours	Erysipelas	Sent in most dangerously ill

[...... and another twelve cases]

Case number 808 was a 50 year-old woman, sent in on the fifteenth day of erysipelas, who died the next day. John commented:-

Can anything more deplorable be imagined than the want of judgement exhibited in this and other cases sent in beyond recovery?[51]

To remedy this defect in the hospital's activities he frequently drew such cases to the attention of the Managing Committee. One was a patient who had been under the care of the Dispensary medical officer at home. She was a forty year-old married woman who was suffering from typhus with bed sores, and was in an 'extremely prostrate condition' when admitted on the fifteenth day of her illness. John considered that a woman in that state of the disease could not safely be moved to hospital, and should have been treated and nursed at home if earlier admission had been impossible. The Managing Committee took the matter up with the Dispensary Committee, and through them with the doctor who had seen the patient. The doctor's reply was:-

I could not at all approve the proposal that fever cases should be retained in their own tenements and nurses obtained for them at the expense of the rates; the other inhabitants of the tenements being turned out, would be most likely to carry the infection to other houses.

This was true in the sense that it was wrong to disperse the disease through carriers, but John protested that the 'saving of life' should outweigh any other considerations, and that the 'provision of a home-nurse and maintenance of a woman so grievously ill' was a fair charge on the rates. He protested again when the same doctor sent in another moribund patient who arrived in a horse-drawn ambulance during a thunderstorm, and died twenty four hours later. The reply to his protest was 'as unsatisfactory as before'. Even if the Dispensary doctor was right about the spread of disease, he could have minimised the risk by early admission and isolation. He seemed to want it both ways, to nurse the sick at home until they were moribund and then send them to hospital, whereas early admission might be a better route to recovery. Public funding of medical care was a problem then, as now, and deterioration of health before admission to hospital is still, sadly, an event that is all too common in British hospital waiting lists.

John continued his interest in fevers throughout his career, for though the severity and frequency of such appalling disease was lessening other conditions arose to take their place and fill the hospital wards. Like his great-grandfather Daniel, who 'contrasted the last century with the present', John's career spanned two centuries. Daniel's 'best days' in the eighteenth century and John's in the nineteenth were both periods of momentous change in the medical world. Eventually the scourges of typhus, scarlatina, puerperal fever, diphtheria, and measles waned as the twentieth century began. Better housing and hygiene contributed to the reduction in severity of scarlet fever and diphtheria, and the need for fever wards declined. The discovery in 1916 that the germ which causes typhus, *Rickettsia prowazeki,* is carried by the body louse made prevention possible, and in most communities the disease has now disappeared. Seventy years on, there are no fever patients in the Cork Street Hospital which now cares for the chronically infirm.

Despite this progress in health and hygiene, two anecdotes remind us of the ever present danger of disease and our susceptibility to it. When Maurice, John's only surviving son fell ill with a fever while home on leave from the Navy in 1931, there was understandable concern. On emerging from the sickroom after John had examined his 45-year old son's rash, he said to his worried daughter-in-law, with more than a hint of gravity in his voice, "I am sorry to say, Ida, that it *is* scarlatina". Her reply "Are you sure?" was followed by a stony silence of disbelief. No one had been so bold as to challenge his authority on the diagnosis of scarlatina for sixty years! Happily Maurice recovered, and his wife's temerity was forgiven.

The other tale is a reminder of the importance of non-medical action in the prevention of disease. Years after the cause of typhus fever was known cases were still occurring, especially in the West of Ireland. It was discovered that second-hand clothing from Glasgow and Birkenhead, where typhus was still occurring, was being exported to

> the poor of Mayo [who] are mostly clad in this type of clothing, which comes here in bundles of jumbled garments of doubtful origin and cleanliness.[52]

Though it is individuals who suffer disease, we can all spread it, and without care we do.

A dead victim of cholera at Sunderland in 1832, coloured lithograph, showing the characteristic blue colour of the face and extremities, like an excess of 'choler'.

(Wellcome Library, London).

CHAPTER SEVEN

Epidemics

.... She died of a fever, and no one could save her,
singing cockles and mussels, alive, alive O!

Popular song

The disease that poor Molly Malone suffered is not named, but the fever that killed her was probably one of the devastating epidemics of typhus or enteric fever, measles, smallpox, and scarlet fever that swept through the country during the nineteenth century. In Europe today a doctor will probably never see a case of typhus. Measles and enteric fever can be prevented by immunisation and proper hygiene, and smallpox has been removed as a practical threat. Even scarlet fever, though it still occurs, is usually a minor problem and easily cured. The number of deaths during these epidemics now seems incredible, especially those in Ireland where one in four children who caught measles died, and every year there were 2,000 deaths from scarlet fever and 1,700 from whooping cough in a population of 5 million. Even those are overshadowed by the thousands of deaths from the epidemics of cholera, which first broke out in Britain and Ireland in 1831–2, when over thirty thousand died[1], and returned many times. The recurrent epidemics of smallpox, measles and scarlet fever throughout the century killed tens of thousands more.

Cholera had long been endemic in India and was therefore known to medical officers of the army and trading stations there, but had not been seen in Europe before the nineteenth century. As a result of increasing travel and trade the disease was carried out of India by travellers, and by 1817 was widespread throughout the Far East and heading westwards in the first 'Cholera Pandemic'[2]. Though it died out for a few years, it was on the march again by 1830, going westwards to North America and the Caribbean, and in 1831 reached continental Europe and the British Isles. Dublin, like other cities of the time, was ripe for the spread of the disease because of the insanitary state of its houses and amenities, and was completely unprepared for a disaster of this scale.

Daniel Moore was over 80 when the first cholera epidemic began, and his son John William was already dead. William Daniel was studying at the Royal College of Surgeons in Edinburgh, and would have seen cholera as it spread through Leith, Edinburgh, Musselburgh, Perth, and on to Glasgow, and when he returned to Dublin he found himself in the middle of the epidemic there. Charles, though only a boy of thirteen, would have witnessed the start of it in Dublin and shared the general alarm caused by the rapid advance of this new and very deadly disease, which no one understood. In later epidemics in the 1850s and -60s he was an active contributor to discussion about its nature, and wrote about his experience of it both as a ship's doctor and as a general practitioner, and William Daniel also took an active interest in how it spread. In the early epidemics deaths had been measured in hundreds, but between 1873 and 1884 when John was at the Meath Hospital the average number of deaths from cholera had fallen to 'only' 56, compared with 770 from typhus and 322 from smallpox, and he wrote little about it[3].

When this mysterious eastern disease burst upon Europe there was a widespread feeling of panic because of its rapid and unpredictable onset, the horrible appearance of its sufferers and the frequently fatal outcome. What caused it? How did it spread? Was it contagious? How could it be stopped or cured? Many examples of its rapid and dangerous course were described in the medical press, such as the case of Mary Johnson of Glasgow, who was taken ill on a journey to Ayrshire:-

While on the road she had purging and vomiting (which her husband attributed to whiskey, of which she partook freely,) became exhausted and weak, so that she required the assistance of her husband to reach [her destination]. She was ill that night with purging, vomiting and cramps, and was attended by two women, sisters, who rubbed her and administered whiskey toddy. Next day she was seen by Dr Anderson, when she was in a stage of collapse, cold, blue and pulseless, and died on the afternoon of that day.

This was on a Tuesday. On Friday one of the sisters who was engaged in rubbing was seized with all the symptoms and died after 12 hours illness. The next case was the other sister who had the disease severely but recovered.[4]

It spread rapidly through some but not all parts of the British Isles, as *The Lancet* reported with alarm:-

It is a curious fact, that from the first breaking out of the spasmodic Asiatic cholera throughout Great Britain, it has invariably shown an attachment to water, or in other words it has followed the inlets of the sea, such as bays, or where the ocean runs up into the land, or the course of large fresh-water rivers; and in no instance has it found its way into the interior or mountainous parts of the country, where little water exists. In Ireland it has raged with destructive violence at Belfast, at Sligo, at Cork, at Dublin; in Scotland at Musselburgh, at Glasgow, up the Murray Frith (sic); in England at Liverpool, London, Newcastle &c, all under such circumstances.[5]

It even reached remote Ross-shire where forty-one people died in a village of 120 inhabitants. In Glasgow it was noted that whereas 3,000 people died 'not one brewer's servant was attacked', which was attributed to there having been allowed a 'liberal quantity of good ale' daily. The writer evidently did not realise that, unlike everyone else, the brewer's men had no need to drink the cholera-infected water. This was twenty years before the famous outbreak in London when Dr John Snow removed the handle of the public pump in Broad Street from which local people drew their water to stem the epidemic there; those who drank from the pump got cholera, but those who worked and drank in the local brewery did not. It was also observed early on that cholera was more likely to break out in low-lying, poorly drained areas, and especially where garbage, animal waste from slaughter-houses or piggeries, and human sewage were unable to drain freely away. In Dublin there were many such places, where the poor were forced to live. An account by Mr McCoy of the 1832 epidemic tells of their pitiful conditions.

I found the population existing in a state hardly to be credited by those who have not witnessed it. Most of the peasantry living in huts, the thatched roofs

of many of which give a free entrance to the frequent showers, as their
unglazed windows admitted of the cold air of an inclement December; their
food but a few potatoes and some salt, for a scanty morning and evening
meal. They were much alarmed at the presence of the disease among them;
the cause assigned to those occurring on the 25th December and two or three
following days [was] the eating of a little flesh on Christmas day by those
who had not tasted animal food for twelve months before!

> *Unwholesome straw, damp earthen floors, steaming mud walls, stinted*
fuel, and uncleanliness appeared to invite disease.[6]

McCoy saw hundreds of cases as resident medical officer in the Grange
Gorman-lane Hospital in Dublin, which had space for more than 700
patients, and had been set up rapidly in 1832 to accommodate the huge
number of cases – nearly a hundred a day during one week. Despite its
rapid spread he did not believe cholera was contagious, because:-

> *On coming into the wards unexpectedly in the middle of the night, I have*
often found [the attendants] stretched on the same bed with a collapsed
patient, sometimes asleep; and yet I have not known any ill consequences to
follow.[7]

An account of various houses in Dublin which were the seat of disease in
the 1846 epidemic was given to the Surgical Society of Ireland by
Mr Tufnell, who had experienced cholera in India, and noted its route to
Europe via Kabul and Teheran.

> *One particular house in Sycamore Alley was depopulated seven or eight*
times, while the houses adjoining remained untouched; a nearly similar occur-
rence took place in a house near Cuffe-street, and in a single house at
Kingstown four or five families died successively of the disease.[8]

It was no better in England or Scotland, where seaports especially were
affected by the arrival of disease-bearing ships. In Sunderland, in 1848,
five of the six members of the family of Robert Henry, a ship's pilot, went
down with cholera and died within four weeks. James Ellemore and four
relatives all died[9]. In Newcastle a sailor who went to his home as soon as

his ship came to port was taken ill that night, and within days cholera had spread through the town.

Faced with the recurrence of severe epidemics the authorities had to do something to prevent them. When cholera began again in 1848 the Central Board of Health in Dublin issued a list of measures to be taken, with advice to the citizens. Because these were lengthy and verbose, they were summarised by Dr M Donovan[10]. Among the items of good advice given were these:-

Shun damp and low situations, and, if possible quit dwellings in such places during the prevalence of cholera ....

An abundant supply of fresh air is as necessary during the night as in the day ....

Remove all stagnant water and dung-heaps from around your dwellings, and clean out all sewers without delay ....

Avoid chills: do not wear wet clothes a moment longer than can be avoided ... Wear a flannel belt around the stomach and loins ...

Abstain from stimulants unless prescribed .... In former visitations both rich and poor resorted to the use of stimulants – wine, whiskey, brandy &c, under the false impression that what was sometimes useful as a cure was also useful as a preventive.

This was good advice for those who could take it and many of 'the better class' moved out to healthier places, but for those who were crowded into the filthy, ill ventilated courts and tenements there was no escape.

The debate about whether cholera was contagious rumbled on, and as late as 1866 Denis Phelan wrote to the *Medical Press and Circular* to insist that cholera was not contagious:-

The friends and relatives of the sick may be under no apprehension of catching the disease, and need not be deterred from affording the sick in their own dwellings every needful assistance and attention. It is a well known melancholy fact that numerous medical men who have been on attendance of fever patients have died of it, but the reverse in remarkable degree has been the case ... in cholera.[11] [original emphasis]

Dr Phelan was right in that cholera is not passed from person to person by bodily contact, as typhus is, but its infectious nature became clear in 1883 when Ludwig Koch isolated the bacterium *Vibrio cholerae* and showed that it is the cause of the disease. Furthermore, because the germ can exist in sewage-polluted water it can spread rapidly through populations at risk.

A curious and very frequent feature of the new disease that was noted by many observers was the coldness and blue-ness of the face and extremities in advanced cases, which often heralded death. They were familiar with vomiting, profuse diarrhoea, pain, headache and fever, and in such cases would not hesitate to bleed, apply blisters and leeches, or 'salivate', i.e. give large doses of mercury, but this new disease was a puzzle. McCoy describes the appearance:-

> *Sometimes in three or four hours the blueness of the hands becomes intense, particularly under the nails, and their skin has a shrivelled appearance, as if they had been two or three days enveloped in a poultice, or like those of a laundress except in colour, and covered in a cold clammy sweat; the insteps get blue, but I have not often seen the colour here present that continuous dye which it does on the hands; in general, the minute vessels can be distinctly traced here, while the hands seem as if they had been immersed in some colouring matter. I have known patients express surprise at this appearance, "wondering what could have soiled them in that manner".*[12]

Charles Moore's career as a ship's doctor for the Peninsula and Oriental Steam Packet Company lasted seven years. The route to India and the Far East was through the Mediterranean and thence slowly overland to the Red Sea at Suez before the Canal was built, through hot and insanitary conditions. There were usually about 250 cabin passengers and crew on the ships, plus 'deck passengers', and ten or twelve persons would be ill in each voyage. Mostly they complained of stomach upsets, but there was the occasional apoplexy or dropsy. He was lucky not to have any case of cholera, for in 1849 they arrived at Suez to find that more than half its population of three thousand had died in a recent outbreak. The party sensibly avoided the town on that occasion, but visiting it another time he noted the 'dilapidated khans, or inns' and the town's 'low lying position, lack of fresh water, and foul cesspools under the houses'. He wrote:-

A number of habitations are crowded round the bazaars, which are generally thronged with people of many nations, not over cleanly in their persons; this most thickly inhabited part of the town is close to the cemetery, a large piece of sandy ground, partly surrounded by the town wall through broken portions of which jackals and hyenas find a ready entrance.[13]

During the cholera epidemic the P&O Company sent its passengers direct from Suez to Alexandria, avoiding the usual visit to Cairo because the disease was rife there. They took special care not to stay in Alexandria itself where '300 were dying of cholera daily, out of a population of 65,000'. They left there free of the disease, but were not allowed to land at Malta or Gibraltar because of quarantine rules. In fact, though they had no cholera on board they might well have got it in Malta, for 'several cases occurred in a line of battle-ship, which was lying opposite a place where a foul sewer opens into the sea'[14].

When Charles returned to Ireland he was involved in an outbreak of cholera in Finglas, now a suburb of Dublin but then a separate village, which he described in the *Dublin Quarterly Journal of Medical Science*. This was in 1854, the same year in which John Snow removed the handle of the Broad Street pump. His account begins by saying that to understand an outbreak of disease it is necessary to understand the locality in which it occurs.

The village stands on limestone rock, for the most part on the sloping sides of the vale, the main street being, at its northern end, 194 feet above the sea. Several parts of the village command a splendid prospect of Dublin city, bay, and mountains, and naturally it has great advantages as a healthful place. But what nature has bestowed on this classic spot man has marred by neglect and carelessness. Thus the site of William the Third's camp, the vicarage of Parnell, and the place where Swift, Addison and other equally celebrated men met together, has become little better than 'a refuge for the destitute', the vagrant, and the bad characters of many a mile round, and a nidus for disease. ....

I consider the apparently capricious selection of certain houses, sides of streets, &c, which are generally held up as proofs of the inscrutably mysterious workings of this fearful malady, are not so in fact, for on close inspection

I have never yet, in any part of the world I have visited, failed to discover a palpable cause for the too often merited infliction of the scourge of cholera and other epidemics.[15]

In other words Finglas had degenerated into the state of filth he had seen in Egypt, and if the sanitation had been better cholera might have been avoided. Charles had a crusading spirit for the newly developing concept of Public Health, though it was tempered with a rather mischievous thought. He believed that if 'occasional visitations' of cholera did occur from time to time it would sharpen the efforts to remove these insanitary conditions, and would:-

> ....*induce Governments, local powers and the people never to relax industry in sanitary measures, which ought constantly to be enforced to prevent the more frequent, and therefore less observed, fatality from fever and other preventable diseases.*[16]

Charles reported that the first case recorded at Finglas was that of a labourer recently returned from Belfast, who became ill 'after drinking a gallon of porter and eating a liberal supply of bacon for his breakfast'. It seems the protective power of 'good ale' was less in Ireland than Scotland, but this was not surprising in the conditions of the poor man's house, which was:-

> ... *of two stories high, very old, without rere★, - owing to another house being built against its back wall on very much higher ground than the wretched clay floor of the front house; the first person attacked lay on a straw bed on the ground, near the street door, close to which is an opening broken into an old foul sewer. The drinking water used by the villagers is chiefly taken from the nearly stagnant stream, which like the Thames and the Liffey receives the filth of the village and the drainage of the ancient and still used cemetery. [In another house there were] eleven persons in a small damp cabin, with only one room, five adults and six children, and five of the inmates lying in one bed, one of them ill with cholera.*[17]

★ rere = Irish spelling of rear

He believed that quarantine was useless, and that:-

> .... *the only true prophylactic is attention to drainage, ventilation, cleanliness, proper drinking water and food, and employment for mind and body.*[18]

While Charles was voluble on the subject of cholera, William Daniel was more restrained. He wrote no account of cholera himself, but in April 1867 when the cause of the disease was still not understood, he presented to a meeting of the College of Physicians of Ireland a translation of a paper by the Dutch Professor Donders with whom he was corresponding. The chairman of the meeting was Dr Dominic Corrigan (whom medical readers will associate with a peculiarity of the pulse,) who introduced William Daniel as 'my friend Dr W.D.Moore'. Donders' paper concerned an outbreak of cholera in Utrecht the previous year, where in a population of 60,000 people one in twenty-five suffered from the disease[19]. It dealt principally with one street in Utrecht where 380 people in eighty-three families lived. One in five of them developed cholera and one in ten died. What was the nature of the disease? Why was this street in particular so badly affected? Why did the houses which had recently been improved have more cases than old houses in lower and poorly drained ground? Donders asked three questions; is the infecting matter transmitted through the air? is the earth the conductor of the contagion? can direct transference from the sick to the sound occur? He did not seem to consider water as a possible 'conductor of the contagion'. Nor could he explain why some inhabitants of a house fell ill while others did not, but concluded that whatever the answers to these questions good hygiene was vital and it was necessary to:-

> ... *provide for good drinking water, for the improvement of the food for the people, for the promotion of cleanliness, and for the removal of injurious filth, for the improvement of the dwellings, and not less for the investigation of endemic diseases.*[20]

The message William Daniel conveyed to the meeting from his friend Professor Donders was that whatever the actual cause of cholera, the way to prevent it was through provision of clean water, wholesome food and proper housing and effective drains. Using Donders paper as evidence, he was saying that the medical profession has a duty to argue the case for appropriate action by government and society. Medicine is not merely the treatment of the sick, but has a wider responsibility to promote healthy living conditions for everyone.

Like his nephew John in his work on typhus, Charles introduces his description of cholera with his view of the derivation of the word 'cholera', which he says 'some authors attribute to the Greek word for 'waterspout'. Nowadays the Shorter Oxford Dictionary says it comes from the same origin as the word 'choler' of the four humours, which describes the horrid blue congestion of the face, hands and feet that was so noticeable. Yet waterspout well describes the profuse vomiting and diarrhoea, which has been likened to 'rice-water'. He describes the blueness and coldness of the patients, but does not say what proportion of his cases recovered. Many did so, it seems, like the twelve-year old boy who for three days was pulseless and passed no urine, but was 'cured' by treatment with mercury and chalk, calomel, James's powder and gray pill with blisters to the neck. In no time he 'was calling for beefsteak'.

Charles and his brother William Daniel must have treated many cases in their homes in the 1848 and 1866 epidemics, for not everyone could go to hospital. In the latter outbreak the Dublin hospitals were more than full, with a mortality rate ranging from 44 to 66 percent. Charles's treatment for cholera was the standard one of the time, and included good nursing, warmth, rubbing, mercury, leeches and, occasionally, bleeding. He wrote elsewhere that he was sceptical of the benefits of bleeding and refused to carry it out even when patients expected it. He cautioned against the overuse of opium which was liable to lead to cerebral congestion; it was better to give small doses of calomel repeated frequently. Blisters, friction of the extremities, and shampooing were helpful, and 'inhalations of oxygen gas seemed useful for a time, at least'. Whatever was done, treatment should be started early:-

> There is an immense amount of evidence to prove that diarrhoea always precedes cholera. The vast importance of treating this premonitory stage cannot be overestimated.[21]

Others had sought new treatments, relating them to a supposed cause, often seemingly bizarre to us now, but plausible then. Tufnell, who had met cholera in India, speculatively attributed it to:-

.... *an absence of electricity in the atmosphere, which exerting its peculiar influence over the animal economy, reduces it to such a state that any powerful depressant or miasm coming upon a constitution thus prepared for the changes which subsequently take place produces the disease in question.*[22]

His description of the cause of thunderstorms is very vivid, but lacks evidence that they cause cholera. His other theories talk of 'electric fluid' being extracted from the rarefied air and causing rain, which paradoxically can both cause and cure cholera. Electricity was a new discovery, of course, and ripe for use in hypotheses to explain mysterious phenomena. McCoy was intrigued but not impressed when treatment involving electricity was tried by another doctor. He wrote:-

I had a notion that taking sparks with an electric machine from the surface of the body might possibly be of some service, and whether it was my appearing anxious to have this tried or not, I cannot say, but a patient was shortly after treated with electricity; but instead of merely stimulating the surface in the way I imagined, the contents of the charged jar were repeatedly sent through the thorax; and from the description of its effects I should not wish to witness a similar experiment; the case was a very bad collapse, no advantage was gained.[23]

McCoy witnessed an intravenous infusion for cholera which was no more successful than 'taking sparks', though he confessed 'perhaps from old prejudices I cannot bring myself to carry it out'. He accepted that in cholera there seemed to be a 'great diminution of the water and of soluble salts' in the blood, and twice saw an attempt to correct this in the Grange Gorman-lane hospital

Four or five pints of water at the temperature of about 112° Farht., having the usual salts dissolved in it, were slowly thrown into a vein in the bend of the arm; after a few strokes of the piston, by which I suppose ten or twelve ounces had been injected, the pulse at the wrist of the other arm became a little fuller and accelerated at the rate of about thirteen beats in a minute; until towards the close the patient did not feel any thing particular from the process, but then began to complain of a tightness about his chest; he expired about half an hour after his arm was tied up, as I learned.[24]

A similar treatment was reported in *The Lancet* by Thomas Latta MD of Leith, also in 1832, with more success. Latta performed the operation with the patient in a vapour bath, a device in which the patient was suspended in a metal case over a bath of heated water. The water to be injected was 'charged with protoxide of nitrogen and holding in solution the salts natural to the blood', but at a temperature of 97° or 98° F, rather cooler than McCoy's colleague used. He treated five cases, all seriously ill and beyond hope of recovery. His first two cases were very promising:-

Pat. Peddie [who] was ... beyond the reach of any remedy except venous injection was dismissed cured; he never had one untoward symptom after being injected.

Geo. Dunne, whose circumstances were truly desperate, goes far to recommend the treatment. ...his constitution was undermined by chronic disease to the stomach and liver of seventeen years duration, but he is now well and declares he is freer from the symptoms of his old complaint than he has been for many years.[25]

Two of Latta's patients died, a child of five and a woman who was an 'inveterate drunkard', though the latter seemed to benefit for a while. One patient was 'convalescent without consequences for some days', and two others recovered. A 60% cure rate for a dangerous disease must have seemed quite promising. Intravenous infusion to counter the dehydration is the basis of modern treatment, of course, so it was a brave try defeated only by the limitations of the technique.

More drastic measures were employed by others who had heard of the benefits of blood transfusion. First done in dogs in 1666, the following year Dr King injected twelve ounces of calf's blood in to the veins of 'a Cambridge student, who was reported to be mentally defective'. The operation 'gave rise to no ill effects, nor to any benefit to his mental powers', and failed to do so again when tried a second time. It was even proposed that kings might have wisdom imparted through their veins in this way, though evidence of this from the Cambridge experiment was lacking. Injections of various substances had been tried to treat apoplexy, hysteria and consumption including, in 1820, the 'successful treatment' of an epileptic girl by the injection of tartar emetic.[26]

The Lancet received so much correspondence in 1832 suggesting that transfusion of blood should be tried that it sought evidence for its benefit, which was not encouraging, especially a report from Professor Diffenbach of Germany[27]. Diffenbach's first patient was Frederick Muller. He had been ill with cholera only seven hours − 'hands and feet purple, pulse completely gone', and was treated thus:-

> The right jugular vein was exposed for about the length of an inch, and a quill-tube introduced into it; the blood to be injected was furnished by a young physician, and an ounce and a half introduced by means of a small syringe previously warmed. The patient immediately fell into a state of insensibility .... And after a few plaintive cries died suddenly six minutes from the time of the operation.

The next case was an older woman who received eight ounces of blood and some warm water, but died two hours later. The third attempt was no more successful. Blood transfusion seemed not to be the answer to the mystery of cholera.

Other, less dramatic treatments were tried, which seem quaint to us now, but to those desperate for a cure were clearly worth the attempt. They include infusion of horse-radish and a teaspoonful of dilute calomel and opium taken by mouth[28]; Spiritus ammoniae compositus, lime-water and milk taken every half hour[29], and toast water − "a gallon of boiling water to one square inch of toast: when cold it is ready for use"[30]. Perhaps the most dramatic after the transfusion debacle was that of putting the patient to sleep by administering chloroform[31]. An example of this treatment was carried out at Peckham House Poor Asylum and reported in The Times.[32]

> Place the patient in bed in warm blankets; give a glass of brandy in hot water, with sugar, and spice; apply friction to the body by means of warm

flannels; and an embrocation composed of lin. saponis co, lin camphor, tinct opii, and extract belladonna; apply to the whole surface of the body bags filled with heated bran; place the patient under the influence of chloroform by inhalation, and keep him under its effect as long as the bad symptoms occur.

No fatalities were reported, fortunately, but sometimes 'the reaction was so great as to require gentle blood-letting'.

Outbreaks of cholera continued throughout the world, and are said to have been responsible for 370,000 deaths in India between 1898 and 1908[33]. It still occurs where insanitary conditions prevail. Charles' suggestion that a little cholera occasionally is a good reminder of the need for proper hygiene, both publicly and privately, seems to have been ignored in such places.

When John entered the profession as house physician at the Meath Hospital, the last great cholera epidemic was receding. It had begun on July 22nd 1866 when a young girl, ill with fever which turned out to be cholera, landed from the Liverpool steamer. Within days a child of three from the same house died, the first of 1,459 people to perish from the disease in the next twenty-two months. Fifty-five years later he recalled that:-

The picture presented by the ill-fated victims of that dread disease left an ineffaceable, a life-long, impression on my memory. To this day I see in my mind's eye the wasted, icy cold, blue-tinted, yet withal conscious, pain-stricken, hapless sufferers for whom medical skill could do so little in their sore extremity.[34]

In that epidemic the hospital resources were stretched to their limits. At the Meath there were usually only twelve beds for fever cases, so the hospital authorities built wooden sheds in the grounds in which the patients actually fared better than in the wards of the main building. The mortality rate in the sheds was 43%, compared with 49–55% in the wards[35]. It was surely early experiences like this, as student and house physician, which motivated John to take such an active interest in epidemic diseases and try to find ways to prevent them through public health measures.

As that last severe cholera epidemic subsided and the fever wards became vacant, he was soon experiencing another epidemic killer – smallpox. He was again much moved by seeing one particular patient with smallpox in 1872, a student at the Meath. William Stokes vividly described the poor man's condition:-

[It] soon showed itself in its worst characters. The fever was very high, ... and the eruption was universal, while on the face the pustules became confluent at an early period. Delirium set in, and the patient tore off the dressings from his face so often that we desisted from further application. ..... The body was one universal sore, and the agonies of the patient from adhesion of the surface to the bed-clothes was not to be described.[36]

At this point a colleague, Mr Smyly, suggested the use of a warm bath 'with a view to relieving the terrible suffering', and one was prepared in such a way that the patient could be placed in it with least distress. As soon as he was lowered into the water:-

The effect was instantaneous and marvellous. The delirium ceased as if by magic; it was the delirium of pain, and the patient exclaimed 'Thank God! Thank God! I am in Heaven! I am in Heaven! Why didn't you do this before". He was kept at least seven hours in the bath, during which time brandy was freely administered, and omitted only when it showed symptoms of its disagreeing with the brain. The bath was repeated the next day ...... From this time his recovery was progressive. That this gentleman's life would have been sacrificed but for the timely use of the bath, few who have had any experience in prognosis can reasonably doubt.

Now, when we have predictably effective treatment for most infectious diseases, and better still know how to prevent many of them, it is well to remember that care is more important than ever when cure is not available.

Smallpox is now considered to be extinct, the welcome victim of research and the international implementation of preventive measures, but for the nineteenth century physicians things were very different. In the Cork Street Hospital, where John became physician while the 1878 epidemic was at its height, admissions in one year reached 1,509, nearly half of them in the fifteen weeks between April and July – fourteen a day. Two hundred and sixty six of them died, more than one in six[37]. In

1879-80 admissions for smallpox fell to six hundred, and in 1880-81 to four hundred and eleven though the death rate was still one in five. But in the next twelve months there were few cases and only one death. Not everyone who had smallpox could be admitted to hospital. In the epidemic of 1847 two and a half thousand beds were available in Dublin as a whole, three hundred of them at Cork Street. There was simply no room for most of the 12,000 people who wanted to go there[38]

Even this appalling outbreak was small compared with the pandemic which had swept across Europe five years earlier in 1871-1874. It was especially bad in France, where 23,000 soldiers died among those mobilised to fight in the Franco-Prussian war. In Paris ten thousand people died, and in Prussia sixty thousand. In England and Wales sixty nine thousand died, most of them in London and Liverpool, though the highest mortality rate was in Sunderland. In Ireland, whose population had been depleted by famine and emigration, 4292 died in the four year epidemic, three quarters of them in 1872 alone. Dublin had 1,557 deaths, the highest mortality rate in Britain after Sunderland[39]. Five hundred patients were admitted to the Cork Street Hospital, of whom one in four died. Unfortunately this mountainous effort left the hospital in debt, which the surviving population seemed reluctant to repay. Six thousand people attended a service at St Patrick's Cathedral to give thanks for the end of the epidemic, but the collection taken to help meet this debt raised only £50 – two pence per head[40]. Small gratitude; in seventeenth century Venice they built the magnificent Basilica of Santa Maria della Salute to give thanks for the delivery from an epidemic of plague.

The suffering of the thousands who died from smallpox was pitiful, as the case of Stokes's student illustrates, yet even in the nineteenth century it could have been largely prevented. Inoculation had been used for many years, despite its risks, before Jenner's famous use of cowpox material made the procedure safe. Various Acts of Parliament made the new method of 'vaccination' by cowpox compulsory and the use of actual smallpox material illegal, but the element of compulsion was widely unpopular and compliance with the law was extensively resisted. Yet it really was effective. Just how valuable it could be was described by John in several of his writings[41]. For instance, in the 1871-2 epidemic the mortality rate in Cork Street was 22%, almost the same as other hospitals in Ireland and England, such as the Hardwicke (20%), the London Smallpox Hospital (19%) and Hampstead (19%). But when this figure was broken down in to the vaccinated and unvaccinated, there were big differences. In those who had been vaccinated it was only 11%, but in those who had not it was more than six times higher – 72 per cent. Looked at another way, of the people who had a mild attack nearly all had been vaccinated, but of those with so-called 'malignant' smallpox just over half had been. Similar figures were reported from the 1878-9 epidemic[42] which convincingly showed the benefit of vaccination in reducing both severity and mortality.

In his book on fevers John refers to a study carried out by Mr Marson at the London Smallpox Hospital. Five thousand patients admitted between 1836 and 1855 were recorded, an unusually large series for that period[43]. Successful vaccination causes a blister which leaves a small round scar. Marson counted the number of scars in each patient, which indicated the number of times that patient had been vaccinated or re-vaccinated, and related that to the death rate among those patients. It was clear that repeated vaccination reduced the likelihood of dying from smallpox.

Number of scars	Death rate %
No scar but claimed to have been vaccinated	21.7
One	7.7
Two	4.7
Three	1.9
Four or more	0.5
Overall, vaccinated and non-vaccinated	18.8

John regretted that so few people were re-vaccinated despite this convincing evidence of its greater protective effect. He estimated that of the thousands of patients admitted to Cork Street in 1876-9, eighty percent had been vaccinated once, but only five percent had ever been vaccinated again. These figures suggest that if even half of them had had a second vaccination the death rate might have been only 8%, and four or five hundred lives might have been saved amongst the hospital cases alone. He was convinced of the greater effect of repeated vaccination, and argued for it vigorously in his book on Fevers:-

There can be no doubt that the protective efficacy of vaccination wears out grad-
ually with the lapse of time. Periodical revaccination every seven or ten years
is, therefore, necessary if smallpox is to be completely prevented.....
[added emphasis]

In view of the thousands of cases still occurring in the late nineteenth
century the idea that smallpox could actually be 'completely prevented'
may have seemed unrealistic. But eighty-two years later smallpox itself
was dead, rendered a virtually extinct species as the result of exactly what
he had advised – a mass vaccination campaign[44]. He did not know that
there would be a World Health Authority which could organise such a
programme, but would surely have welcomed it.

Treatment was ineffective. As well as the high mortality there was a
need to reduce the appalling suffering while the acute stage lasted, and
disfiguring scars on the face and body after recovery. Brettoneau, in 1830,
advised puncturing every blister with a gold needle to prevent scarring. If
this had been applied in the Franco Prussian War he would have had an
immense task treating the thousands of cases in the French army, and it
would have been extremely expensive if his gold needles had been disposable as they would be now. His colleague Dr Guersent opened all the
blisters and inserted silver nitrate, an equally painstaking process[45].

When John came to write his text-book *Continued and Eruptive*
Fevers in 1892, much had been learned about the infectivity of smallpox,
its dangerous course, and the effectiveness of vaccination in preventing
the development of the disease in individuals, and also therefore in the
prevention of devastating epidemics. He describes the great variety of
treatments which had been proposed over the years, but had to admit
their uselessness. For example in medieval times the treatment was the
'hot regimen' advised by John of Gaddesdon in the *Rosa Anglica,* but, he
says, this 'barbarous and disastrous system' had been supplanted by Thomas
Sydenham with a 'cooling regimen', which is the principle on which
nineteenth century treatment was based[46]. Huxtable, in 1764, advised
'cataplasms of milk and bread, boiled turnips, and the like applied to the
feet'. Later, the benefits of bathing were introduced, such as the system
invented by a Professor Hebra in 1862 and recommended by John.

The apparatus consists of a bath, six feet long by three feet broad, made of wood lined with copper or zinc. Exactly fitting its interior is an iron frame to which are fastened transverse bands of webbing as in an ordinary bed. About two feet from one end is attached a head support, which moves on a hinge and can be fixed at any angle by a simple piece of rack-work. The frame is covered with a blanket and is also provided with a horse hair pillow; it does not rest on fixed supports but is suspended in the bath by cords attached to it at each end..... At the head of the bath, but at a higher level, is a vessel made of copper which can be heated so that water may be supplied at any temperature.

In this way water could flow through the bath continuously, and the patient would remain there for hours at a time. John mentions a case where the patient remained for five and a half hours at 98° F, after which he was:-

....put to bed perfectly free from delirium, and with the help of 15 grains [1 gramme] of chloral (of which 60 grains had previously had no effect), he slept uninterruptedly for eight hours.

What is not mentioned is the spread of the virus by sending the bath water down the drain, but then they did not know that there was a virus.

Such symptomatic relief must have been blissful, but was not curative. John admitted that "no physician has ever yet *cured* a case of smallpox", but set two principles for treatment, namely to guide the essential disorder to a favourable termination, and to combat secondary affections as they arise. The search for a cure continued, or at least for something to reduce the misery. The sick room or ward should be well ventilated and warm, the patient 'skilfully nursed', the hair cut close and the skin washed with carbolised water or with a weak solution of corrosive sublimate – mercury again. Pain could be relieved with dry cupping, or by hypodermic injection of ergotin. Ice-bags applied for headache were effective, though ice must have been hard to find before refrigerators were common. John's colleague, Dr Arthur Wayne Foot, recommended carbolic acid to be taken internally in the form of 'sulpho-carbolate of sodium, one drachm in a wineglassful or two of iced water as the usual drink' – or by spraying the throat with it. Foot also recommended 'throwing pure sulphurous acid about the bed and bedclothes of the patient; and burning sulphur in the sick room'.

At the London Smallpox Hospital Mr Marson used only the 'best olive oil', or glycerine and rose water. In America they excluded sunlight, an idea John followed enthusiastically following a chance observation of his own[47]. One of his patients was being nursed at home in a sick room with dark red curtains drawn close over the windows and door, excluding all natural light, and where a fire glowed redly in the grate. When the patient recovered there were no scars on the face, but as he had also been advised to take 'a claret-glassful of good burgundy every six hours', one could hardly say the experiment was well controlled for confounding variables. Even in 1894 he recorded seeing a patient who probably had smallpox, with swollen red eyes and flushed face. He advised 'local depletion' to reduce the eruption on the face, which he did by applying a leech and allowing the bleeding to continue for thirty minutes after it had fallen off. In the most severe cases John says that:-

Stimulants are imperatively called for – brandy, whisky, or wine according to circumstances, and especially "egg-flip" mixture and "turpentine punch".

In this last remedy he was supported by Alexander Collie of the Homerton Hospital in London, who, to make up for the loss of appetite during the illness, advised:-

Let your patient then have milk in abundance, as many raw eggs beaten up with a little whisky as can be stuffed into him, beef-tea, arrowroot, sago, tapioca, &c. ..... Or what we have often found to succeed when drugs proper failed [in restlessness, sleeplessness and delirium] was two or three ounces of whisky in warm water, and a little sugar.[48]

As a last resort John says 'Curschman recommends a trial of transfusion of blood, which he admits, has so far disappointed expectations. This 'transfusion', which Stokes had also recommended for typhus in the 1830s, simply consisted of the removal of a few millilitres of blood from a vein in one arm and re-injecting it in the other.

The effectiveness of treatments has often been judged by their number; the more there are, the less effective they appear to be. By this standard none of these treatments could hope to achieve a cure, but the physicians of the time must be admired for their care for the sufferings of their patients and their persistent search for an effective treatment. As there is still no cure we must be thankful that the scourge of smallpox has been removed, hopefully for ever. Vigilance is essential in cholera, indeed in any infectious disease, as is maintenance of public and private hygiene. Smallpox has been defeated, measles is preventable by immunisation, and cholera, typhus and typhoid have been eliminated, at least in countries where sanitary standards are good. Yet the battle against disease must continue because the human race, as part of the natural world, remains vulnerable. Just as cholera emerged two hundred years ago as a new and mysterious disease, we now have AIDS, E. Coli 157 and BSE. It seems that new forms of disease are one step ahead of us; we should not be complacent.

If the spectre of Molly Malone is ever seen pushing her ghostly barrow in the broad and narrow but now prosperous streets of Dublin, it would be a safer reminder of the constant need for hygiene than Charles's 'occasional episodes' of cholera. Charles, William Daniel, and John saw many Mollies in their time, but as well as treating those patients individually they directed their thoughts and efforts to the control of disease through better sanitation and hygiene. They were early pioneers of what we now call Public Health, that is to say, the prevention of disease and the promotion of health by methods which go beyond medicine to engineering, legislation and education. We should be grateful to them and their contemporaries who saw what was needed and changed the attitudes of a sceptical public.

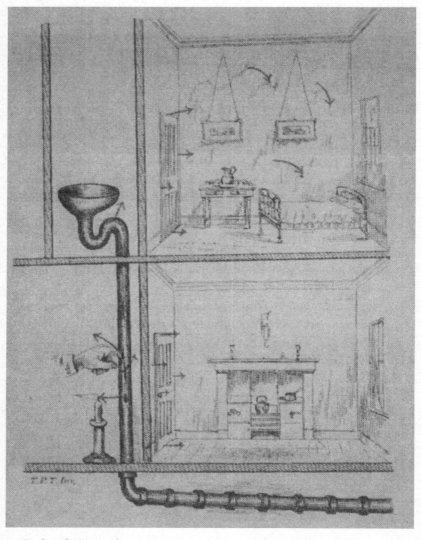

Broken drains, such as occurred at a house in a fashionable Dublin Square,
where escaping gas blew out a candle.
From: Dangers to Health; a pictorial guide to domestic sanitary defects.
T. Pidgin Teale, J & J Churchill, 1878
(Reading Pathological Society)

CHAPTER EIGHT

Mysterious Miasms

Upon this subject of epidemics we require facts and faithful records[1]
The Lancet, 1855

Anyone tempted to return to a nineteenth century lifestyle should think again, at least as far as health is concerned, because there was little chance of a life as long and healthy as can be expected today. In Ireland fever and famine had devastated the population, and it was not much better across the Irish sea in Manchester or Liverpool, where in 1839 the average age at death of even the more prosperous citizens was less than forty years. For the labouring poor the outlook was even bleaker; in those big cities their average age at death was less than 20 years, though in rural Rutland, with luck, they might reach the age of forty[2]. In 1860 a leader in *The Medical Circular* said:-

The great mortality that characterises urban life occurs among the lowest classes; and mainly so because they have not breathing room, and wilfully exclude the limited supply of air to which they might have access. For the sake of warmth in cold seasons, every cranny is stuffed with rags, and every casement carefully sealed, so that not a draught of cool air shall lower the temperature of the close and foetid atmosphere which is insidiously poisoning the blood of the wretched beings, who ... huddle round the dying embers of a coke fire, doing their best to keep warm[3]

This wretched state of things provided ample material for philanthropists to speak out against the poverty, squalor and filth. *The Medical Circular* joined them in appealing for the construction of 'model dwellings' for the poor. This unhealthy state pervaded the whole of London and other great cities, including Dublin where the Moore family then lived and practised.

The British Medical Journal, a new force in the field in 1858, remarked on its universal effect:-

> *In the Lords' library, there is a great smell which comes from the river; and their lordships are fluttered beyond measure at the fact. Alas! There has been a very great smell for years lower down the river: but there plebeians alone smelt it, and they were of little consequence. We rejoice, however, that their lordships' library is nothing better than a stench-trap. If the Lord Chancellor would only have a mild diarrhoea, it would be of infinite service; and the fainting of a few cabinet ministers from a similar cause would be indeed an invaluable service to the nobodies of this vast town, who have so long suffered from the state of the Thames in silence.*[4]

The reason for their lordships being so was that the river flowing through the very heart of the capital of the British Empire was little more than an open sewer. The unplanned and primitive drainage system of London was overloaded by the biological waste of its millions of inhabitants. No less than 87 million gallons of sewage poured into the river whose daily flow at Teddington lock was only 400 million gallons, so more than a fifth of the water under the windows of their Lordships' library was untreated sewage. Even royalty had to share the experience. The *BMJ* said that Queen Victoria:-

> *…was bold enough to venture upon the river the other day at Deptford; but she soon repented her temerity, and was obliged to neutralise the dreadful smell by keeping her bouquet close to her nose.*[5]

Indeed, she was lucky to avoid worse consequences, for in 1844 it had been discovered that at Windsor there were more than fifty unemptied cesspools within the Castle[6]. Other members of the royal household were less fortunate. In 1861 Prince Albert died of typhoid fever[7], and ten years later the Prince of Wales was gravely ill from the same disease[8]. These well publicised illnesses intensified the debate about how such catastrophic diseases were spread. Was it through the air as 'sewer gas', through water or food, or simply by the appalling smells? And what was the agent or *'materia morbes'* that carried the disease? Some doctors even thought scarlatina could come through the post on materials handled by an infected person; if it could travel on aprons, why not on letters?[9]. Until today's germ theory was developed no one could say for certain, but the idea prevailed that foul atmospheres, euphemistically called 'miasms' were to blame.

The *Medical Circular's* assertion that it was the lowest classes who bore the brunt of the high mortality was borne out in 1878 by the Registrar-General's 40th report[10]. William Farr, the eminent and pioneering medical statistician and Assistant Registrar General, tried to confirm the theory of miasms[11], and went to a great deal of trouble to show that mortality rates were much higher in places with very dense and crowded living conditions than in more sparsely populated areas. He calculated 'the proximity of the population' in the cities of Manchester and Liverpool and another 591 smaller urban and rural districts, and defined it as 'the average distance in yards between people living in a given area', by which he meant the area in square yards divided by the number of people in it. He showed that where that distance was very low, such as the seven yards in Liverpool, the mean duration of life was only 26 years, but where it was higher the lives were proportionately longer, being as much as 51 years in the districts where 'proximity' was 147 yards or more. Figures 8.1 and 8.2 show this expressed as proximity in relation to mortality rates, and as proximity in relation to years of life lost in comparison with populations of different densities.

William Farr's work proved that infectious diseases spread more easily in crowded conditions, as had been suspected. But what caused them, and how did they spread? The idea that disease was spread by 'miasms', mysterious poisons that pervaded the atmosphere, was then generally accepted. Miasms were 'infectious or noxious exhalations from putrescent organic matter' (OED), of which there was an abundance in the overcrowded streets and alleys of big cities, and the diseases which they caused were called 'zymotics' because they arose from 'zymosis', the contemporary word for fermentation and putrefaction. Therefore, any attempt to prevent these diseases depended on controlling and removing the sources of these offensive miasms.

Figure 8.1 (after William Farr)

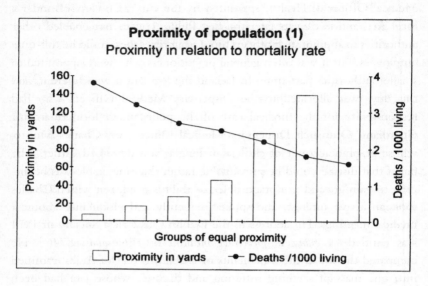

Figure 8.2 (after William Farr)

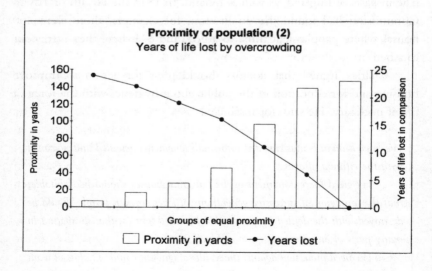

On 1st January 1847 Dr W.H.Duncan began work as the first ever Medical Officer of Health, appointed by the City of Liverpool under a local Act, and two years later the first Public Health Act enabled other authorities to appoint such officers too. In big cities they could be full-time employees, but it was often general practitioners who were appointed to smaller authorities part-time. In Ireland the legislation was different, and this duty was allocated to the Dispensary Medical Officers who had responsibility for the medical care of the poor, under local Boards of Guardians. One such Dispensary Medical Officer was Charles Moore, whose graphic account of cholera in Finglas was described earlier. The belief that disease could be preventable rather than inevitable was beginning to gain ground as a practicable possibility, an idea in which Charles took an active interest, and spoke frequently and eloquently about at medical meetings. His address to the Dublin Obstetrical Society in 1874 was entitled '*A glance at preventive medicine in 1769 and 1874*'[12]. He compared the lot of the inhabitants of Dublin to that of Arabs 'rammed into one mass of seething suffering and disease', whose fate had been described to him as 'worse even than the black-hole of Calcutta'. He had, after all, seen many Arabs in his travels as a ship's doctor. The same was true in parts of England, as well as Ireland. In 1845 the Health of Towns Commission had found that in Preston, for example, there were 400 houses where people slept three to a bed, and 84 where they were four to a bed[13].

Charles argued that doctors should press for action to improve housing and for education of the public about hygiene, with the force of law if necessary. He said, for instance:-

We have human beings crowded into small tenements befouled and poisoned with the effluvia of ages.

We need the enforcement of the law, that houses should be habitable, that the contagion of successive generations of fever stricken people should be destroyed with the defiled heaps of rubbish, called houses, that so abound in many parts of our city.

We need protection against the results of ignorance and of habits of want of cleanliness, so common among the poor denizens of our courts and lanes. Such people should be taught the consequences of using the same vessels for

*the removal of everything offensive from their dwellings and for the bringing
in of water from the fountains.*

*Those medical men who are, with the clergy, too often the sole visitors
of the poor, can tell the suffering and sickness, and degradation of mind and
body, so common among the people of the city alleys and back streets.*

On another occasion[14] he scathingly condemned the filthy state of dwelling
houses in connection with the care of parturient women. Puerperal fever
was an increasingly frequent and devastating complication of childbirth,
especially in the years 1874-5 which 'seem to have been notable for what
was probably the most deadly pandemic of puerperal fever ever recorded'[15].
It was so bad in Dublin that demolition of the famous Rotunda Lying-in
Hospital was contemplated, in favour of separate bungalows in its extensive grounds which would provide more space and air to disperse the
deadly miasm. Charles sought the opinion of an architect on this matter,
but had to report to the Obstetrical Society that he had been advised that
the bungalows would be so polluted by smoke from the surrounding
houses that the miasms would be as bad as ever.

Charles agreed with the prevailing view of a link between scarlet
and puerperal fevers, though their common cause had not been proved.
How could women escape this infection, he asked, if they had to give
birth in conditions such as one house he had recently visited where 'the
hall and back-yard were flooded with liquid sewage in a state of fetid
fermentation'. He promptly reported this to 'the sanitary police', but alas
even they did not, or could not, remedy everything. He pointed out the
futility of merely whitewashing the walls of houses which were 'a mass of
infection', while 'leaving undisturbed under the floorboards the debris of
persons who had suffered countless epidemics'. His address concluded
with considerable passion, in sentences such as these:-

*Witness the instantly fatal effect, every now and then recorded of poisoning
by sewer-gases and the frequent attacks of a more insidious nature, from
which even royalty itself has not been free. What is it that aids unbelief in
such causation of disease?*

*I saw today two children thickly out in measles. The eldest, a girl of
about nine years, was suffering such agonising pain of heart that it rendered*

her almost insensible. Her condition was but a step removed from starvation; filth and misery characterised her dwelling – the heat of the burning June sun rendering the air of the overcrowded room almost unendurable.

I would weary your patience to record the experience of a single day in the life of a Dublin City District Medical Officer. I would add that city authorities should not permit decomposing filth to accumulate in our streets and lanes, and be blown by every blast of wind down our throats. Nor should the miasmata of a thousand manure yards be allowed to befoul the air we breathe, and their offscour [contaminate] the sewers and water-courses and the river of our city.

A few years later, in 1880, Charles spoke to the Society of Metropolitan Medical Officers of Health when they met in Dublin[16]. His topic was 'Domestic Scavenging, in which he described the 'ash-pit system', or as it was known in Great Britain the 'midden-privy'. The phrase 'ash-pit' was an euphemism for a festering hole in the ground in the communal back yards of houses into which all rubbish and sewage was thrown. Charles described numerous examples, saying the ash-pits were:-

..... rarely provided with masonry or water tight cement lining. Some are covered over, several are not, and the size is so considerable generally, that a very large accumulation occurs before the necessity of cleansing become apparent to the casual observer.

... the basements of some [tenements] were being used as receptacles for filth of the most injurious description. In not a few houses, even in some of the best localities, the area cellars are even now used in this way.

A resident in a court near St Patrick's cathedral complained that the only overflow from the privy was through the court.

Though all too familiar with this so-called 'system' in his work as a District Medical Officer, he said the matter had also been 'urged on him by influential citizens as an evil needing a prompt and permanent remedy'. Sometimes by 'repeated reporting and remonstration &c' he was able to get some improvement, but:-

even in many of the leading fashionable and important business localities cases of great neglect, in this particular, exist at the present moment.

Dublin, like The House of Lords and Windsor Castle, was ripe for outbreaks of disease. Education of the public was clearly needed, and it
should begin with the leaders of fashion and business.

The following examples of the 'sanitary police's' activities come
from the Dublin Sanitary Associations 'Nuisance Reports Book' of 1874,
in which were recorded complaints and any remedial action taken[17].

No 35.   12, Cork St.
Choked drain at rere; passage choked with dirt
Result; No cause for complaint.
Observations; A case of pneumonia lately admitted to hospital from this
house.

No 43.   39, Coombe.
Filthy passage, back-yard and privy; drainage runs in at back door.
Result; No cause for complaint.
Observations; A fatal case of pneumonia contracted here

No 47.   8, Newmarket.
House in bad repair, filthy cellar; no back yard, but the yard of next house
is used by the occupant of this. In this yard is a filthy privy and ash-pit.
The ruins of No 9 are used as a dust hole.
Result; No cause for complaint.
Observations; A man admitted to hospital with miasmatic pneumonia.

Action was sometimes taken, however, although it is not clear why
Case 41 merited it while the others did not.

No 41.   5, Engine Alley.
These premises consist of a house and three cottages in the rere; they are
filthy and dilapidated. Filthy privy at rere.
Result; Acted on since receipt of complaint.
Observations; All these tenements unfit for habitation.

Charles was by no means the only one to express his horror at this state
of affairs. Commenting on the Report of the Royal Sanitary Commission
in 1880, *The Medical Press and Circular* said:-

The public has before it a solemn declaration of the fact and of conclusion which is of priceless value as putting beyond dispute the causes of the monstrous unhealthiness of "the second city of the empire" ..... No possibility of doubt remains that Dublin, though truly called "second" in size and in population amongst the cities of the empire, is proudly first in the pre-eminence of dirt, neglect, and un-civilisation, and unquestionably last in decency and in the executive capacity of its sanitary administrators.[18]

The following week the same journal reported that the death-rate of Dublin and its suburbs was 33.5 per 1000 – "nearly double that of London (18.0) or Glasgow (19.8) and one-third more than Edinburgh (22.4)"[19]. It was glad that the City Corporation was adopting a new code of sanitary bye-laws, for:-

The Lord Mayor said that he had been through some of the tenement houses of Dublin in the last few days and had been appalled at their condition. The scenes of filth he witnessed had been beyond description, and had made him determined, as far as he could, to do something by way of remedy. .... It really made him wonder how human beings existed at all in such hideous filth.

The Medical Press was not entirely convinced of his Lordship's commitment, however, for it remarked that though this was no joking matter there was 'a grim funniness' in it, and suspected the Lord Mayor of speaking ironically:-

Be it known that the Lord Mayor is, and has been for many years, the Chairman of the Public Health Committee; that the Dublin sanitarians have, during the whole tenure of his office, never ceased from (metaphorically speaking) thrusting the filth of the Dublin tenement houses down the throats of his Lordship and the Public Health Committee; ...[but] that [he] had attempted to prevent the Royal Sanitary Commission from enquiring into the state of these tenement houses; [and was] determined not to see the state of affairs which now exercises his indignation and horror.

The erudite and determined though less outspoken William Daniel had died in 1872, but Charles had an ally in his newly-qualified nephew John, who had good personal reasons for wanting to prevent disease as well as being professionally convinced of its necessity. When the family moved to Fitzwilliam Square it was one of those 'leading fashionable locations' mentioned by Charles, though not exempt from the all-pervasive miasma. Within a few months of moving in, his aunt Hannah, who lived in the same 60 year-old house, 'fell ill with enteric fever, her attack proving fatal'[20]. A maidservant was also taken ill but recovered. Investigation revealed a drain running under the floor of the kitchen 'seen to be filled to the brim with black decomposing sewage', which was presumed to be the source of the illnesses. Nine years later, when John had become the head of the household, his first wife Ellie died within days of giving birth to their daughter Elsie. Puerperal fever was rife, and since John was assistant physician at the Cork Street Fever Hospital he would have been in daily contact with patients with erysipelas and scarlet fever, and may well have brought home the deadly germs, and tragically passed them on to his young wife.

Medical men were urgently trying to answer the questions of how these diseases were caused and spread, and how the appalling toll of death could be reduced. John was encouraged to join the search for answers by his mentor and senior colleague William Stokes, whom he described as 'one of the earliest, ablest and most disinterested advocates of the doctrines of State Medicine'. Years later, when addressing the State Medicine section of the newly formed Academy of Medicine in Ireland[21], he recalled words from Stokes' 'Prelection' address to the University of Dublin in 1872:-

Ignorance, selfishness, the grinding of the poor, the consumption of human life, like fuel, for the production of wealth, vicious indulgence and everything that deteriorates the body, and with it the mind, come within the scope [of State Medicine]. Its object is health, and therefore the happiness and prosperity of man – its instruments are science and common sense, ... And it would be a bold man who would dare to limit its results or predict its triumphs.

Although Charles had been passionate in his condemnation of the filthy state of Dublin, and insistent in his demands for action, he was the product of an earlier age. He used common sense, not science, to support his arguments which were pragmatic: housing and sanitation were appalling and if they could be improved there would be less disease. John, however, was determined to bring 'facts and faithful records' to bear on this important part of the practice of medicine. It was therefore no surprise that he was one of the first candidates when, in 1871, Dublin University instituted the first ever course and examination in State Medicine, later to be called Public Health. Twelve years later he was a member of the Council of the subsection of Public Health in the Irish Academy of Medicine. When the Medical Act of 1886 empowered the General Medical Council (GMC) to register higher degrees and diplomas, it was John who, as Registrar to the Royal College of Physicians in Ireland, signed the college's letter proposing a scheme for a Diploma on a national scale[22]. He subsequently became chairman of the GMC's Public Health committee, and remained so for many years.

Candidates for the new diploma had to be Doctors in Medicine of Dublin, Oxford or Cambridge Universities. As well as medical subjects such as pathology and chemistry, the syllabus included law, engineering, vital and sanitary statistics, meteorology, and medical jurisprudence. Among much else, candidates were required:-

> to understand maps and plans of buildings without being dependent on the explanations of engineers or architects; to master the details of two or more completed waterworks for large towns'; to study 'in like manner the Sewerage of Cities and the Ventilation of Sewers .... by visits to works in progress.[23]

All this was a far cry from the study of *Xenophon's Anabasis Books I, II, and III*, and *Lucian's Dialogue (Walker's edition)* necessary for his matriculation into the university as an undergraduate[24]. For John, however, the inclusion of meteorology in the syllabus was a pleasure. For years he had been collecting data on rainfall, temperature and humidity, first at the house in Anne Street and then at Fitzwilliam Square, and continued to do so until shortly before his death 70 years later[25]. It was to be a life-long interest, both as a current science and a historical study, and was the subject of his book *Meteorology Practical and Applied*[26] published in 1894. In his early years as a doctor he was determined to identify the link between meteorological conditions and the miasms believed to cause disease, if there was one. He was convinced that if disease could be prevented in this way it was an essential part of medical practice.

While still a student, and long before he sat the Diploma in State Medicine, John began to think that variations in the prevalence of diseases might be explained by variations in the weather. The first paper he ever published was an essay on the relationship of disease to the environment, entitled *Notes on Mean Temperature in its Relations to Disease and Mortality*[27]. He quoted earlier writers who had studied the link between health and weather, such as William Heberden's description of the effects of cold on the inhabitants of London in the eighteenth century. In his own time others were thinking along the same lines, including William Guy, a physician at King's College Hospital who had written about it in 1842 and 1881. Guy's first paper[28] showed that in London there were 14% more deaths in the three coldest months, January to March, than the three warmest, July to September. Deaths from respiratory disease in particular were 73% commoner in the cold period than the warm. In the second[29], dated 1881, he showed that not only was respiratory disease more common in winter but also more often fatal. Furthermore, although in summer there were many deaths from alimentary disease, winter deaths were highest of all because of respiratory illness and the effect of cold on the elderly. Guy's second paper, subtitled '*an application of the numerical method to discover the truth*', included data from many parts of Europe over more than 100 years.

In order to describe the situation in Dublin John added his own observations to Guy's, basing his study on two hypotheses:-

> *That death and morbility (sic) from diarrhoea and dysentery were highest in summer, but bronchitis, pneumonia and pleuritis deaths were highest in winter*
> *These tendencies increased in summers when the mean temperature was above the average over the years, and in the winters when it was below.*

Although statistics on weather were available from the Irish General Registry they were recorded in the open and uninhabited Phoenix Park, so he preferred to use his own records because they represented a residential area. When the number of deaths from respiratory disease were compared with his record of temperatures his hypotheses appeared to be correct as shown by the examples in Table 8.1.

Table 8.1 Deaths in Dublin and their relation to temperature

Thoracic deaths in winter		
	1867	*1868*
Total deaths in the year	1664	1302
Deaths in first quarter (% of all deaths)	794 (49.7%)	469 (36%)
Mean temp in relation to average over several years	–1.6 F	+2.5F
Dysentery and diarrhoea deaths in summer		
Total deaths in the year	337	434
Deaths in third quarter (% of all deaths)	135 (40%)	289 (66.6%)
Mean temp in relation to average	–1.0 F	+0.7 F

After Moore J W, *Notes on Mean Temperature in its Relations to Disease and Mortality.*

When proportions of deaths are examined, variations in temperature appeared to have an important effect. For instance in 1867 as a whole, one fifth of all deaths were of people aged 60 or more, but in the very cold first quarter they amounted to one quarter. In the great heat of the summer of 1868, deaths of children under 5 years doubled, accounting for 42% of all deaths in the city, compared with the annual rate of 23%.

These figures are only a few of those in *Notes on Mean Temperature*, which was based on mortality data over five years and meteorological data for the previous twenty. Although the modern reader may say they lack tests of statistical significance, there were other data to support his hypotheses. One source was records from Manchester, where the week ending 29th December 1866 was unseasonably warm, with a mean temperature of 44° F (6.7 C), but by the week ending 19th January 1867 it had dropped to 22.6°F (-5.2 C). The number of respiratory diseases each week reported in *'public practice'* (original italics) rose from 246 to 463 in three weeks, and as a proportion of all recorded cases rose from 16.6 to 25 percent. While the total number of cases rose by a fifth, respiratory cases almost doubled. There was also data from Sweden, readily available to him because his father William Daniel received copies of the Swedish journal *Hygeia*. No doubt this prompted an interesting discussion between them, including, perhaps, why in Sweden during the years 1865 to 1867 the numbers of cases of diarrhoea and of dysentery were consistently higher in warm months than the cool, as Table 8.2 shows.

Table 8.2 Sweden; Maximal and Minimal incidence of cases of dysentery and diarrhoea (figures in brackets show increase in incidence)

	1865		1866		1867	
	Jan	Sept (increase)	Mar	Aug (increase)	Feb	July (increase)
Cases of dysentery	40	467 (x 11.7)	19	99 (x 5.2)	22	108 (x 4.9)
	Mar	Aug	Mar	Sept	Feb	Aug
Cases of diarrhoea	623	3041 (x 4.9)	663	3397 (x 5.1)	754	1831 (x 2.4)

Most Swedish doctors at that time held state appointments, and since the eighteenth century had been required to keep statistics. These showed that dysentery occurred in 'violent outbursts' in 1783 and 1785, but was 'almost quite absent' in the cool year of 1782. It occurred again in 1808-11, and in 1813, but not in the intervening year of 1812 which was famously cold, as Napoleon discovered in Russia.

John realised that recording only the number of deaths from these diseases but not the number who were ill gave a very inadequate picture of their extent and effect on the population. Taking the ratio of cases to deaths shown by the Swedish figures as a model, he calculated that in the week ending August 8th 1868, for instance, there might have been as many as 3,100 cases of diarrhoea in the registration district of Dublin –

something like one person in twenty-five. The number of people who were ill was therefore very much greater than the number who died. There were some places in the United Kingdom such as Manchester where the incidence of disease was reported, and it had been common practice in Sweden and other countries for many years. If it could be done there, John reasoned, why could it not be done everywhere? How could the spread of an epidemic be halted if the earliest cases were not identified? When people began to die it was too late to halt the spread of infection. This was the starting point for his campaign for a system of notification and registration of occurrences of disease as well as of deaths from them.

The hypotheses relating to incidence seemed to be proved, but what actually *caused* the diseases? One widely accepted theory was that of Justus von Liebig, who believed that everything in the plant and animal 'economies' depended on chemical interactions, so that unhealthy chemicals such as those produced by fermentation of rotten matter might corrupt them and cause disease. He was partly correct, for this is indeed the cause of the toxic effects of alcohol produced by fermenting yeast and sugar, and many plants contain substances poisonous to animals. It was not surprising, therefore, that the bad smells and plentiful heaps of rotting rubbish in the streets of Dublin should be seen as the cause of the diseases that devastated its population.

A colleague and friend of John's was Dr Thomas Grimshaw of Cork Street and Dr Steevens' hospitals, who was also interested in statistics. Together they published a paper in 1875 entitled *Pythogenic Pneumonia*[30]. This name, unfamiliar and meaningless to modern doctors, comes from the supposition that whatever causes pneumonia might be conveyed in the noxious gases arising from sewers*. They had noticed that whereas bronchitis was less common in summer than winter, pneumonia was just as frequent in warm as cold weather. Could this be accounted for by the heat of the summer accelerating fermentation in the sewers and producing more gas? Was there a poison in the sewer gas that caused pneumonia?

Similar cases had been reported elsewhere, such as one in East Sheen in London. There, the Sanitary Authority had inserted a ventilator into a

---

* Pythos = filth + genic = arising from

sewer near a boarding school, where the sons of some eminent doctors lived. Unfortunately a day or so later the sewer outfall was filled by a high tide, which forced the gases back through the new ventilator and into the nearby buildings. The very next day a boy was taken ill with pneumonia, followed by two other boys and two servants, one of whom died. The ventilator was promptly removed and no further cases occurred. Nearer to home, when the drain-cover was removed in the scullery of a house in a fashionable square where four people had died of typhoid, the draught coming up from the drain was enough to blow out a candle[31], which was a routine test for such draughts.

Grimshaw and Moore noted that there had been twice as many cases of pneumonia admitted to the Cork Street Hospital in 1874 than usual; sixty-three compared with the average of twenty-eight in the previous five years. They described the details of five of these cases, of whom one died and four survived on treatment with wine, whiskey and a mixture containing quinine, nitrate of potash and dilute nitric acid. Could these extra cases be associated with an excess of sewer gas caused by some variation in the weather? The weather conditions of 1874 were therefore compared to the previous five years, and were found to be identical as far as average temperature was concerned, so a rise in temperature could not be responsible. However, the early part of the year to midsummer was very dry, followed by a very wet period in August, as shown in Figure 8.3.

To show that Dublin was similar to other cities as far as the occurrence of pneumonia was concerned, they compared the seasonal incidence of pneumonia in Dublin with that in Paris and found it was identical, as Figure 8.4 shows.

If escape of gas from the sewers varied with the weather the number of cases of enteric fever and associated pneumonia might also vary, so they compared the number of deaths from those diseases in 1874 and the averages for 1865-74 with weather conditions in 1874 in each of thirteen 4-week periods. The mean temperature of 1874 was the same as the average for the previous five years, confirming that excess heat was not to blame, but the much greater rainfall of the summer of 1874 appeared to have a marked effect.

Figure 8.3 (after Grimshaw and Moore)

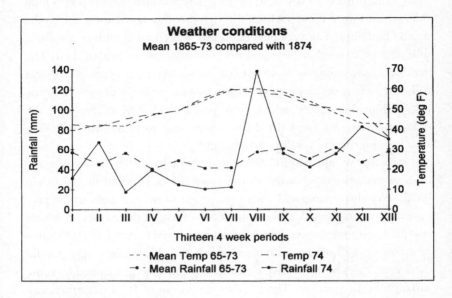

Figure 8.4 (after Grimshaw and Moore)

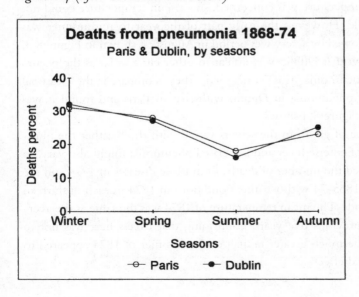

Figure 8.5 (after Grimshaw and Moore)

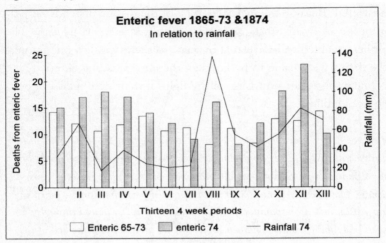

In 1874 enteric fever was only a little more common than usual during the drought of the first six months, tailing off as expected from May to July, but the way it increased in the exceptionally wet periods in summer and late autumn was unusual. Also, pneumonia increased as the drought continued, but fell abruptly when it rained heavily in August, and increased again in the warm autumn months (Figure 8.6).

Figure 8.6 (after Grimshaw and Moore)

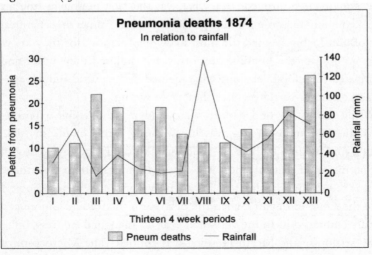

They asked themselves 'Why does a *warm dry air* increase pneumonia?, and answered 'Because the *pythogenic* type of the disease depends on pollution of the air by miasmata, which is greatest in *warm dry weather*'. The atmosphere seemed to be cleaned by rain, so there was less pneumonia, but the drains were liable to be flooded, thereby spreading enteric fever. This conclusion is not surprising in the light of their description of contemporary Dublin:-

> *After the heavy downpour of February 25th, no rainfall of half an inch occurred until May 28th, and almost* two months *then elapsed until, on July 22nd another fall of that amount took place. What was the consequence? The rivers were nearly all dried up; even perennial springs failed in many instances. A comparatively scanty quantity of water flowed through the sewers of Dublin, which remained unflushed for months; and the bed of the Liffey became such an intolerable nuisance, under the combined influence of the drought and the hot sun, that, from his Grace the Lord Lieutenant down, the inhabitants of the city murmured. Ashpits, whether cleansed or not by the Public Health Committee, contributed their quota to the nuisance; and, in fine, the air reeked with miasm.*[32]

The association between variations in temperature and rainfall and the prevalence of zymotic disease supposedly emanating from rotting matter seemed convincingly proved. But what was the fatal poison in 'the air that reeked with miasm'? To the physicians of the time the chemical theory of von Liebig seemed the most likely explanation, for they knew little or nothing of the invisible life forms that polluted their water and contaminated their food, let alone what teemed in the putrid and sewage-laden bed of the River Liffey. But they were wrong.

While Grimshaw and Moore were studying the visible environment, Louis Pasteur in France was investigating forms of life invisible without a microscope. In 1878 he announced to the French Academy of Medicine his belief that infection was caused by minute living creatures, or 'germs'[33]. Although John had his own zymotic and meteorological ideas of the cause of disease, when the new germ theory was announced he rapidly embraced it. In the very next year his Inaugural Address to the 1879-80 session of the Meath Hospital was entitled 'The Microcosm of

Disease', and covered in erudite fashion the current state of bacteriological knowledge[34]. He felt this topic was important for the new students because:-

> For some time past such expressions as "zymotic disease", "blood-poisoning", "germ theory of disease" , "antiseptic medicine and surgery" have been on everybody's lips. It occurred to me, therefore, that it would be neither uninteresting nor uninstructive were I to give a brief summary of the present state of our knowledge.

He talked about the disease-causing organisms with strange new names – *bacteria, vibrio-bacillus, spirillum,* and the extra knowledge that the students and practitioners alike would have to acquire. He said that micro-organisms had been suspected of being the cause of typhoid fever, malaria, and autumnal diarrhoea, and referred to the work of Oertel and Klebs in diphtheria, who had:-

> ... put forward the view that this deadly disease is, in all probability, set up by a specific organism which exists in solid particles suspended in certain atmospheres.

This was the era of Lister's antiseptic innovations in surgery, and in the same year as this address was delivered Ludwig Koch published his famous 'Postulate'. This stated that if a germ that could be shown to pass through an animal which suffered a disease, and recovered from that animal and passed on to another which then suffered the same disease, it was indeed the cause of that disease. Here was a plausible explanation of how atmosphere and environment could affect the spread of diseases; they could help or hinder the conditions in which these living germs might thrive or perish. The idea that miasms actually caused disease died its own death, though a slow one. In 1911 Sir James Barr recalled that for most it was 'ancient history, except in the Law Courts where it still does duty'. What exciting times to be living in! This was a revolution in medical thinking as great as the discovery of anaesthesia, introduction of antibiotics and, maybe, the mapping of the human genome.

The new Germ Theory identified the cause of many diseases but not all, and in any case variation in weather conditions was undoubtedly an important factor in their occurrence, so John continued recording and analysing weather in relation to mortality. As yet he had found no answer from his data, but he felt the subject was so important that he contributed quarterly *Sanitary and Meteorological Notes* to the Dublin Journal of Medical Science from 1875 to 1909, and included comprehensive weather tables in his hospital reports. He also devoted two chapters of his book *Meteorology, practical and applied* to the subject of the effects of weather and season on the incidence of disease. Some examples of this association based on data in *Meteorology* are shown in Figures 8.7, 8.8 and 8.9.

Figure 8.7

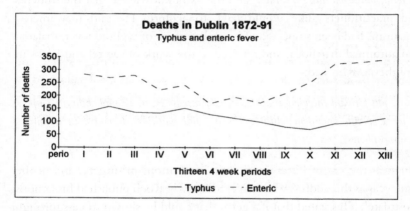

Figure 8.8

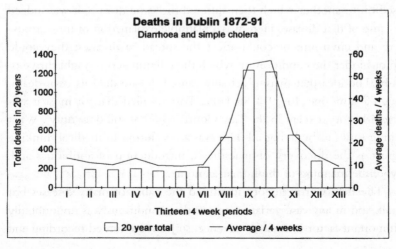

Figure 8.7 shows the total number of deaths from typhus and enteric fevers during a 20 year period from 1875-94 in relation to thirteen four-week periods of the year. Typhus was lowest in the autumn but increased slowly in winter as people huddled together and even shared their clothing and beds, and therefore their germs. Being a long illness before death occurs the highest point of the curve comes in the spring, months after the illnesses began. On the other hand enteric fever declines from winter to early summer, then rises sharply in autumn as those patients die quite soon after developing the disease in the hot months of July and August. More dramatic is the rise in deaths due to diarrhoea and what was called 'simple' cholera, which was not really cholera but various forms of food poisoning (Figure 8.8). This was clearly a summer phenomenon, with the incidence falling rapidly as the weather cooled off at the end of September. Scarlet fever and measles both declined through spring and summer from their winter high-point. Measles continued falling to its lowest incidence in the late autumn, but scarlet fever began to rise sharply in September until November when it tailed off again (Figure 8.9).

Figure 8.9

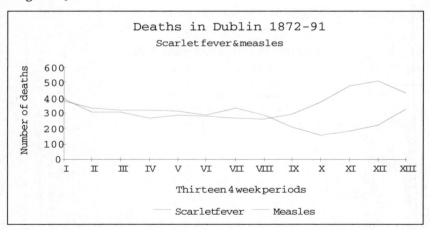

The germ that causes typhus, that most intractable of fevers, was not discovered until the twentieth century, and other diseases were shown to be due to viruses too small to be seen by the early bacteriologists. At the end of the nineteenth the concept of miasmata was therefore still accepted as plausible in the absence of knowledge to the contrary, and seemed a reasonable way to explain the severe influenza outbreak which swept through Dublin in the winter of 1889 to 1890. John examined the episode in the light of the weather at the time, and found that in the first five weeks of 1890 there were 367 more deaths than the average in the equivalent weeks in the preceding ten years[35]. Of the extra deaths recorded 142 were from pneumonia, 83 from bronchitis and 115 from heart disease. Only twenty-seven deaths were certified as due to influenza, probably because the certifying doctors did not recognise that influenza can cause death. He had already shown that there were more deaths from respiratory causes in cold weather than warm, especially in very cold winters, so were the extra deaths due to the cold weather while influenza prevailed? No, he said, because the weather was unusually warm during the epidemic and the increase in deaths followed the rise in temperature by about seven days, long enough to catch influenza, develop pneumonia and die. During the early weeks of 1890 in which the influenza outbreak occurred the temperature was as high as in the warm year of 1884, but the number of deaths was much greater, actually double at one point

Figure 8.10 (after Moore J W)

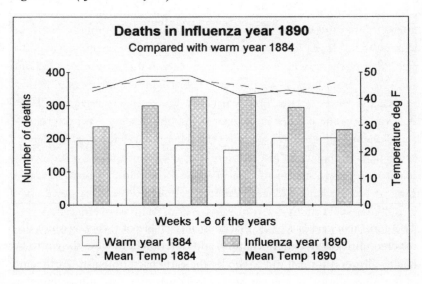

Figure 8.11 (after Moore J W)

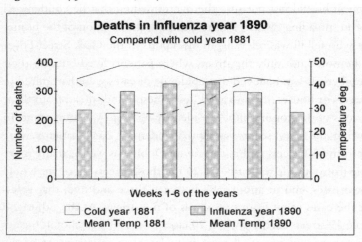

The pattern of deaths was very similar to that of the cold year of 1881 when the average temperature was 10°F (5.5°C) lower over the same six weeks of the year (Figure 8.11).

He concluded that susceptibility to influenza was independent of the seasonal factors that influenced other chest diseases, and that the disease was *pandemic* rather than *epidemic* (original emphasis) because it 'affected multitudes at the same moment'. Influenza, he thought, was ' an acute specific disease of the miasmatic rather than miasmatic–contagious type', that is, the causative 'agent' was 'already in the atmosphere and did not spread from person to person'. There was no incubation period because the 'virus (*sic*) was already hatched' at the time of infection. What that 'virus' was he did not know, nor could he offer any form of prevention, let alone a cure. He used 'virus' in the sense of a force or influence, rather than as a specific kind of micro-organism, but the use of the word 'hatched' suggests that he thought it was a living rather than a chemical thing. It was certainly a killer, though mercifully not one that killed children, like measles and summer diarrhoea. Four of his own children developed influenza in that outbreak. The youngest at that time was Maurice, who had the mildest attack, which was fortunate for he was the only one to have descendants who have lived into the twenty-first century.

William Farr related mortality to 'proximity', that is to density of population. John did not measure the overcrowding that he condemned as a factor in spreading disease, but he did think the location of the homes of people who fell ill was relevant. In his reports of the Cork Street Fever Hospital he noted not only the streets where patients lived but also their house-numbers. It was believed that epidemic diseases were harboured in certain streets or houses, the so-called 'fever-nests', and spread from there to all sections of the community[36], so identifying them was important. In 1879, during the very severe smallpox epidemic, 2032 patients were admitted from 530 streets within the city of Dublin, as well as many more who came from outside the city[37]. In 260 of those streets there were only one or two cases, and in another 87 between three and five, that is less than half the cases came from two thirds of the streets. At the other end of the scale 19 streets each provided 20 cases or more, a total of 496 cases of smallpox: one quarter of all cases from less than four percent of the streets. Eight came from one house alone, No 13 Nicholas-street, while Meath-st, Francis-st, Cork-st, Aungier-st and Bride-st had 30 to 36 patients each. The worst, by far, was the Coombe with 49 cases. None of these streets was very large, but all were densely populated and in poor condition. The difference between streets is highlighted in Figure 8.12, which plots the number of admissions against the number of streets from which they came.

Figure 8.12 (after Cork Street Hospital Report, 1879)

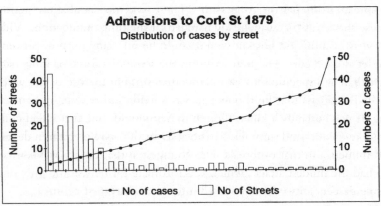

In 1881 the smallpox epidemic was subsiding but the hospital still took in 1083 patients, most of whom (960) had typhus, enteric fever or scarlet fever[38]. The addresses of the patients were again recorded, and the number from each street and dwelling was analysed in all of John's Cork Street reports. The 1881 report, after smallpox had receded, lists 186 streets with one case each of various kinds of fever, and 116 with two, and four streets with more than 20 cases. Of the latter Bride-st again featured with 21, Coombe with 23, and Golden-lane with twenty-seven. The worst this time was Plunkett-st, with sixty★. Twenty four of these came from seven houses, and a further twelve came from No 17 alone. Many cases came from other single houses, such as No 18 Ardee-st with nine, No 117 Clanbrassil-st with six, and Nos 10, 22 and 91 Coombe with seventeen between them.

This selection is probably not representative of the city as a whole, for many patients must have been admitted to other hospitals or not at all, but it is by no means exceptional. Similar reviews of the location where fever cases arose had been done by John's friend and colleague Thomas Grimshaw[39]. In 1871 he found 41 houses had produced 270 cases of fever in the previous two years. In one house 'the small back yard was ankle deep in human filth, ... a privy and ash-pit totally unapproachable, ... a running tap converted the broken sewer into a cesspool'. Inside all fifteen inhabitants were ill with enteric fever. Such houses were neglected by the sanitary authorities, said Grimshaw, and 'few people besides clergymen and medical men were acquainted with the existence of these places'.

Such was the fear of hospitals that admission was dreaded and even resisted, though for the poor in desperate times the benefit of rest and nourishment must have been attractive. Indeed one of the purposes of the Cork Street hospital was reflected in its sub-title '... and House of Recovery'. People living in more prosperous conditions were less at risk from the miasm, and would have considered admission to hospital not only very uncomfortable, but dangerous. We would find the conditions described in the report very distressing, whether we had to endure them as our domestic circumstances or as professional duty. Yet today there is

---

★ The Plunkett-st of 1881 was near Patrick Street, not today's north Dublin road with the same name.

still an excess of deaths in the winter and we are rediscovering what was known more than a hundred years ago, that cold is a killer.

By the time these reports came to be written the surviving patients had returned home to the same overcrowded and insanitary conditions. The medical authorities could only describe the state of affairs. The civic authorities had the responsibility to put things right, but the medical profession had an important duty to bring the matter to their attention and persuade them to take action. That is the field of Public Health, which grew steadily in importance and effectiveness as the nineteenth century came to a close, and in which John is acknowledged to have played a prominent part. He would be sorry to know that, one hundred years on, both hot and cold weather still wreak havoc with our health. And he would be nothing less than amazed that the Meteorological Office can now forecast the weather with such accuracy that they can predict the effect it will have on winter diseases, heart attacks, and even accidents, so that health services can be prepared to meet whatever the weather might bring.

PREVENTION BETTER THAN CURE.

Old Lady. "But, going in Four Wheel, Cab! I'm so afraid of Small Pox!"

Cabby. "You've no call to be afraid o' my Cab, Mum, for I've 'ad the Hind Wheel Vaccinated, and it took Beautiful!"

A woman refusing to get into a cab believing she will catch smallpox. The cabbie assures her his cab's 'hind wheel' has been vaccinated. Wood engraving after J.Leech. (Punch 30 May 1863.) (Wellcome Library, London).

CHAPTER NINE

Science, Wisdom and Charity

*How far premature mortality, which in this country amounts
to nine-tenths of the total deaths, is dependent on causes capable
of being avoided or counteracted, is a question deserving of
the most careful investigation.*

British Medical Journal 1858

These words come from the *British Medical Journal's* comments on the *Inquiry into the Different Proportions of Death produced by Certain Diseases in Different Districts in England*[1]. This report, presented to Parliament in 1858 by John Simon and Edward Greenhow, showed that while it was perfectly possible to live for seventy, eighty or more years, nine out of ten people actually died younger than that. They calculated that if everyone lived to 80 the death rate would only be 1250 per 100,000 living, but in fact it was as high as 3300 in some places. These variations were due to local circumstances which were 'fully possible to counteract'. They believed that:-

*of all the total mortality ascribed to these influences in England, a very
large share is preventable.*

The extent to which the death rates from three diseases varied in different places is shown in Table 9.1. In Britain today a death rate such as that for measles in 1858 would result in between 20,000 and 65,000 deaths annually, and in Ireland between one and four thousand.

Table 9.1 Variations in death rates

Location and Mortality per 100,000					
	Smallpox		*Measles*		*Scarlet fever*	
Highest	E.Stonehouse	146	Liverpool	107	Manchester	142
Lowest	Manchester	26	Portsea	34	Nottingham	66

After Simon and Greenhow

Apart from the frequent epidemics, this high mortality was due to tuberculosis and to crowded or dangerous conditions in work-places. Although the authors of the *Inquiry* believed that it was possible to reduce epidemics of 'infectious disorders like smallpox, measles, hooping-cough *(sic)* and scarlet fever to their minimum destructiveness' they feared that they could not be 'absolutely preventable'. Fortunately the story of the next 100 years was to prove them almost completely wrong. The process they began involved medical and statistical science combined with political persuasion, but it could not bear fruit until public apathy and professional opposition had been overcome. Throughout his long life John was prominent among those who argued for action, both in the form of statistical information and proper provision for care and treatment, and was scathing in his criticism of those who failed to grasp the gravity of the situation.

In 1865 *The Lancet* described scarlet fever as 'the deadliest of fevers' because it:-

> ....*chiefly infects the very young, and not unfrequently carries off the whole of the children of the family, – its irruption into a household is regarded with dismay.*[2]

Despite this deadly virulence, said *The Lancet*, the attitude of the public and the medical profession was 'strangely contrary', for both looked upon scarlet fever as a necessary contingency of childhood:-

> *We suffer it to persist amongst us with barely a protest, and assuredly without any systematic efforts to hold it in check. As a family evil we look upon it with just dread: as a public evil we deal with it as if it were of little more*

moment than a quinsy or a catarrh. We call upon the legislature to protect us from ... smallpox and the ruck of continued fevers. Every community and local government is agog with energy if typhus lodges in its skirts. But if scarlet fever breaks out with malignancy the profession and people alike become possessed with an aimless and impracticable dread. Is this a compelled result arising from sheer inability to help ourselves?

Ten years later *The Lancet* reported that in only four weeks 456 people had died of the disease in London, and in 18 other towns a thousand more had perished[3]:-

There is something shocking in the plague-like deadliness of some forms of scarlet fever, especially when considered in connexion with the uncivilised carelessness with which it is spread. It is lamentable to receive the accounts of the utter recklessness with which in populous places whole families free from the disease intermix with families in which a child or two is laid down with it. ... We must not omit one word of allusion to the carelessness on the part of medical officers which will allow a child once ascertained with suspicious symptoms to present itself a second time at the same institution. It is one of the opprobious facts in medicine that we can record no improvement in the gross mortality from this disease.

The writer went on the castigate the 'want of knowledge on the part of the people' and 'the laxity of the so-called sanitary authorities', and to forecast its dreadful consequences:-

Within a week ... a hundred children will lie dead in London from scar-latina, and a very much larger number variously maimed for life, by this disease. But the circumstance does not occasion so much sensation as would be caused by a member of Parliament being fatally run over at a crossing in Whitehall.

These words were from the London-based *Lancet*, but were just as valid in Dublin where, as a medical officer of health, Charles was making outspoken comments on the appalling state of sanitation, and his nephew John was beginning his campaign for improvements in public health.

By the last quarter of the nineteenth century the way diseases spread was beginning to be understood, even before the germ theory was proved. For instance, milk was suspected as a means of conveying typhoid fever. Dr Charles Cameron, the Superintendent Medical Officer of Health for Dublin, reported a case in which a milk-man had the disease, followed in turn by each of his children[4]. Their house had neither water-closet nor privy, nor any means of hand-washing, and the cows were milked next to the household's midden in a 'byre of the most primitive description'. It is no surprise to hear that 'sixty or seventy persons who drank his milk' suffered the disease.

Scarlet fever was also thought to be conveyed in milk, as a remark-able piece of sanitary detective work records. At Fallowfield near Manchester, when thirty-five people fell ill with the disease within a month, twenty-four of them within thirty-six hours, it was found that all the families in which scarlet fever occurred had bought milk from the same farm[5]. The milk was distributed via one large can to fourteen families, in ten of which several members fell ill with the fever. One of the dairymen, 'an old man called Hill', lived in a house with 'confined space, imperfect ventilation, low standard of cleanliness and want of sanitary intelligence', where his grandson was ill with scarlet fever. The milk handled by the other dairymen went elsewhere, and none of the people who drank it were ill. Naturally 'old man Hill vehemently denied he had been near the child'

In Dublin enteric fever and pneumonia broke out at a teacher train-ing school to which John was the doctor, which he thought was due to contaminated drinking water[6]. He asked Dr Cameron to investigate, who discovered that the water was kept in an outside tank with a stone roof, with an overflow pipe passing into a drain below the tank, but 'the whole area was dirty and the drain was choked with foul matters'. Microscopic examination revealed various 'infusoria, monads and rotifers', and the water was declared unfit to drink. Infection could be water-borne in other ways, too. Addressing the BMA conference at Cambridge in 1880, Dr Cameron reported that oysters had been 'transplanted' from the sea at Wexford to Dublin Bay, but in recent years 'had been much subject to disease and had died in large numbers'[7]. He blamed this on the increasing amount of sewage entering the bay from the many newly installed water closets, which was directed towards the oysters by a new pier near the outfall. He argued that if enteric fever could be transmitted by water and milk, it might also be transmitted by oysters that lived in contaminated water. The sickly oysters in Dublin Bay remained a problem, for in 1899 John reported a series of cases, possibly enteric fever, in which the patients had 'supped on oysters' from Dublin[8]. One detects a degree of *schadenfreude* in this report because he thought Dublin's Medical Officer should have done more to prevent the illness of both its citizens and its oysters.

Clearly, to prevent disease spreading by contaminated food and water it is necessary to know where the contamination comes from, but in the mid-nineteenth century it was usual to treat each case on its own without looking for any common source or association between cases. In other countries, however, doctors were required to inform a central authority about all infectious or contagious disease. From their reading of foreign journals John and William Daniel knew that such information could be supplied by doctors and collated centrally. In the first paper he wrote, *Notes on mean temperature*[9], the 24 year-old John who was still a student, said:-

> It is much to be deplored that, in the United Kingdom, there does not exist an official registration system in connexion with morbidity (sic); that while statistics relating to mortality are elaborated with assiduous care, the even more important subject of the prevalence of disease receives little or no attention. In this way we are surely far behind most of our continental neighbours.

Deaths had been registerable for many years, and voluntary registration of certain diseases had been required locally in some places since about 1860. John advocated a more comprehensive and nationwide system to register and publish statistics about the prevalence of disease as well as deaths. That was in 1869, but it was to be another twenty years before all doctors were required by law to notify certain diseases. Even then the system was imperfect and widely resented by the profession. In 1875 the new Public Health Act drew attention to the wider need for it[10], and the following year the BMA set up a committee on registration of disease to consider its position in regard to proposed legislation. The committee found that infectious disease reports in Poor Law practice were inefficient and ineffective, and medical officers of health were calling for a more universal system to limit the spread of epidemics[11]. They feared, however, that introducing such a system would present three controversial problems.

1. Whether the onus of reporting the case [should] rest on the householder or on the medical attendant
2. To be obliged to furnish information to a public official, with regard to sickness occurring in a family, might reasonably be resented by the medical profession. It would be regarded by many not merely as an unnecessary addition to their work, but as an inquisitorial test of the extent of their practice, and as leading to breach of professional confidence that might cause annoyance to both doctor and patient
3. The cost of medical reports alone [if a fee were to be paid] would be so great as practically to be a bar to the whole enterprise.

This attitude hardened into 'grave objections to the proposal'. These were many, such as that doctors should not be put in the position of 'informers' on their patients; proposals to impose heavy fines on doctors for non-compliance were objectionable; it would be self-defeating because people would refuse to call a doctor to avoid being reported themselves, and might even call an unqualified practitioner instead; and if a householder's trade were ruined by his being reported he would probably blame the doctor. To overcome this the BMA proposed that the onus should be entirely on the householder to tell the medical officer about a notifiable illness in his house, though it was acknowledged that 'in poor districts ignorant and illiterate persons' might need a little help with identifying the illness and knowing what to do. In such cases doctors would be willing to oblige by giving 'an authoritative declaration of the nature of the case' – assuming they had been called in[12].

John entered the debate again in 1880 with a vigorous speech at a meeting of the BMA's Dublin Branch[13], published in both the *BMJ* and the *Dublin Journal of Medical Science*. He recalled that 'many years previously Dr Rumsey of Cheltenham regretted that there were no published records of sickness attended at the cost of the community', so that the extent of illness had to be inferred from the number of deaths, and quoted similar remarks in 1864 by Dr Arthur Ransome[14]. Death registration, though more or less complete, lacked precision and scientific value. He went on:-

> *But even granting that our registration system may be perfected, we may well ask whether there is not a further step to be taken – whether it would not be politic to extend the principle of registration, which has hitherto been restricted to* mortality, *to* disease *also. Despite improvement in mortality rates chronic disease has increased resulting in increased misery. [original emphasis]*

John quoted some historical examples of how disease rather than death had interrupted or paralysed human activity. According to Mercatus, in 1557 influenza attacked 'all parts of Spain *at once*', and in St Petersburg in 1782 'the temperature rose 30 deg Fahrenheit, and the next morning 40,000 people were taken ill with influenza'. It was certainly possible to record the incidence of disease, even though doing so might be difficult:-

> *... the fact that several European governments have long since inaugurated and prosecuted such a system, should encourage us in essaying to follow their example. For many years the College of Health at Stockholm has received monthly and annual reports of the sanitary state of the country, including an account of the prevailing endemic and epidemic diseases. ... A similar organisation exists in Norway and Denmark. ... Our American cousins have adopted a system of registration in some of their large cities, and the authorities of some of the Swiss cantons are following their example.*

If this could happen elsewhere, why could it not do so here? True, the BMA had appointed a committee to promote voluntary registration, and to urge the government to legislate, but:-

> *... a national system of registration of disease in general unfortunately still remains a thing of the future.*

To demonstrate the need for such a system, and its probable benefit, he said that epidemics of scarlet fever, smallpox and measles advanced rapidly because:-

... the first case of illness, either through wanton neglect or ignorance was not isolated in due time. Some weeks ago several cases of scarlet fever were admitted into the Cork Street Hospital from a tenement house in which a child had died of the disease and was waked. No medical man was called in to the patient, nor was any report made to the sanitary authorities until other children in the house had been attacked. At least two lives were lost in this instance, which is one of many that might be adduced.

The system he envisaged needed two things, namely 'the immediate compulsory *notification* of outbreaks of disease to the sanitary authorities', and 'the early *registration ... and publication* of tabulated results at frequent intervals...' Little had yet been done towards this apart from the power obtained from Parliament to notify diseases in fifteen large towns in England and Scotland. He called for similar legislation in Dublin and throughout Ireland, and supported the BMA's policy that the duty of notification lay upon the householder, who would forward a certificate provided by the doctor. If a doctor had not been called the householder must still notify, having identified the disease himself. Dr Cameron also supported this system of information from doctor plus householder[15], and justified it in this way:–

Whereas the upper and middle classes would not neglect their duty, the denizens of tenement dwellings where notification was most necessary might neglect it, so would need the help of a doctor.

The weakness of this argument was that it was the 'ignorant and illiterate' 'denizens of tenements' who were least likely to call a doctor.

In a leading article in the issue which reported John's speech, the *BMJ* said[16]:–

Dr Moore's acknowledged position as a sanitarian entitles his views to very great weight, and it is eminently satisfactory to us to find him warmly endorsing the [BMA's] report on this important branch of State Medicine which was recently submitted to the Parliamentary Bills Committee.

John's ideas on notification were not yet universally acceptable, and one of the first to reply was his near neighbour Dr Quinlan of Fitzwilliam Street who wanted to put the other side of the question[17]. While he agreed with notification of infectious disease in tenement houses, where it was right to give the local authority power to intervene and even compulsorily remove people to special hospitals, the case of 'private houses of the better class is entirely different'. Such people's lives were separate from the crowds, so danger of spreading the disease was small. In his view notification would:-

> ... *seriously impair the honourable confidence between physician and patient. The patient's malady is the patient's secret, and it is my duty to keep it. Should the patient object to my notifying, I would not notify; and if he [the householder] did not, no legal obligation would induce me to go into the witness box to convict him.*

The notification system in the fifteen towns John mentioned had been introduced under separate Acts of Parliament which applied only to those towns, and were strangely inconsistent in what had to be notified, as Table 9.2 shows. Some required notification of 'infectious or contagious disease' without mentioning any by name. Others specified from two to nine conditions. Some would pay no fee, some a shilling, and others half-a-crown, but all would fine doctors up to £10 for non-compliance. In Jarrow, for instance, the fine was £5, one hundred times the fee of a shilling, plus £2 a day for 'continuing offence'

Table 9.2 Towns requiring notification of disease in 1879

"Any infectious or contagious disease"	Specific diseases to be notified (numbers listed)				
	2	6	7	8	9
Greenock	Huddersfield	Llandudno	Burton on Trent	Edinburgh	Bolton
Jarrow	Rotherham		Nottingham	Leicester	Warrington
Derby			Norwich		Blackpool

When 6 or more disease were specified they all included smallpox, cholera, typhus, typhoid, scarlet fever, diphtheria. Others were variously measles, erysipelas, relapsing fever, puerperal fever.

NB. Blackburn also had a local act but is not referred to in this source

(after *BMJ*[18])

The medical men of Leicester vigorously opposed the Local Act there[19], protesting that its:-

> ... *penal nature and stringency will act prejudicially to the interest of the public, and interfere with that social confidence which must of necessity exist between medical attendant and patient, [and that] the information given would be likely to injure the tradesmen in their business, professional men, schoolmasters, and school mistresses.*

They appealed to 'the medical profession throughout the kingdom' to resist such impositions, and declared that the Local Government Board was trying to 'smuggle' legislation into a few towns and then spread it to the whole nation. In a letter to *The Medical Times and Gazette* they raised a rallying-call[20]:-

> *This Machiavellian advice has succeeded only too well, and unless the whole profession now comes forward to help Leicester in opposing this Bill in the House of Lords next July a fatal precedent may be created.*
>
>   *I am &c,*
>
>   *C.R.Crossley, President of the sub-committee of the Leicester Medical Society.*
>
> *P.S. Subscriptions should be sent at once to me – the New Walk, Leicester.*

Dr Hutton of Jarrow dismissed the objections from Leicester[21]. There were heavy penalties in his own town, so why should the Leicester medical men be exempt when every law had to have penalties to ensure enforcement. Others objected to payment, asking 'whether it is fair and right' to receive a fee for doing something for the public good. Dr Bond of Gloucester[22] said writing a certificate was not hard work and took only a moment, and in any case death certificates were given without fee. The proposed fee was 'simply a *placebo*' to the profession, and authorities 'should not be called on to pay gratuities to doctors' because it would 'materially increase the rates'. The *BMJ* was ambivalent, believing that doctors could not be exempt from the law, but that the authorities had acted with 'excessive harshness and want of tact' in the cases of two doctors who had been prosecuted[23]. In one case a Huddersfield doctor did not notify scarlet fever in a house from which milk was being sold, because in his view the patient was not 'without proper accommodation', a state which would have justified notification under Huddersfield's Local Act. The authority prosecuted on the grounds that there was a danger of conveying disease through the milk. In the other, in Blackburn, a child died of scarlet fever which the doctor failed to notify in life, but certified as the cause of death. The registrar noticed the discrepancy, and the doctor was prosecuted.

Another objection was that in places where the Medical Officer of Health was also in private practice he had an unfair advantage. An anonymous 'Member of the BMA' wrote from his 'seaside watering-place' where there were many boarding houses and hotels[24]. He complained that if he was required to notify a case in a boarding house, the MOH would probably close the house resulting in serious loss of trade, and therefore cases would not be seen by a doctor. But if the householder notified directly, the MOH would visit, fumigate the house and immediately allow business to resume, and might even attract those patients to his own practice. He alleged that the MOH in his own town:-

> ... has rapidly got himself into a large practice, which seems likely to become so large as to include the whole town. In fact, this law gives him an advantage that places him at once out of the way of ordinary competition.

Even where authorities had taken powers to ensure notification it was not always used. In Nottingham, where the penalty imposed on doctors for non-compliance was £5, the notification clause in their Local Act had still not been implemented two years after it came into force[25]. The MOH, Dr Edward Seaton, said in his annual report that this was because, 'it would cost money to work'. The *BMJ* commented:-

> The Town Council apparently do not regard as important enough for their notice the economy of human life which would result from their having knowledge of infectious cases immediately on their occurrence, and being thus able to direct the necessary precautionary measure to prevent the further spread of the disease. ... Indeed it may be a question of law whether, having asked Parliament to clothe them with powers of notification, they can, under the terms of their Act of Parliament, decline to exercise those powers.

The whole matter was put into simple perspective by Dr Littlejohn, the MOH of Edinburgh[26]. There, he said, in the year 1879/80 there had been 4502 notifications, and from this 412 people had been taken to hospital. The cost of fees for notifications was £519, but there had been no complaints from doctors about the scheme. Most importantly:-

> *Intimations [i.e. notifications] have proved of great service – first, in showing how inadequate was the existing accommodation for infectious diseases in our various hospital; and, secondly, in enabling us to arrive at the true cause of outbreaks of these diseases, and thus prevent their spread.*

Science and wisdom were employed to reduce premature mortality in Edinburgh, at least.

Ireland was subject to separate legislation from England, Wales and Scotland, so it fell to the Dublin Sanitary Committee, of which John was a prominent and active member, to persuade the Lord Mayor of Dublin to campaign for similar provisions. In 1880 a delegation of all the most influential medical men, brought together by the Dublin branch of the BMA, waited upon the Lord Mayor, Mr Gray MP, to press for legislation throughout Ireland[27]. In the delegation were the Secretary of the Irish Branch Dr George Duffey, with Drs Charles Cameron, John Moore, and F.J.B. Quinlan, who seem to have settled their differences and become united in their proposal. The *BMJ* said the meeting had been successful, and that the Lord Mayor had brought the subject to the attention of the Dublin Corporation who were unanimously in favour of compulsory notification of infectious disease. Commenting again the following week[28] the *BMJ* said 'What Dr Duffey and Dr Moore do, they do well'. *The Lancet* commended the introduction of a Bill to this effect[29], though it doubted that it would pass into law, and was not at all pleased with the parsimonious fee of *one shilling (!)* proposed for each certificate (original emphasis).

The Bill failed as *The Lancet* predicted, but the campaign continued. John addressed the Social Science Congress meeting in Dublin in 1881 on the subject of notification[30], emphasising the difference between notification and registration. The former simply informed the local authority of a new case, but the latter recorded it in tables published nationally, so

Daniel Moore (1750–1847)
as Governor of Apothecaries' Hall, Dublin, 1806.
The original of this portrait hangs in
Apothecaries' Hall, Merrion Square, Dublin.

William Daniel Moore (1813–1871)
from Photographs of Eminent Medical Men, *J.A.Churchill & Son, circa 1865.*

*Sir John Moore (1845–1937),
in Court Dress at his Investiture as Knight Bachelor, 1901*

Maurice Moore (1886–1972)
pictured August 1939
in the full dress uniform of a Surgeon Lietenant RN

John Moore (b1926)

Ian Moore (b1920)

*Left: Sir John Moore,
pictured (circa 1894) as
President of The Royal College
of Physicians of Ireland*

Above: Richard Moore, (b1930) author of Leeches to Lasers

Facing Page
Top Left: James Moore (b1956) as Fellow of RCGP, 1996.
Top Right: Jane Moore (b1963) on graduation from Cambridge, 1984
Below:
Sir John Moore on the Sugarloaf Mountain, Co. Wicklow,
in 1935, with his grandsons
John Moore (on right) and Richard Moore (on left).

The Hospital Ship Maine,
leaving Grand Harbour,
Malta, 1914.

Maurice Moore,
as Surgeon Lieutenant RN,
while serving on
HMS Temeraire, 1922.

that trends and developments could be observed. He referred to a speech by Mr (*sic*) John Simon, co-author of the 1858 *Inquiry*, in which he quoted advice given in the eighteenth century *Mrs Glasses' Cookery Book* .... "first catch your hare, *then* skin it!". Much had been said about isolating and disinfecting when disease broke out, but first you had to know where the cases were. He disapproved of the doctors who had petitioned Parliament against the Leicester Bill 'on the ground that "it imposed upon them new, onerous and unnecessary obligations"', and noted with satis-faction that just as the Leicester Act came into force a severe epidemic of scarlet fever began there. Despite their objections the doctors of Leicester notified 496 cases of the disease in fifteen weeks with the result that the epidemic ended sooner than expected. Leicester's MOH estimated that 'through notification 41 lives were saved and 287 homesteads were preserved from an invasion of scarlet fever'.

In that speech John made one of his most impassioned pleas in the cause of preventive medicine:-

What shall we say as to the bearing of notification of infectious diseases upon home-life? With all reverence, let us speak of such affections as "preventable", and, if they are preventable, how best can they be warded off? Surely by timely warning of the threatening danger. My heart bleeds as day after day I see on the wards of our epidemic hospitals the fever-stricken victims of sanitary neglect, and in our general hospitals the still more miserable sur-vivors of the pestilence, dying a lingering death from one or other of the dread sequelae of scarlatina, measles or typhoid fever.

Despite this passionate plea, opposition by the profession and inaction by the legislature continued. In 1887, when notification had still not been universally introduced, he again complained of his colleagues' intransi-gence in an address to the Royal Academy of Medicine in Ireland[31]:-

Personally, and as an ardent lover of my profession, I deeply regret the uncompromising attitude which the vast majority of my brethren have taken up in the matter of notification of disease. Rightly or wrongly, a grievous stumbling block has been placed in the way of general legislation on the sub-ject, and year by year an incalculable amount of injury is being done by the systematic concealment of the presence of preventable disease among the population.

Gentlemen, I would conclude this address with the heart-stirring words of a master whom I never tire of quoting – Dr William Stokes. "The great instruments of Preventive Medicine will be science, legislative wisdom and charity. The time may come when no man for his own ends or his profit will be permitted to damage the health or well-being of his neighbour or his servant".

Eventually the campaign for legislation was successful. Ireland was included with the rest of the United Kingdom in the Infectious Diseases (Notification) Act of 1889 which made it compulsory for local authorities to be informed of cholera, smallpox, typhus and relapsing fever, typhus, typhoid and paratyphoid fevers, diphtheria and scarlet fever[32]. Curiously one of the biggest killers was excluded. Measles, which in 1901 still had a mortality rate of 3.5 per 1000 children under 1 year of age[33] was thought to be so rapidly infectious that it was impossible to prevent it spreading. Notification was therefore pointless, and was not required until 1940. The BMA held out for the system that placed the duty of notification on the head of the affected household, to whom the doctor would give a certificate of diagnosis. If there was no head of household the duty fell on the nearest relative, or if there was no relative on the patient, unless too young. It did not say what should be done if such a lone patient was too ill to comply. The BMA insisted that the doctor's duty was only to give a certificate to the householder and tell him to send it to the MOH.

Even after the Act was in force doctors resisted notification. Dr Biddle of Kingston-on-Tames accepted that 'England expects every man to do his duty', including the duty to report an outbreak of disease in his house. For doctors, however, it was 'un-English and unprofessional to send information directly to the authorities except at the householder's request'[34]. W.C. Crofts, Secretary of the Liberty and Property Defence League agreed[35]. For middle and upper class people in spacious houses there was no problem because isolation was simple, but:-

... the small tradesman and the working man are not so well posted up in the germ theory as their betters mostly now are, nor is the consequent

necessity for the separation of the sound from the unsound; their household accommodation is straitened and business considerations, particularly with the petty shop-keeper, make strongly against letting their outside acquaintance (among whom are their customers or employers) into the damaging secret of domestic afflictions of a catching nature.

The argument raged on as to whether the single system (doctor reporting directly) or the dual (householder delivering doctor's certificate) was preferable, but eventually the principle of direct notification by the doctor was accepted and is now a matter of course. The people of these islands are now free from those disastrous epidemics, but in the rare event of a case of infectious disease developing another preventive measure is necessary – the patient must be isolated.

It is understandable that so long as the cause of infectious diseases was still not fully understood, there would be reluctance to accept measures to control it which not only seemed ill-founded but invited intrusion by officialdom. After all, it was argued, if disease was caused by miasms wafted on the air how could telling a Sanitary Inspector about it and removing the patient to hospital prevent others from catching it in the same way? It was necessary to understand the new germ theory to know that microbes were living things, and could be spread from person to person in the air, by contact, or on clothes and other materials. In the 1870s this was still the subject of research accepted by some but still unproven, and required new thinking. Pragmatically, however, it made sense to isolate people who were ill with diseases known to occur in epidemics, which by their nature clearly spread from person to person.

The Cork Street Hospital had been founded for the dual purposes of isolation and convalescence. It was a Fever Hospital and House of Recovery. Its foundation in 1804 had been achieved by a government grant of £1000 for buildings and £500 annually for support, to which was added £8935 7s 1d from public subscription[36]. It was generally accepted that the public should help the 'labouring poor' by their generosity in building this hospital and others such as the Hardwicke, because it was 'felt that the health of the poor was the security of the rich': the wealthy had a duty to be benevolent for their own self-preservation as much as for its intrinsic charity. Cork Street admitted 205,000 people in the next 80 years, of whom over 90% survived. Similar hospitals existed in England, at Manchester and Liverpool for instance as well as in London. If isolation was to be prolonged into convalescence better facilities would be needed for everyone, because when the Notification Act was passed in the late 1880s social structures were very different from the start of the century. The greater populations of the cities required much more accommodation in times of epidemics, and the legal requirement for notification increased the demand because more cases were being reported.

Ten years earlier, when advocating notification of diseases, John had foreseen the need for more accommodation during convalescence. At the annual meeting of the BMA in Cork in 1879, he opened the Public Medicine Section's session by speaking on the subject of *'How are we to deal, by isolation or otherwise, with convalescents from acute infective disease, so as to prevent the spread of disease?'*[37]. It was well known that patients convalescing from an illness could still pass it on to others, which in turn would make more people ill. Limiting the spread of disease needed careful and prolonged separation of the convalescent from the general population. He described how one of his patients, a girl with scarlet fever, spent six weeks in strict quarantine 'in an isolated room at the top of a house', but accidentally met her younger sister who had been confined to another part of their home. Within days the younger sister was ill with the same disease. In hospitals the problem was even worse, especially during epidemics such as that of smallpox in 1878 when he had 1500 cases 'under his observation'[38]. During that time, he said:-

> *Often and often was I an eye-witness of the untoward effects of a prolonged sojourn in the necessarily tainted air of the hospital. Abscesses, bed-sores, diarrhoea, pleurisy, pneumonia, scarlatina, were sequels of the disease in too many instances, and I could not help thinking how different it might have been had the sufferers been removed in good time to a purer air.*

Beds in the wards were needed for the acutely ill, but early discharge and return to 'their wonted employment' would be harmful to people weakened by illness. It was therefore necessary to provide special convalescent homes, situated in a site of 10–12 acres in the fresh air of the country. They would be staffed by a resident medical officer, a lady superintendent, nurses, wardmaids, general servants and porters. He showed a proposed plan for such a home, with rooms for both public and private patients, the latter being charged no more than their costs of 1 or 2 guineas per week, for it was not feasible to make a profit in such a place.

In England the 'wealthy and generous public' might provide such homes voluntarily, but in Ireland he feared that would not happen. Attempts in Dublin to raise £4000 for a convalescent home had only reached £1200 after 'immense labour'. Therefore the cost must fall on the Local Government Board, which was legally empowered to meet such costs. He closed his address with a plea, which foreshadowed the now widely accepted view that society has a duty to help its needy members:-

> *The plan I have proposed is, no doubt, a costly one. But the duty of the physician who is true to the traditions of his noble profession is calmly and thoughtfully to devise means whereby, under Providence, the health of the people may not merely be restored, but preserved. In one scale of the balance lie the gold and silver, and in the other the precious lives of fathers, mothers, children rescued from disease, or, it may be, death. Can we doubt for a moment to which side of the beam the balance will incline?*

Although his paper included a design, there is no mention of a completed scheme in any of his writings.

Improvements to hospitals became the subject of a dispute in 1895 between him and his occasional rival Dr (now Sir) Charles Cameron, as Superintendent MOH of Dublin[39]. At that time John and Cameron both held office at the Royal College of Surgeons in Ireland, Cameron as Professor of Hygiene and John as Professor of Medicine. Cameron proposed building a special hospital for infectious diseases in Dublin, but failed to consult his professional colleagues before announcing it to the public. John said such consultation was usual, but as Cameron:-

> *thought otherwise he should not complain if his scheme is fated to be severely handled in searching criticism [from the profession] to which it is bound to be exposed.*

Cameron proposed that the hospital would be available to patients with any infectious disease, especially smallpox, and would be paid for with borrowed money as allowed under 'the Poor's Rate'. It would be run by its own Board with the powers of a Sanitary Authority, and would therefore potentially be a rival to the Dublin Sanitary Authority of which John was a member. John's objections were fourfold: it was 'unnecessary, inexpedient, injurious to medical teaching, and would probably be a costly failure'. He said accommodation was already provided under the Public Health (Ireland) Act 1878 in the many hospitals in Dublin, and when the demand was great extra wards and convalescent space were always provided in wooden huts. Cameron's proposals were based on the example of London where, according to him, smallpox cases were not treated in the city, yet the famous London Fever Hospital was surrounded by dwellings and at least a mile and a quarter from open country, while the Cork Street hospital was less than a third of that distance from fresh air. Already nine Dublin hospitals received government grants which would probably be lost if the new hospital was built. And how would students learn about infectious disease if there were no cases in the teaching hospitals, and they could not get out to the distant new hospital for lack of transport? The public bodies concerned had assembled to 'hear, not to vote for or against, the scheme' at a meeting presided over by the Lord Mayor, where the scheme was viewed with scepticism. But with unusually strong words the gentle John said the *coup de grace* was given 'by the infanticidal hand of Sir Charles Cameron himself. He said that the hospitals would probably be *mainly used for smallpox*, but this disease was 'absolutely preventable by periodical vaccination', and if more were done to prevent it in this way a new hospital would be unnecessary.

This speech was made to the Royal Academy of Medicine in Ireland, who had met to debate the proposal, with Sir Charles Cameron there to respond in person[40]. In his defence he pointed out that infective diseases were 'propagated through the medium of the air', so it was important to keep 'persons suffering from such diseases apart from healthy persons'. There had been a welcome decrease of 40% in the zymotic death rate in the previous ten years, 'largely due to the enlightened actions of bodies composed almost wholly of non-medical men'. At that very moment there were 300 cases of smallpox in the two fever hospitals and the workhouse, and the wooden sheds there were 'very defective'. In Leicester it had been shown that smallpox could be spread more than 600 feet to adjoining houses, so separation of at least 1000 feet was needed. In Hull, Dr Mason had specified that there should be no more than 20 patients to an acre in a fever hospital, which should also be more than a mile outside a town. The cases in the general hospitals were inevitably a source of infection to other patients, because diseases were carried by the physicians and students to the wards in which non-infectious cases were treated after they had visited their fever patients. And as for distance, surely the fit young students could walk a mile to the fever hospital?

A lively discussion followed, in which both sides were supported. One of those present was the 75 year-old Charles, always keen to attend a meeting and offer his comments. On the matter of teaching he said that as a student he had seen only one case of smallpox, and was therefore in difficulty when he had to decide whether or not a passenger on a large steamer had the disease, but 'if he had not seen that one case he would not have been so conversant with the disease'. As for the way smallpox was spread he thought it came not from Cork Street hospital, but from 'the public houses in the neighbourhood, and from the mountains of filth forty or fifty feet high in Marrowbone-lane where the Corporation carts empty their rubbish'. Each principal speaker heard the other out, passions were calmed and order restored.

The Notification Act of 1889 specified that those acute epidemic diseases that had been so devastating should be notified, but not the chronic though often infectious 'Great White Plague' of tuberculosis. John was proud to record that Ireland was the first division of the United Kingdom to make it a notifiable disease by the Tuberculosis Prevention Act (Ireland) which became law in 1909, whereas it was not until 1913 that notification of tuberculosis, along with poliomyelitis, was required in England and Wales[41]. Making it notifiable was one thing, but making the provision useful was another, and it was to his profound regret that this promising development failed. Under the Act notification was voluntary at the discretion of each local authority, and few of them saw the need for action. Four years after the Act only one in four urban districts and one in eight rural districts had introduced the measure in their areas. In any case, only the pulmonary disease was notifiable, and then only if the patient slept in the same room as an uninfected person, or handled food for sale to the public, and had infected sputum. In 1914 in Dublin thousands of people must have had the disease, for 1069 of them died of it, yet only 1015 were notified, while in Belfast 806 died but only half that number were notified. The measure was a failure, and tuberculosis remained rampant throughout Ireland for years. John made proposals for improvement, but by now he was an ageing man. Though he lived another 20 years he did not see the battle against tuberculosis turn in Ireland's favour.

The fight against disease due to insanitary conditions was fought on many fronts beside notification, but there too it met with obstruction and apathy. The foot-soldiers that carried on this struggle were the medical officers of health, who had to contend with opposition from local authorities and other vested interests. Authorities spent little or nothing on sanitation before the 1878 Act, and were reluctant to pay their new medical officers more than the minimum[42]. If the MOH's annual reports or other activities were not to the liking of their authority, the reports would be rejected or contested, and the medical officer might even be threatened with dismissal. In 1884 Dr J Byrne Power, the medical officer for Kingstown Township (now Dun Laoghaire), read a paper to the Sanitary Institute of Great Britain. John later recalled that:-

> Dr Byrne spoke in plain and unsparing terms of the decadence, poverty, insanitary state of the once flourishing township of Kingstown. For this Dr Power was summoned before the authority, and ordered to apologise under threat of dismissal from his appointment. Happily, he stood firm, and the threat was not carried into effect. But the incident conclusively demonstrates the necessity which exists for independent supervision if medical officers of health are to be held privileged in the discharge of their functions.[43]

This was not only an Irish problem, for the same difficulty faced Dr Parsons of Barking who had offended his authority by a report which called for urgent reforms. The authority said his report was 'damaging and discourteous, and resolved that it should lie upon the table'. He sought advice from the BMA, and was advised to go over the head of the local authority to the Local Government Board, which would have required some courage as it would probably have offended his employers even more. Stokes' plea for 'science, legislative wisdom and charity' was falling on deaf ears.

The Moore family is not given to political comment, but in 1921 John came as close to it as any of us. For his Presidential Address to the Royal Academy of Medicine in Ireland he chose the title of *'Existing Hindrances to Public Health work in Ireland'*[44]. When notification had at last been introduced in 1889 the fee for notifying had been set at half-a-crown. This was a sizeable sum of money, equivalent to £10 or more now. A year after the First World War began, in order to divert money to the war effort this fee was reduced to one shilling (which *The Lancet* had actually considered derisory thirty-five years earlier). Three years after the Armistice in 1918 it still had not been restored. John caused a question to be asked in Parliament as to when the profession might expect restoration of their proper remuneration, only to be told that it could not be done as hostilities had not been concluded – the United Kingdom was technically still at war with Turkey which was not party to the Armistice. This was bad enough, but worse was to come. The Chancellor of the Exchequer refused to allow money to be spent on planned health schemes that had not yet started, thereby halting urgent work on the prevention of tuberculosis in Ireland. At this time, 1921, pressure was building up for an independent Ireland, and tension was running high. Whereas England and Scotland had their own Ministries of Health, Ireland remained dependent on London, once again the poor relation. John 'had the curiosity to ask what burden the annual cost of the Irish Public Health Council imposes on the Imperial Exchequer'. The answer was a mere £4000. He concluded his speech with following words:-

The only comment I would make upon this fact is that the sum is negligible when compared with a statement published in the newspapers a short time ago that the battle-cruiser H.M.S.Repulse had been re-fitted and re-commissioned for active service at a cost of £750,000 – over three-quarters of a million of money! This fact needs no further comment, and must serve as my most eloquent peroration.

Within months Ireland was a Free State. Before long Repulse was a torpedoed wreck at the bottom of the Pacific Ocean, victim of another World War.

Members of the BMA, as gladiators, conceding the introduction of the National Health Service to Aneurin Bevan, as Nero. E.H.Shepard, 1948. (Wellcome Library, London).

CHAPTER TEN

New Centuries, New Ideas

Health, which is a state of physical, mental and social
well-being and not merely the absence of disease or infirmity
is a fundamental human right
World Health Authority[1]

F
or the Moore family the twentieth century opened with
honour and acclaim. Although John had many years of life and
work ahead of him still, as the new century began he was publicly honoured and the achievements of his already successful
career were nationally acknowledged. He was one of four medical men
who were knighted by Queen Victoria in the last year of her long life.
The Medical Press said 'his knighthood will be a popular one'[2], and the
BMJ commented:-

> *Sir John's fair-mindedness has won him popularity and esteem, while his*
> *high sense of honour in all dealings with his professional brethren has earned*
> *their confidence*[3].

Besides his hospital and private practice, he was President of the Royal
College of Physicians in Ireland (RCPI), Professor of Medicine in the
Royal College of Surgeons in Ireland, and editor of the Dublin Journal
of Medical Science. He was chairman of the Dublin branch of the BMA,
and sat on several important committees, including the Irish Branch of
the General Medical Council (GMC), and in 1905 was elected to represent the RCPI on the central Council in London.

In 1904 the University of Oxford conferred on him the degree of
Doctor in Science, *honoris causa*, and in 1933 he was admitted as
Honorary Doctor of Law in the National University of Ireland. His final

and possibly most cherished accolade came in 1935, his ninetieth year, when he was admitted to the rare distinction of Honorary Fellowship of the Royal Academy of Medicine in Ireland[4]. This was a particularly apposite tribute to the length and success of his career, because the Academy had been formed by the amalgamation of four existing bodies, one of which, The Dublin Medical Society, John had joined sixty-five years earlier. He was already a prominent figure in the profession when, in 1882, these societies were amalgamated to create the Academy to which he was now being admitted as an Honorary Fellow, and it was he who had formally proposed the motion that brought the Academy into being.

Sir John was active in medicine until the very end of his life. He was unwavering in his determination to control the tragedy of tuberculosis, which was still causing the deaths of between three and four people of every thousand in Britain, though the death rate was falling. But it was still all too common in Ireland[5], where in 1911 more than nine thousand people died from it in a population of 4.2 million (1926 census). He campaigned for additional resources and personnel to eradicate it, calling for compulsory notification, whole-time medical superintendent health officers, domiciliary nurses and sanitary inspectors, and most importantly public education about the risks of tuberculosis and how to avoid them. He applauded the development of special TB hospitals, encouraged patients to get out in the fresh air, and insisted that windows should be opened on the 'lee' side of hospital buildings. When the Bishop of Norwich told a BMA meeting that he believed an open window was an 'accident', Sir John's response was that it was a more unfortunate accident when windows remained closed[6].

He owed his greatest allegiance to the Meath Hospital, for it was there he had trained under his much admired mentor William Stokes, and had been on the staff himself for sixty years. His career had been largely devoted to combating infectious diseases, and glad though he was to see the end of the havoc they wrought, he was reluctant to lower his guard. In 1930, when the hospital Board proposed to convert the infectious diseases wards to more modern purposes, he 'stoutly opposed' the move because every year since 1827 the hospital had received a grant of £600 for fever cases[7]. But by this time, like his great-grandfather Daniel, he was 'a venerable grey-bearded old man from the last century' – indeed their two lives had already spanned the 180 years that had passed since 1750 when Daniel was born. He was overruled, and medical progress moved relentlessly on.

In 1933, at the age of eighty eight, he resigned from the Meath to live in contented retirement, during which he still had the energy to visit his son Maurice and grandsons John and Richard in Malta, where Maurice was then serving. In October 1937, a few days before his ninety-second birthday Sir John's long life came to a close, only months after the introduction of what promised to be the complete answer to those infections which he had fought against for so long – the sulphonamide drugs.

Soon after the new century began an earlier generation also passed into the sunset with the death of John's uncle Charles. The last of the apothecaries, Charles lived until 1904, long enough to see medical science begin to produce truly effective results. A determined advocate of sanitary progress, he had been President of the Public Health Section of the Royal Academy of Ireland. He was a thinker and an activist, and a frequent contributor to discussions at medical meetings, though his reported remarks suggest he was also an able jockey of his favourite hobby horses. He never married, so no medical inheritance passed through him to later generations. With these deaths an era in the Moore family's practice of medicine came to an end, for though many of John's descendants and relatives were to become doctors, medicine itself was about to change beyond recognition.

The Moore doctors of the twentieth century witnessed these changes from various viewpoints. Maurice continued his career in the Royal Navy, and made his home in England. Consequently his sons John and Richard entered the British rather than the Irish medical profession, so it is mostly through their experience of general practice in England that this story continues in the later twentieth century. In Ireland Sir John's cousin George completed a distinguished career at the Dental Hospital like his father. Medicine continued into another generation in 1944 when George's son Ian qualified at Trinity College, Dublin, and joined the Medical Department of Guinness's. Cecil and Hugh LeFanu, nephews of Sir John, qualified in Aberdeen and entered the Colonial Service in the Gold Coast. Of Sir John's two doctor cousins, Thomas remained in Ireland to practice in Co Monaghan, while his brother Frederic was medical officer to the *Sardinia*, before entering general practice in various parts of

England. This minor diaspora of the family presented the opportunity to enter several of the many medical specialties then developing. Whatever their field, the twentieth century Moores and their relatives were to witness a veritable explosion in medical progress, and a remarkable improvement in the health of the population. Though the bright light of laser technology was still to come, the era of the leech was already a thing of the past – or so it seemed.

In the 1850s, of every thousand people alive at the start of a year more than twenty would have died by the end of it. In the decades that followed, as housing, nourishment and sanitation were improved the death rate began to fall, mostly because of the reduction in infections as a result of better living conditions[8]. By 1900 medicine had become an organised profession, centrally supervised by the GMC as regards education and conduct, and seen by its practitioners as a branch of science. Changes in social, scientific and medical fields enabled the children of the new century to live healthier and longer lives than their forebears. Boys born in 1901 could expect to live 4 years longer than their grandfathers from the 1840s, and girls 6 years longer than their grandmothers. The children of 2001 can expect even more, for their lives should be 30 years longer still[9]. Now, in the twenty-first century, citizens of developed countries expect to have long and healthy lives, and as medicine has grown in effectiveness and availability such prospects have become a realistic aspiration for people everywhere. When the World Health Organisation met at Alma-Ata in Khazakstan in 1978, it called on all governments, health and development workers, and the world community to 'promote and protect the health of all the people of the world'. Government action was essential, as Article V of the Declaration states[10]:-

> *Governments have a responsibility for the health of their people which can be fulfilled only by the provision of adequate health and social measures. A main social target of governments, international organisations and the whole world community in the coming decades should be the attainment by all peoples of the world by the year 2000 of a level of health that will permit them to lead a socially and economically productive life. Primary health care is the key to attaining this target as part of development in the spirit of social justice.*

Governments in developed countries had accepted responsibility for ensuring the provision of medical services long before 1978, of course, though regrettably there are still many nations too poor to respond to the aspirations of Alma-Ata. Our medical forebears might be astonished to discover that in Great Britain now ninety percent of medical services are funded from general taxation, and that medical care is available for everyone free at the time of need. Government intervention in health care in Britain began almost unintentionally with the National Insurance Act of 1911, which was introduced as a financial measure by the then Chancellor of the Exchequer, Lloyd George. It was not originally intended to control the medical services, but only to pre-empt the financial losses due to illness in a work-force who could not afford doctors' fees. The BMA reluctantly accepted the terms of the 1911 Act on condition that 'six cardinal points' were safeguarded, which unsurprisingly included free choice of doctor by the patient and adequate remuneration by a method acceptable to the doctors. There was no consistency in what doctors considered acceptable, however, and their willingness to participate therefore varied from place to place[11]. The popular journal *The Medical Press* had welcomed the Bill cautiously[12], saying:-

> *If ever there was a need of strong and united action on the part of medical men it exists at the present juncture of affairs. It is a sad reflection that, after some four hundred years of existence, the dawn of the twentieth century should find so learned a profession as ours weak in Parliament, practically defenceless against unqualified competition, miserably underpaid, betrayed and neglected by some score or so of selfish corporations, and saddled by a mockery of government in the shape of the General Medical Council. ....*
> *Happily the scheme advanced by Mr Lloyd George promises to bring succour to a struggling profession ... by way of proper payment for solid and valuable personal services of a highly skilled nature.*

After it became law the Act was not greeted so eagerly elsewhere in the profession. At one 'Mass Meeting of Medical Men' attended by 'upwards of 2,000 medical practitioners', doctors were urged to 'unite' to achieve their objectives[13]. The chairman, Sir Watson Cheyne, told the meeting:-

*A very able and astute statesman has conceived an idea of a national insur-
ance against sickness and unemployment. ... This statesman has gone to the
public and he has said to them "If you will subscribe a small sum weekly, I
will arrange that if you are taken ill you shall have a great variety of benefits during your illness, and among them you will have free medical attendance". ... This offer has been accepted ... and before long insured persons
will be asking about this free medical attendance. Well, now, it is a very
extraordinary thing, and indeed hardly conceivable, that up to the present
time no definite arrangements have been made with the medical profession to
provide the attendance which has been promised.*

The Lloyd George Act changed the pattern of medical care for the rest of
the century, but the Royal College of Physicians had misgivings[14], for
they warned that:–

A system of per capita *contract practice, if it should become universal, as it
appears to be contemplated, throughout the working clauses of the National
Insurance Bill,* will lower the standard of medical practice, and will
prove in this way injurious to the public and the profession. *[added
emphasis]*

The provisions of the National Health Insurance Act (NHI) lasted thirty
five years until the National Health Service Act (NHS) came into effect in
July 1948, when its protagonist Aneurin Bevan boastfully called it the envy
of the world. Successive governments of all persuasions have developed it,
and political parties have used it as a bait to attract votes, but this has not
prevented it from suffering from the complacency and defects of all
monopolies. As far as general practice is concerned its structure had
already been determined when the NHS took over, because it was 'path-
dependent' on the previous scheme of a fixed payment for each person on a
registered list of patients[15]. Although the place of the GP in a state-funded
system was assured, the next ninety years were not always characterised
by security or contentment. The frequent policy changes of government
still generate passionate discontent, while under-funding and bureaucracy
have stifled initiative and innovation. Today's equivalents of *The Medical
Press* carry headlines such as *'Reforms Driving GPs to the Brink'* and
'National Doctor Day May 1st – It's Time for Action'[16].

Such antagonistic publicity obscures two significant consequences of the Act of 1911 that have shaped British attitudes to medical services. One is that the relationship between patient and doctor is now mediated by the State, which is a party to the doctor–patient relationship because it pays the bill. Therefore, whatever the relationship between the individuals concerned, the circumstances of medical care are determined by national government on a political and financial basis, which do not necessarily reflect national, local or individual needs. The other, which is particularly significant for the four doctors of the family who have been in modern general practice, is that this field is no longer the province of the doctor alone, but has become 'Primary Care'. The work of 'Primary Care Teams' is shared between people in several disciplines whose roles are increasing and developing, and even the doctor's leadership role is disputed. The long-term and personal relationships between doctor and patient are in danger of being lost in a system of medical supermarketing in which the political piper calls the tune, and risks confusing value with cost.

When the National Health Service was introduced in 1948 morale among general practitioners was low, and prospects were poor because the system created by the 1911 Act was ill-organised. It depended on a variable mixture of inadequate capitation payments from the National Insurance scheme and private fees which often remained unpaid. While John and Richard were still students two years after the start of the NHS, a visiting Australian doctor named Joseph Collings carried out a review of British general practice[17] and published a highly critical report on the 55 practices he visited. He found that nearly all of them were badly housed, inefficient and overburdened, especially those in industrial towns. In one practice with four doctors and 20,000 patients there were:-

...a small dilapidated waiting room, three equally small and untidy consulting rooms, [and] a kind of cupboard which served as a dispensary. The consulting rooms were dirty and ill-equipped. There were no examining couches and no apparent means of sterilising anything; indeed apart from a few rusty and dusty antique instruments, there was no sign of any sort of equipment ..... I found a queue of people extending 200 yards down the street .... During my stay of an hour and a quarter 120 patients came in ... seen by three different doctors who replaced one another with almost bewildering rapidity.

He ended his report with this challenge:-

> *My conclusions have led me to write what is indeed a condemnation of*
> *general practice in its present form; but they have also* led me to recognise
> the importance of general practice, *and the dangers of continuing to pre-*
> *tend that it is something which it is not.* Instead of continuing to com-
> pensate for its deficiencies, we should admit them honestly and try
> to correct them at source. *[added emphasis]*

The British Medical Association, stung by Collings' criticisms, commissioned a review of its own[18], which, though wider and more carefully
selected, revealed a similarly gloomy picture. It found that 10% of
premises were 'dismal, bare, dirty and inhospitable' and unsuitable for
medical work. Little or no effort was made to keep medical records,
which some regarded as a 'sort of red-tape imposition'. Forty percent
of the doctors were considered to be 'good', and an equal number
'adequate'. The other twenty percent were presumably bad, though
that word was not used and the criteria for these judgements were not
defined. Collings and Hatfield had revealed that the Royal College of
Physicians was right in its prediction in 1911 that such a scheme would
be 'injurious'.

Not long after this, the eminent physician Lord Moran enraged general practitioners by telling the 1961 Royal Commission on Doctors' and
Dentists' Remuneration that general practitioners were those who had
'fallen off the ladder to consultant status'. The implication of failure was
deeply resented, for there was no other ladder to climb for those who did
not wish to work in hospitals, but whose medical schools had failed to
prepare them for anything else, and certainly not general practice.
Dr John Horder, eminent himself as the President of the Royal College
of General Practitioners, has said of Lord Moran's remark[19]:-

> *It made a beginning for them in which jealousy of their more successful*
> *colleagues was combined with a degree of contempt for the inferior circum-*
> *stances of the job they had been forced to take and for which they had not*
> *received any special training.*

Although general practice was weak and under stress in the 1950s, else-where medical science was advancing rapidly. In his book *The Rise and Fall of Modern Medicine*[20] James Le Fanu, eighth-generation descendant of William Moore of Ballymahon, lists thirty-six developments of great importance. Among these are some which he calls 'Definitive Moments', and though none of them originated in general practice several of them have had a major impact on the way it has developed. Among them are:

Sulphonamides and Penicillin	*Helicobacter as the cause of peptic ulcer*
Chlorpromazine to treat schizophrenia	*Cortisone*
Prevention of strokes	*Smoking identified as a cause of cancer*
The contraceptive pill	*Poliomyelitis immunisation*

Until fifty or sixty years ago general practitioners had virtually no effective medicines except antiseptics, a few 'potions for the motions' such as rhubarb and senna, a minor sedative in bromide, and a major analgesic in morphine. In the early twentieth century scarlet fever was still dangerous, and through another of its manifestations, puerperal fever, the germ that caused it, *Streptococcus,* was killing one mother in every five hundred births[21]. At Queen Charlotte's Hospital in London, one in five of those mothers who were admitted with this fearsome infection would die. But in 1936, when the new sulphonamide drug Prontosil was used for the first time, all but three of thirty-eight very ill patients recovered. The doctors who prescribed this remarkable treatment were careful to play down their success[22]:-

> *It behoves us to be very cautious in drawing conclusions as to the curative effect of any remedy upon puerperal infections due to the haemolytic streptococcus.*

Their caution proved unnecessary, and the success of sulphonamides, penicillin and other antibiotics that were to follow has almost eliminated the terrible waste of life from acute infections. Yet previously unknown causes of infection are still being discovered, or old ones taking a new prominence. Peptic ulcers used to cause prolonged pain and distress to patients, whose doctors spent much time and effort treating them with medicines and operations, often unsuccessfully. In the 1980s it was shown that this disease was actually due to an infection by a newly discovered germ, *Helicobacter pylori*. Such a thing had been assumed to be impossible – how could bacteria survive the acidity of the stomach? Now with a simple breath test the germs can be detected, and a few days treatment with antibiotics cures the problem. This diagnosis can easily be made and effective treatment given in general practice, removing the need for boringly bland diets, useless medicines or radical operations for millions of people. Another curious organism, *Campylobacter*, long known to exist in earth, was thought for years to be harmless until it was shown to cause troublesome and sometimes severe gastro-enteritis in 30,000 people in Britain every year.

The illnesses caused by *Helicobacter* and *Campylobacter* can be treated successfully with antibiotics, but the old menace of meningitis can still be a frightening emergency, reminding us in nineteenth century manner how sudden and overwhelming infections can be. And the wily *Staphylococcus* which can resist all but the toughest antibiotics still kills thousands of people, especially in hospitals where it lurks ready to pounce on patients already ill from other causes. Such deaths from infectious diseases are all the more distressing because they are now so unusual. Despite these powerful cures and remedies, our lives are as vulnerable as ever.

Acute infections have disappeared, but the time that was spent on them by doctors is now taken up by the concept of 'long term care' which has crept silently into everyday practice. New medicines have been introduced, like chlorpromazine for major psychoses, antidepressants, and tranquillisers; drugs to reduce blood pressure and cholesterol, and to control diabetes; treatments for arthritis and rheumatism, and others for cancer. No longer need patients stay in hospital for months, because continuing medication allows them to live at home with psychological support where necessary. But patients must attend the doctor or clinic periodically to ensure the medicines are being used properly and effectively. Other drugs require monitoring by a doctor, such as cortisone and its derivatives, and their companions the non-steroidal anti-inflammatory drugs for arthritis, and those for asthma, anti-coagulation and … the list is long.

The prevention of disease, an idea championed long ago by Sir John and his contemporaries, is still a vital part of medical practice. Now it is more than the attention to hygiene and immunisation that they advocated, for now that strokes and heart attacks can be forestalled, and cancer detected before it endangers life, the hunt is on to identify people at risk of getting a disease years before the first symptoms develop. Clinics to detect and treat symptomless heart disease and diabetes have become an essential part of general practice. People who feel perfectly well are now encouraged to attend to measure their blood pressure and weight and be advised against smoking; babies must be seen to check their growth, and the elderly to see if they have begun to suffer from the effects of their age. The introduction of contraception by pills and other means created a huge demand, because those who take the pill, and its allied treatment hormone replacement therapy, need to be seen regularly. Advice on health promotion, travel, mammography and cervical cytology have created new functions for doctors which would seem strange to our medical fore-bears. The general practitioner may now see more people who believe they are well than who think they are ill. The emphasis is on staying well, with the expectation of a full and healthy life span. From the cradle to the grave some medical manoeuvre seems to be available to dispel the spectre of illness. If not preventable, the problem is surely curable – 'a pill for everything'. If not a medicine, then an operation – every year millions have artificial hips or knees, or heart pacemakers, and even have the organs of other people transplanted into them. Medicine has become a technological industry.

Yet in the long history of medicine it is less than one lifetime since the miracle of penicillin and sulphonamides was discovered. The amount of penicillin available to treat the first patient ever to have it was so small that it ran out in three days, but he was brought back from the brink of expected death[23]. Other innovations were just as amazing, if less well known. When a 46 year old 'Mrs S' developed myxoedema in 1891 it would probably have killed her within a year or two. It was already known that this disease was due to a defect of the thyroid gland, so Mrs S accepted the offer to be the first person to be injected with an extract of sheep's thyroid gland. Within weeks she could 'walk about the streets' again. She lived to the age of 74, having taken medicine derived from the glands of 870 sheep. Nowadays a patient with this disease can keep per-fectly well, with a daily tablet prescribed by their general practitioner at a cost of less than a penny a day. So too do people with diabetes, but when Sir John treated the 14 year-old Elizabeth R (not the royal one) in 1922 he was powerless to cure her, and within six months she had wasted away and died. He commented on the case:-

> In regard to treatment my only regret is that I was not aware of recent researches by Professor J.J.R.McLeod in the University of Toronto on an antidiabetic hormone to which the term "Insulin" has been given. ... The Medical Research Council has taken the matter up, and a supply of insulin will shortly be available[24].

When it did become available insulin was so expensive that few could afford it at £1 5s for a week's supply when a man's wage might be £2 or £3 a week. In 1923-4 the British government was pressed to pay for this new and life-saving treatment, but declined on the grounds that it had no duty to pay for treatment, which was for 'the Guardians on the advice of their medical officers in cases of destitution'[25]. In Ireland it was proposed to set up a charity to make insulin available free to those who could not afford it. Now insulin is cheap, and, in the NHS at least, the patient pays nothing.

When cortisone was introduced in 1949, the first patient ever to have it was so crippled by rheumatoid arthritis that she could hardly get out of bed[26]. Amazingly, within a few days of starting treatment she was able to go shopping, but the miracle medicine cost $18,000 a week and she needed it continuously. The modern equivalent, prednisolone, costs less than 2p a tablet, which allows it to be used for a wide variety of minor and life-threatening conditions. Treatments for thyroid disease, diabetes, rheumatism and many other long term disorders are now straight-forward and routine, but although the cost is small for individual cases, for the millions who need treatment the total is huge. Miraculous though these innovations would have seemed to William Daniel and Sir John, a new problem came with them – how to pay for them. How much is a cure worth? Or a life?

While the tools available to cure disease have become increasingly effective, the diseases that afflict people have changed. Smallpox has been abolished and we are no longer afraid of other sudden and disruptive epidemics. It is not enough, however, merely to eradicate some diseases, for having apparently mastered the dangers of the environment mankind has created new threats to take the place of the old. Among the extensive writings of William Daniel and Sir John between 1840 and 1925 no mention is made of several major conditions that kill and cripple people today. High blood pressure, and its consequences of myocardial infarction and stroke, do not feature in their writings; indeed the means to measure blood pressure was not invented until Sir John was more than 65 years of age. Smoking, once advised by doctors as a means of relaxation, is now recognised as the cause of many diseases which nearly half the population of western nations inflict on themselves and their neighbours. The disease-inducing habit is spreading to developing countries, too, under commercial pressure from the tobacco producers. Much medical effort, especially by general practitioners, is expended on the prevention of smoking, or, if that fails, on the cure of the disease it has caused.

In December 1952 the usually benign climate of the British Isles smothered London in a dense and poisonous fog, which provoked a surge in hospital admissions – 500 a day, five times more than four months before[27], and hastened the deaths of over 3,000 Londoners[28]. Since then the clean air policies have eliminated the dense and acrid fogs of years ago, but the air we breathe still harbours danger. Pollution from vehicle exhausts alone has been estimated to cost European health services more than traffic accidents, amounting to 1.7% of gross domestic product in the three countries studied[29]. Whereas our forebears poisoned their food and water, we poison the air with a new man-made miasm, causing thousands of people to be admitted to hospital every year with respiratory and cardiovascular diseases, which are all too often fatal[30].

In the nineteenth century it was clear that the poor were more prone to disease than the rich. It is so still. Death rates in the poorest areas are more than twice those of the richest[31], largely due to inadequate housing and exposure to winter cold[32], which makes the inhabitants of northern regions die younger than those of the warmer south. The situation is improving gradually in many places, but even in the well-to-do residents of Merseyside mortality is still higher than it was among their social equivalents in Oxford or Surrey ten years previously. Those in the North

and North-West trail behind them all, regardless of their individual prosperity[33]. Unfortunately, because the most deprived towns in England are
also the coldest, they have up to 70% higher mortality from ischaemic
heart disease; the people of Dewsbury and Halifax fare worse than those
of Redbridge and Worcester, for instance[34]. These findings would have
intrigued Sir John, who surely would have liked to compare the meteorological state of his native Dublin with other towns and cities.

While some excess mortality can be attributed to cold because of
where people live, much is due to *how* they live, and indeed how they die.
In the most deprived tenth of the population of England and Wales the
death rate from all causes is 15% higher than in the least deprived tenth.
In northern districts it is 23% higher than southern ones[35]. Every year
about 100,000 people in England and Wales die prematurely, half of them
from heart disease, lung cancer or chronic bronchitis and emphysema,
and exposure to cold is a factor in a quarter of these early deaths. Nor is
this premature mortality only due to heart or lung disease. People in
deprived areas are more likely to die from ten of the twenty commonest
cancers, which are all related to smoking, and account for 20,000 cases of
preventable cancer every year[36].

Nutrition has improved so much over the last few decades that a
boy of 14 in the 1990s is as big as a working class adult of the mid
eighteenth century. Sixteen year old boys at Christchurch School are now
10-12cm taller than their predecessors of a hundred years ago[37]. But
cheaper, readily available food encourages over-eating. In England now
one person in five is clinically obese, three times as many as 20 years ago,
with an increased risk of ill health, premature death or disability. However
good this may be for the trade in books on slimming and 'dieting',
it means that on an average GP list of 1,900 people there are up to
300 whose own weight is a danger to their health. If the doctor were to
see half of them once a year twelve extra consultations would be needed
every week.

The effect of this trend on general practitioners was observed by
Pereira Gray[38] in 1987 when he began to realise that his patients' problems
were increasingly the consequences of their own choices and behaviour,
and needed to be managed differently:-

The pattern is the same throughout the western world: the conditions caus-
ing the greatest concern are ischaemic heart disease, lung cancer, alcoholism,
obesity, depression, accidents, self-injury, abortion, and venereal disease. All
have one common factor, conscious human behaviour.

Human behaviour in housing, smoking, eating, drinking, working and even leisure presents a twenty-first century phenomenon to medical practice – 'life-style consultations' intended to promote healthy habits or to mitigate the effects of unhealthy ones. While the statistics quoted here relate to England and Wales, similar factors are at play all over the developed world.

The World Health Authority has a view of health that is much wider than the mere absence of disease. The Alma–Ata Declaration includes many objectives that involve political and economic dimensions[39], such as:–

Health is a fundamental human right (Article I)
Existing inequalities in health are politically, socially and economically
unacceptable (Article II)
Sustained economic and social development depends on everyone being
healthy (Article III)
People have a right and duty to be involved in their own health care
(Article IV)
Governments have an essential part to play (Article V)
National health care systems must include practical, scientifically sound
primary health care for individuals (Article VI and VII)
Governments of all countries should co-operate and direct their expenditure
towards these ends for all people, and attain them by the year 2000.
(Articles VIII to X)

However much WHO aspires to convert swords into ploughshares, and promote health by using all available resources to improve living conditions, the deadline of the year 2000 for its aspirations of Alma–Ata has been passed. Indeed WHO's publicity now declares:–

Tobacco is a Greater Cause of Death and Disability than any Single Disease[40]

The Seventh Cholera Pandemic is now in Progress[41]

Malaria causes 1 million deaths a year and kills a child every 30 seconds[42]

At least 22 new infectious diseases have been identified in the last 25 years[43]

And AIDS is an increasing threat on a scale that is reminiscent of the epidemics of the nineteenth century, and totally unfamiliar to most of us in modern times.

The comfortable citizens of Europe might think these are largely problems for the rest of the world, but it should be remembered that the White Plague of tuberculosis still exists in our midst. There were 6,000 new cases in Britain in 1999, and the prevalence is rising[44]. Underfunding of services to prevent and treat the disease, a problem for Sir John in the 1900s, still delays effective treatment and hastens spread of the disease[45]. Though malaria is mainly a disease of the tropics, there were 2364 cases in UK in 1997[46]. Food-poisoning by the typhoid-like germ *Salmonella* is now as common as typhoid used to be, though less serious. New problems like Creutzfeld-Jacob disease from BSE-infected cattle, and the potential consequences of genetic modification of crops and animals causes widespread concern.

That the aspirations of WHO are achievable should not be doubted if the political will is strong enough. Sir John predicted that smallpox could be defeated, and was proud to report that between 1905 and 1910 in Ireland where vaccination was compulsory, only one person died from smallpox (and he caught it in Glasgow). In England, where it was voluntary and unpopular, twenty one people died in the same period. The abolition of smallpox raises hopes for the elimination of another scourge. Poliomyelitis, first described in 1790, common by the 1870s, became epidemic in the twentieth century and has killed and disabled millions. The means to abolish it by vaccination exists, and WHO has embarked on a global campaign to remove the disease from the human population. The Director-General of WHO, Dr Gro Harlem Bruntland, has said: 'At the dawn of the new century we have it within our grasp to eradicate polio for ever'[47]. Let us hope that this bright dawn will spread its light on the means to prevent other devastating diseases that plague the world.

The medical challenge of the last two centuries was to prevent disease by building a healthier environment, and to bring treatment within the reach of everyone whether or not they could afford it. Our medical predecessors knew that cold and poverty contributed to disease and death. Yet despite the efforts of philanthropists and politicians to improve living conditions, deprivation still exists and people suffer the consequences. We have found new ways to damage the environment, and our individual choices expose us to risks our predecessors never had. While governments must lead the efforts to improve environmental and social conditions, individuals must also accept responsibility for their own health. In modern Europe most of us are very much more prosperous than our forbears, but we need to remember both that our own health is our own responsibility whose costs must be met, and that we have a duty to others to promote a healthy society. New eras demand new thinking.

A century has passed since Sir John's achievements were honoured, during which his grandsons John and Richard have played their part in general practice, which will be sketched in the next chapter. At the start of another century his great-grandchildren James and Jane continue the tradition he exemplified so well. While they are immeasurably better equipped to promote health and cure disease than he was, like him they have problems to face. The important and traditional relationship between doctor and patient remains a powerful and supportive force, which Sir John once described as 'that part of the treatment that is not in the Pharmacopeia', but the rising expectations of the public and improvements in technical possibilities create a demand that is increasingly difficult to meet.

James, as senior partner in his own practice and therefore technically self-employed, is increasingly required to deliver a system of health care prescribed by government and directed by official guidelines and regulations. Whereas his forebears were free to decide their own programmes and activities, for James there is pressure for compliance and accountability. His colleagues have recognised his qualities to the extent of electing him as Chairman of the Tamar Faculty of the Royal College of General Practitioners, but finding time even to do this extra-mural activity is difficult. It is on him and his colleagues in the field of primary care that the World Health Organisation's aspirations of 'Health for All' will lie.

From the reduction of infant mortality in developing countries to the preservation of health in the elderly citizens of western nations, primary care physicians and their ancillary colleagues will have a central role in tomorrow's medical profession.

For Jane the path to consultant status in her chosen specialty of obstetrics and gynaecology has been long and slow. In taking this direction she has broken new ground, by being both the first woman doctor in the family and the first to specialise in gynaecology. She has also learned the complex operating theatre procedures made available to medicine through advances in technology. She is skilled in the use of 'minimally invasive' techniques of laparoscopy, and the use of lasers for removal of diseased tissues, achieving results that were hardly considered possible in the past. But however complex the techniques she uses or the skills required to use them, she is well aware of the part of her work which is 'outside the Pharmacopeia', or indeed outside the technical manual of the apparatus she uses. Her approach is illustrated by the subject of her thesis for her MSc degree.

A comparison of this thesis[48] with that presented by her grandfather Maurice[49] for his MD in 1911 reveals how much more complex it is to learn the advanced skills of a doctor compared with two generations ago. Jane's thesis was compiled after three years of original research, involving the examination, interview and management of hundreds of patients from whom twenty were selected for detailed study – and this was only a small part of the long road to competence as a senior gynaecologist. Her thesis was 100 pages long, with references to 120 other original papers. Her subject was not simply how to diagnose or treat a particular condition, but what her patients actually thought and felt about the procedures they were undergoing and her part in it. Unfortunately, investigations do not always reveal a satisfactory explanation or a treatable cause, and treatments do not always achieve the patients' expectations. What do patients feel when no cause for their symptoms is found, or when no remedy is available? For doctors to be fully effective, patients must feel confident that doctors understand their patients' feelings and anxieties and will do what is best for them. Jane was learning how to create that mutual confidence, and how to employ the 'treatment that is not in the Pharmacopeia', or in the operating theatre. By contrast, Maurice's thesis simply consisted of a report on two patients with the recently described condition of Henoch-Schoenlein purpura who 'had come under his observation' at the Meath Hospital. He also had to answer a *viva voce* examination, but no original research was required. As a student who had achieved distinction in surgical examinations this presented no more than a comfortable challenge.

Where, then, has the progress of the twentieth century brought us, and where may developments lead us in the next? As medicine becomes more complex, each individual doctor plays a smaller part in the totality of medical activity, but the available remedies and techniques are ever more potent. One of the family, James LeFanu, has dared to look ahead[50], and sees both promise and failure:-

> *Medicine will continue to be a powerful and immensely successful enterprise, ameliorating the chronic diseases associated with ageing and, where possible saving the lives of the acutely ill. But equally medical discontents are likely to continue. The next surveys will reveal a yet higher proportion of doctors 'with regrets', and a yet higher proportion of the public who are neurotically concerned about their health. Yet more unanticipated hazards of everyday life will be identified and the cost of medical care will continue to spiral upwards.*

He also warns of other dangers within and without the profession, inevitable in those who sail a course of compassion in the uncharted waters between the Scylla of science and the Charybdis of commercial profit. He advises that we formally investigate:-

> *.... how the combination of statistical sophistry and the subterfuge of 'expert' committees has systematically misled the public, and indeed the profession, over the last twenty years. It will not be easy to admit that much current medical advice is quackery, but it must be done.*

For all the 'statistical sophistry' that surrounded the introduction of the laser, Jane and her colleagues now realise that it has its own peculiar hazards and disadvantages, and may not be the great technical advance that it once seemed. And the humble medicinal leech, so useful to William Daniel and his contemporaries is now returning to favour after its years in the wilderness of medical quackery. At the height of its popularity in the

1800s, more than 30 million of them were sacrificed every year in France alone[51] in erroneous attempts to save their human masters. The doctors who applied leeches by the dozen did not then know the complex chemistry of this creature which has evolved the ability to make an anticoagulant to prevent its bloody meal from clotting, a vasodilator to increase the flow of blood, an anaesthetic to render its bite painless, and a dispersal agent to spread them quickly through its victim's tissues. The future of the medicinal leech is looking bright again, for it is now being used to reduce troublesome swelling after some kinds of plastic surgery. In the light of modern knowledge researchers have focussed their attention on this humble creature, in the hope that it will provide answers to a variety of problems like arthritis, and lead to new discoveries in pharmacology[52].

Sir John said that 'the life of a medical man is that of an everyday student; the term of study and observation is being constantly exemplified'[53]. We have discovered much in the last hundred years, but there will be plenty left for our successors to learn. One lesson is that while we need the power of governments to implement health-promoting policies, as doctors we must still care for our patients as unique individuals. And we should remember that the main road to good health lies as much through the actions of ordinary people and the societies they live in as it does in the deeds of doctors.

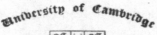

University of Cambridge

Know all men by these presents that

Maurice Sydney Moore
M. D., Dublin.

having been duly examined by the Examiners in that behalf appointed by the CHANCELLOR MASTERS and SCHOLARS of the **University of Cambridge** and having approved himself to the Examiners by his KNOWLEDGE and SKILL in SANITARY SCIENCE to wit in Chemistry and Physics in the causes and prevention of Epidemic and Infectious Diseases and in the means of remedying or ameliorating those Circumstances and Conditions of life which are known to be injurious to health as well as in the Laws of the Realm relating to Public Health is CERTIFIED to be well qualified in respect of his Knowledge and Skill aforesaid to fulfil the Duties of a **Medical Officer of Health** IN TESTIMONY whereof the VICE-CHANCELLOR of the said UNIVERSITY by the authority of the said CHANCELLOR MASTERS and SCHOLARS has hereto set his Hand and Seal the *third* day of *May* one thousand nine hundred and twenty-*two*.

E. Pearce Vice-Chancellor.

H. J. Kynan Registrary of the University.

Parchment awarded to Maurice Moore in 1922.

CORNER·OF·BUTCHER·ROW

Butcher Row, Shrewsbury in 1905. Richard's surgery was in the
Abbot's House, the building on the right of the picture. From 'Shrewsbury,
A historical and topographical account of the town', Thomas Auden,
illustrated by Katherine M. Roberts.
(Shropshire County Library)

CHAPTER ELEVEN

General Practice – The Past Revisited

...that such a medical man may be a very useful person,
we do not mean to deny, but...
The Medical Press[1]

My brother John and I followed our family's footsteps into the medical profession expecting to treat patients, but with little thought how we would do so. John started at Magdalen College Oxford in 1945, moving to Guy's Hospital London for clinical studies. Three years later I went up to Corpus Christi College Cambridge. At the time entry to that prestigious university was simple; all that was required was a letter of application to Dr George Carter, the admissions tutor, which resulted in an interview with port and dessert in his rooms after dinner in Hall .... and the little matter of passing the First MB examination. My clinical studies were done at the London Hospital in Whitechapel. After qualifying we both joined the Navy for our compulsory National Service, though whatever else this experience offered it did nothing for postgraduate development.

Neither I nor John, on his own admission, had been distinguished students and were unlikely to complete the long road to consultant status, so general practice seemed the natural course. John took a post in Reading as a trainee–assistant, a kind of appointment that usually made more of the assistance than the training, and later joined the practice as a partner. I spent a short time as an Assistant Medical Officer of Health but found the job I was assigned to in infant welfare and school clinics bore no resemblance to the pioneering preventive work of my family predecessors.

I received no training or advice on constructing a career in that field, and the future there seemed barren. I therefore determined to regain some clinical experience before looking for a practice. I hoped to do this in a hospital under supervision, but the job I held was inappropriate, consultant support was minimal, and facilities for study or learning were non-existent. I considered looking for a practice in a post-war New Town, thinking that working a displaced and disorganised community would be a valuable service, and in a short-lived moment of altruism wondered if I had a calling to an older deprived area. Eventually, whether from pragmatic desire that my family should live in a congenial place, or an atavistic search for practice like that of my forebears, I found a partnership in Shrewsbury, an ancient town with good medical services, educational opportunities for my family, and in a beautiful part of the country remote from the hurly-burly of big cities.

Alas, I was totally unprepared for it. Until very recently there has been a lack of career guidance and proper training for general practice, and thousands of doctors have entered the profession as haphazardly as John and I did in the 1950s and 60s. My only undergraduate medical experience outside a hospital was to accompany Dr (later Sir) John Ellis on a domiciliary visit to an elderly man struggling to live in a cold, dilapidated house surrounded by acres of bombed-out ruins. This brought home to me very forcibly that people are ill where they live, not just in hospitals, and the challenge intrigued me. But Cambridge University and the London Hospital Medical College failed to teach me the skills necessary for general practice, and GPs then often had no access to the modern medical techniques of laboratory or radiological investigations. Before finding a partnership I had done some locum work, and had seen how the expectations of doctors were diminished by lack of equipment and facilities, unsatisfactory organisation of their practices and lack of reward for initiative. One surgery was in the doctor's house, where patients waited in the hall. Little equipment was available, nor resources for investigation, and the single handed doctor felt quite capable, for instance, of diagnosing anaemia by the colour of the patient's face and considered further tests unnecessary. Subsequent management was therefore erratic, like his use of the newly introduced medicine cobalamin as a general 'tonic', though it is only of value in one uncommon form of anaemia. In another practice the waiting room at the branch surgery was barely heated, and often the patients waiting on hard benches for the benefit of my opinion, or more realistically for a sick note or a tonic, were hidden by the dense miasm arising from their clothing and the puddled floor. There was an examination couch in the consulting room, but no incentive to lie unclothed upon it. The main surgery was rather better, with an auriscope and a burnt-out steriliser, and patient records were available but unhelpful. In a rural practice in Lincolnshire, which I visited as a candidate for partnership, one of the doctors was very proud of his surgery, newly converted from the stable block of his substantial house. The consulting room even had a separate examination room, formerly a loose-box. The straw and hay had been removed, but no further adaptation for its new role seemed to have been made. The offer of partnership was declined, and it was all too apparent that the revelations of Collings and Hatfield described in chapter ten were true.

Hope triumphed over experience, however, and youthful naivety led me to believe that while general practice was clearly not perfect I might be able to offer a service that was rewarding to both me and my patients. I became one of three partners looking after 9,500 patients, based in a 500 year-old 'black-and-white' half-timbered building in the centre of the mediaeval town of Shrewsbury. The surgery was on the first floor, and the only ancillary staff was one part-time receptionist. Such equipment as we had could mostly be contained in a doctor's bag, apart from that for obstetrics which was kept in another. By the standards of the 1960s it was a forward-looking group practice, and the financial prospects seemed rosy even though it would take six years to achieve an equal share of the profits, which was quite usual then. I set about trying to become that difficult thing, 'an able general practitioner', but soon discovered that general practice is also a business requiring many different skills which I did not then possess. It was necessary to develop working relationships with partners and personnel, as well as knowledge and skills in management, accounting, budgeting and planning. No attention had been paid to such mundane but fundamental matters in preparation for my life's work, and my new partners lacked these vital qualities, too. Change was therefore slow, and further hindered by the low expectations implicit in the NHS terms of service.

After education at a teaching hospital with specialist resources of laboratory, radiology, and supporting disciplines, I found myself wandering in a world of tonics and placebos more reminiscent of the nineteenth than the twentieth century. Many of the medicines and attitudes would have been familiar to my predecessor GP and great-grandfather William Daniel. Almost all the work was demand-led. Patients would arrive before a surgery session, queuing in the street if they arrived before our part-time receptionist. When the door had been opened and their names recorded they would take their turn to be seen, in order of arrival. Missing the start of the queue by two minutes might mean a wait of an hour or more, and arriving late might preclude admission altogether. When patients eventually reached the doctor consultations were rushed, overshadowed in the doctor's mind by the knowledge that there were others waiting with resigned acceptance of the antiquated and unfriendly system.

What puzzled me most was the variety of complaints which could not be fitted into the pattern of presentations I had learned about at medical school. What did it mean when they said 'Doctor, I think I need a tonic', or 'I was in my two doubles'? The problem was even worse at the branch surgery, a pre-war device for attracting patients in an expanding suburb, where there were no records, and no facilities other than what we carried in our bags. Therapeutic options were primitive apart from antibiotics, expected by patients and all too easily prescribed for common but self-limiting infections, a selection of barbiturates as sedatives or hypnotics soon to be replaced by the new tranquillisers, and a few other medicines such as digitalis and thyroid extract. The popular tonics contained bromide and strychnine, with optional phenobarbitone, and the linctuses and mixtures involved mysterious substances like Syrup of Tolu and Pulv Tragacanth, relics of a bygone age. Prescriptions were written in a complex system of scruples, drachms and ounces, and the doses were directed to be measured by the patient in tea-spoons, tablespoons and wine-glasses of widely varying capacity. Even if the medicine contained a powerful agent little heed was taken of side effects or interactions, and, alas, scant check was made how, or even whether, they were used.

Communication with patients was not good. Few people expected to understand the nature of their illnesses, and some information such as the level of blood pressure or a diagnosis of cancer or tuberculosis was

considered too frightening to mention. On visiting one patient with terminal cancer I was taken aside by his wife to be told in urgent tones that
her husband 'must never know' that he had cancer. When we went to his
bedside his first remark was 'tell me, doctor, exactly what is wrong with
me?'. The dilemma was awkward, but I chose to tell him the truth, as
gently as I could. The attitude that 'doctor knows best' made life simple,
but engendered complacency. Each of the partners had his own list, only
seeing another's patients during absences. While this encouraged close
relationships with patients, it also inhibited communication between
doctors on matters of clinical or practical interest and prevented proper
accountability to each other and to the patients. This increased the sense
of isolation, all the more so because there was very little contact with
colleagues in other practices, and no facilities for meetings or exchange
of ideas.

This pattern of working was patronising and time-wasting to both
patients and doctors, and the inflexible schedule made it difficult to
accommodate other obligations. Clearly a system of appointments was
needed, but to make the change was far from easy. It needed more tele-
phones, and staff present throughout the day to answer the calls, and
the expenses of new equipment, printing and information. It was also
necessary to argue its benefits with my partners and patients, and to get
the consent of the NHS bureaucracy which had no precedent for such a
startling innovation. When the system was eventually introduced the effi-
ciency and convenience of the practice undoubtedly improved, but we
were unable to recover the cost either by reimbursement from the NHS
or from an increase in practice income. It was clear that improving the
practice's facilities was not financial good sense. The inherent perversity
of the system discouraged development and originality in everything from
maintenance and decoration of premises to staffing, equipment and
working methods.

When medicine was nationalised in Britain by creating the National
Health Service in 1948, many general practitioners were glad that the
burden of keeping accounts had been lifted, but why should the cost of
medical care not be counted by those who provide it? Keeping accounts
is not synonymous with running an efficient organisation, but it does help
to reveal its strengths and weaknesses. Perhaps it was too redolent of the

taint of 'trade' that the profession had shrugged off in the nineteenth century, and an attitude prevailed that doctors need not be concerned with financial matters or effective management. So, ignoring such diversions, I concentrated on the medical aspects of the job and found a satisfaction that deepened as I grew more confident. After the initial bewilderment at what I was supposed to be doing I came to a three-fold view of my role: first, to accept and define the problems that patients brought to me, whether they were physical, psychological or even non-medical; second, to resolve those that I could or refer those that I could not to the appropriate specialist; and third, to help those patients for whom there was no cure to tolerate their illnesses or problems, for however long that might be necessary. Experience was my teacher, for the academic discipline of primary care was only just beginning, and little help was to be found in books.

My lack of training was soon exposed. At medical school I learned to think in ordered sequence of 'history, examination, investigation, diagnosis and treatment', but my new patients in the rushed surgeries did not behave so conveniently. I found myself dealing with what seemed to be a jumble of everyday maladies and misfortunes among which there might be hidden the first symptoms of serious disease. The general practitioner has been described as a specialist in the beginnings of disease[2], and must therefore sometimes deal with situations where the problem is actually the suspicion or fear of disease rather than the disease itself. Helping people to cope with such fears is a valuable if inconspicuous service, whether or not those fears are well founded.

'From cradle to grave' is a cliché of the health service but a reality for the general practitioner, who is concerned with people of all ages, from Shakespeare's 'muling, puking infant', to 'the schoolboy with shining morning face', and 'the second childishness, and mere oblivion, sans teeth, ... sans everything'[3]. Variety of people, of situation, of challenge, and of medical content are all features that make being a family doctor a fascinating if demanding career for those who feel drawn to it. Others with different expectations may find it dull, trivial or below their intellectual level. That was not my experience, which was one of feeling privileged to serve those who sought my help, and interest in human nature and the variety of its responses to challenge. I found a satisfaction akin to that of gardening, that most satisfying of pastimes, where the seemingly tedious ground-work of preparation and cultivation is rewarded by the blooming of flowers and harvesting of crops. Similarly, the way a doctor organises the facilities and trains the surgery staff to respond to the patients' problems all affect the way their problems are presented in future. The building of an effective relationship is the groundwork which facilitates a successful resolution of problems.

In the early years my two partners and I covered all demands on our practice for 365 days a year, including domiciliary obstetrics (twenty-five to thirty births a year), and night and week-end calls, allowing ourselves three weeks holiday and a half-day off once a week. We did three surgeries and ten or twelve home visits on most days, and all did a surgery on Saturday mornings. This did not seem arduous because in the 1960s such commitments were usual. Many visits would be to see children with the usual infections, when understandably the parents would be anxious, especially in cases of measles and whooping cough. They remembered their own childhood when such diseases were common, often with serious outcomes though thankfully not as serious as they had been a hundred years before. There were no cures, but it was important to assess each patient, and take appropriate action where necessary. These visits were opportunities for education and forming a trusting relationship. Sometimes a case was linked to others, as when an elderly lady with shingles was the grandmother of a child seen the previous week with chickenpox, from whom she caught the shingles – a troublesome and painful disease for the elderly before anti-viral medication was available. The person looking after them both would be the mother of one and the daughter of the other. This is the notion of the 'family doctor', typified by one family in which five generations were on my list at the same time. The oldest was a lady of ninety, and the youngest her new-born great-grandchild. Increasing dependency and degenerative problems in the oldest lady, and arthritis and chronic bronchitis in her daughter, herself a grandmother, all needed attention. The mother whose elderly relatives depended on her needed support, while her own daughter and son-in-law suffered the physical and psychological stresses of work and home. When one of the family was terminally ill they all grieved. As each generation grew older, I began to do for one generation what I had done for the previous one. While the family doctor cannot do everything, he or she is often the only person who sees them all and is the link with other helpers.

Care in general practice is continuous, perhaps life-long, even if cure seems impossible at the time. Many problems begin with minor symptoms, and while it is often tedious to be consulted about trivialities, as the 'specialist in the beginning of disease' the family doctor has to look for suspicious signs that might reveal a more serious condition. When does a baby with diarrhoea need to be investigated? Will it settle or is it the start of a long and serious illness like cystic fibrosis? If it is serious, how can we best help the young patient and his or her family? And if in the present state of knowledge there is no cure, how can we hold on until future research brings hope of relief by new methods like transplant surgery or dialysis?

Some people seem to attend the surgery or demand a visit simply to make use of the state's free service. Others, having been investigated and found to have no serious disease, continue to appear with a variety of complaints, requesting a 'tonic' or sleeping pills. Doctors often find their hearts sinking when such patients appear, but these people may have problems just as troublesome as those with a clearer diagnosis. Psychiatrists, and dermatologists, too, used to employ almost Galenic terms such as 'involutional melancholia', or make diagnoses or write prescriptions in doggerel Latin. Their patients might spend months in hospital or out-patients with little or no improvement, and would then be returned to their general practitioner for what was euphemistically called 'continuing care'. One lady who had been in a psychiatric hospital used to ask why I kept black snakes in the waiting room, and during consultations would suddenly 'see' a snake which had evidently followed her into my consulting room, which I believed to be reptile-free (my confidence in the absence of wild-life was shaken when a real mouse appeared in one consultation soon after I had seen this lady). She hated all things male, including me and even her infant grandson, but when given enough time she unfolded a story of childhood abuse by her father and his 'friends' fifty years before. It was too late to remedy the consequences, but with sympathetic non-confrontational listening punctuated by occasional threats of violence on her part, she gradually regained some of the self-esteem which had eluded her for years. Christmas presents from such people, given with varying amounts of gruffness or gratitude, are a generous acknowledgement of the value of time spent on their behalf.

Sudden illness can present challenges, none more so than a heart attack. In my student days such patients were put to bed for six weeks and led to expect another, possibly fatal, attack. At one time there was a vogue for treatment at home, at another hospital admission for anti-coagulants was recommended. Later there were special Coronary Care Units, life-support machines and clot-busting drugs. But heartache may have causes other than physical disease. The stresses of life, such as marriage, divorce, moving house, unemployment and changing jobs can all produce symptoms that are just as real as those with a physical cause. When a person goes to a doctor, symptoms must be investigated sufficiently thoroughly to exclude serious disease. But what if that risks adding to the burden of stress? It may not help a person whose heart is aching for the loss of a loved one, or the threat of unemployment, to be admitted to hospital at the critical moment. More than once I judged that a patient with symptoms suggestive of a heart attack would be better if he stayed away from Coronary Care. Such a decision taken on my own would have been arrogant and foolish, but if the patient chooses to remain at home after a full discussion of the situation, that is probably the right course of action. But it is a worry to the doctor, for the consequences of error are serious for both parties.

While I experienced the stresses of both clinical and organisational problems there were diverting moments too. One dismal November day I visited a house where I was not known, and while waiting to be admitted I noticed on the doorstep a sample packet of detergent with a plastic tulip attached to it. The incongruity of tulips in November amused me, so I picked it up and handed it to the woman who opened the door. I gathered from her immediate and colourfully-worded response that hawkers were not welcome, and when the door was slammed in my face I had to eat humble pie, ring again and explain that I belonged to a more respectable profession than door-to-door salesman. On another occasion, a teenage boy from a jovial but somewhat disorganised family living in a council house developed abdominal pain which might have been appendicitis, and was admitted to hospital. It turned out that he had a form of gastro-enteritis due to a most unusual germ. The microbiologist telephoned to say that the organism they had found is common in monkeys but not in humans, and was there a monkey in the house? Indeed there was, so to complete the diagnosis of this interesting case I re-visited the house to take a swab from the monkey's rectum. Having recruited five members of the family to hold the animal's head and limbs to protect me from the monkey's anticipated self-defences, I approached the business end of my simian friend. As soon as he felt his sensitive parts being investigated he wrapped his prehensile tail around my arm in a vice-like grip, locking the swab inextricably in place. The source of my patient's illness was proved, and I discovered how monkeys have the strength to swing from trees.

After a few years I began to feel I was doing the job with some degree of success, finding experience to be a great teacher. The inadequate preparation and lack of experience of newcomers to practice had long been recognised by some leaders of the profession, but a remedy was slow in coming. A leading article in the BMJ in 1950 said 'It is infinitely harder to be an able general practitioner than to be an able specialist'[4], yet it was commonplace for doctors to 'drift into practice'[5]. In a 'snapshot review'[6] carried out by the *BMJ* in 1951, one doctor was appalled to see 'the mistakes, sometimes fatal, made by such inexperienced people', and another said:-

> *Great damage has been done to the reputation of general practitioners by the ease with which anyone can enter practice without special qualification or experience except a simple medical qualification.*

For a hundred years before these comments were made, half of all medical graduates became general practitioners yet preparation for this work almost never featured in the curriculum of medical schools. It was often derided by teachers, and by implication was dismissed as unworthy of a place in the curriculum. About 1970 some medical schools began to include general practitioners in their teaching staffs to offer glimpses of their work to students, although St Mary's Hospital London began doing so twenty years earlier[7]. But doctors could still find employment in general practice whatever their level of competence, and if their standards were low questions were rarely asked. Even in 1975, a quarter of a century after these warnings, Dr (later Sir) Donald Irvine, then chairman of the Royal College of General Practitioners (RCGP) and subsequently chairman of the General Medical Council, had to insist that general practice was a medical discipline in its own right[8] and the RCGP had the same responsibility as other medical Royal Colleges to set and maintain professional standards. It was not to be seen as a 'fall-back' option:-

We must make it clear to other specialties that we are no longer prepared to be the dustbin of medicine.

As recently as 1980 in Britain it was even possible to pass the final MB examination, and become a GP without any special training or experience other than the one compulsory year in hospital as a house officer. Even today an attitude prevails that general practice is an escape route from hospital medicine, young doctors seeing themselves as possibly 'falling back' on it or 'entering it by default'[9]. As late as 1999 one GP teacher was moved to protest that 'general practice should no longer be tolerated as the easy option'[10].

The roots of this deficiency of education go back to the early years of the nineteenth century. General practice is the archetype of medical work and existed long before the increase in scientific knowledge created the need for specialists, so when special interests began to emerge during the nineteenth century general practitioners also came to see themselves as a distinct group who needed appropriate education and mutual support[11]. This was the period when Daniel and his son William, along with their fellow apothecaries and shopkeepers, founded the Dublin school for general practitioners. By the 1840s general practitioners in England, as in Ireland, were demanding their own educational system in a proposed 'Royal College of General Practitioners'[12]. The profession had become fragmented into specialists and others, but in trying to re-establish a collective identity it failed to include those doctors who had little influence in the medical Royal Colleges because they were working on their own rather than in hospitals. A new organisation called the National Association of General Practitioners was formed to establish the right of general practitioners to govern and educate themselves in the same way as physicians and surgeons[13,14]. Representations were made to the Home Secretary that a college should be founded, with bold aspirations such as the following in 1845:-

> *It would prove to the best interests of the public generally, and most conducive to the advancement of medical science, and be also a measure most serviceable to the profession, if the general practitioners were to be incorporated by charter into an independent college, with a governing council, power to frame bylaws and provide for the future education of the general practitioner, and placed as respects the management of their own affairs in every respect on a footing of equality with the existing colleges of physicians and surgeons.*

Unfortunately the attempts to obtain a charter of incorporation failed, largely due to the difficulties in recruiting enough support from widely scattered practitioners. The movement to create a College of General Practitioners equal in status to the Surgeons and Physicians faltered, and general practice failed to be recognised as an independent discipline with its own teachers and representative organisation. The very idea that it should have one continued to be scathingly received in some places, with comments like:-

> *Now, that such a medical man of all work [a general practitioner] may be, and in many cases is, a very useful person, we do not mean to deny, but that he is to be substituted for the present Physicians and Surgeons directly or indirectly, we cannot admit[15].*

The new medical schools which were being founded in association with hospitals were dominated by specialists, and general practice found no place in the curriculum. Since then medical journals have often warned of the poor prospects for the general practitioner, in comments like this[16] from *the Medical Press* just before the 1911 National Insurance Act:-

> *It is not to be wondered at that [a father] declares that, although he has the greatest admiration for many country doctors, some of whom are leading truly heroic lives, he would be very sorry to see a son of his start with a view to becoming a country G.P.*

Half way through the twentieth century it could still be said that:-

Even before the [NHS] Act the lot of the general practitioner was not too happy, and today it is demoralising. We do not refer to overwork, rather to the fact that he seems destined to a professional life that does not offer the necessary facilities to practice good medicine and which fails utterly to offer the normal incentives which lead to the continual growth of a physician[17].

The Collings and Hatfield reports had warned of the defects of the system. What was to be done? General practice had been the Cinderella of the profession for so long that no one knew about the failure to create its own college a hundred years before. A new movement arose among leading GPs, notably John Hunt and Fraser Rose. They gathered evidence from colleagues in support of an academic home for general practice, which would offer leadership, influence undergraduate and postgraduate education, advise on policy and promote research[18]. It would set standards, improve quality, offer a postgraduate diploma and thereby 'improve the status and prestige of practitioners' – almost a paraphrase of the aspirations of 1845. As a result of the energy and enthusiasm of these pioneers, the College of General Practitioners was successfully founded in 1952, and twenty years later received the honour and grant of a Royal Charter[19]. Now the Royal College of General Practitioners, it has had a far-reaching impact not only in Britain, but throughout the world, by entrusting basic and continuing education for general practice to those who practise and develop it, and has at last established it as a medical discipline in its own right. It is a tragedy that this was not achieved before, despite the efforts of those who tried to do so in both England and Ireland.

Though it took several years for the young college to establish itself, an early task was to determine what GPs do and how they should be educated for their responsibilities, and in 1977 a Working Party reported on educational needs. The report, entitled *The Future General Practitioner*[20], at last provided a job definition, which I was glad to see accorded with my own ideas.

The general practitioner is a doctor who provides personal, primary and continuing *care to individuals and families [added emphasis].*

But if education was the key to progress, facilities for it in places such as Shrewsbury were non-existent. There were friendly relations between GPs and consultants in which some useful tips might be passed down, and once a year there was a grand meeting between the local branch of the British Medical Association and the hospital Consultants' Club. This, of course, echoed the top-down orientation of the teaching hospitals and was an opportunity for consultants to show their superiority to those 'useful persons', the general practitioners. Clearly what was needed was a place where all doctors could meet on equal terms, with a library and facilities for lectures and seminars. One day in 1963 I happened to mention this to a consultant colleague in the course of conversation, and found myself recruited as secretary to a committee whose remit was to create just such a place. My remark had coincided with a movement from the Regional Board to promote local postgraduate educational facilities, and the person to whom I had spoken had just been appointed as the local postgraduate tutor with £5000 available to build and equip an educational centre. We managed to fire the enthusiasm of nearly all the hospital staff and GPs in the area and raised a further £10,000, and the Board was so impressed by this, or perhaps by the financial reality of what had become a sizeable project, that it found a little more money which enabled us to add some refinements, and to spend another £800 on books for the library.

The outcome was a place for educational meetings, the audio-visual equipment necessary for modern teaching methods, and a meeting place for doctors of all disciplines on equal terms, as the original attempts to found a college for GPs has envisaged. This equality of status helped to overcome the fragmentation of medicine into hospital doctors and others, and to develop a better mutual understanding of our respective roles in the medical care of our local population. In retrospect it seems extraordinary that so many doctors working for the same health service in the same area had no place to meet and no collective facilities for continuing education, let alone any kind of library or reference system.

The new Shrewsbury Medical Institute enabled me and my colleagues to become more like my grandfather's 'everyday student'. I was often reminded of my first tutorial at Cambridge, in which we were left in no doubt that the more we learned, the more we would discover how much else there was to learn, and with local facilities for continuing education I became even more aware of the inadequacy of my own knowledge. And if I had come to the job unprepared, what of those doctors then just entering practice who still lacked opportunities to learn the necessary skills? By the late 1970s the Royal College of General Practitioners had won the argument for both undergraduate and post-graduate education for practice, and funding had been provided for jobs to provide both hospital and general practice experience, and for teachers and courses related to general practice. When a vacancy occurred for someone to organise such a course in Shrewsbury I readily applied, thinking that if I could organise local education for new doctors I might learn something myself. I was dubious of my academic credentials, but such was the rush of applications that I found myself appointed from a shortlist of one compiled from the only application. Devising a curriculum and running the course was a valuable experience, for it enabled me to examine the nature and quality of my work in depth, and discover something of my strengths and weaknesses. I like to think that the trainees, or registrars as they are now called, also enjoyed it and learned something. Certainly, the assessment forms they completed after each session showed a high level of satisfaction, but whether anything was learned remained unproved. One registrar, who later became a colleague, admitted in a light-hearted moment that I had taught him everything he knew, but later amended this to my having taught him everything *I* knew. Another, when introducing me to his wife some years later, told her that I was 'the man with the woolly waistcoat'. I did actually have such a garment, so clearly I had created some lasting impressions.

Involvement in teaching in this way, as well as in our own practice which had itself been approved for teaching, led to my becoming an examiner for the membership examination of the RCGP. The examination had been started in 1965, and by the 1990s more than two thousand candidates were sitting it every year, making it one of the largest post-graduate medical examinations in the world. There was a little difficulty to my becoming an examiner, however, because the rules very reasonably required that examiners must have passed the examination themselves. I had not done so, because I joined the College before the examination was introduced, so I would have to sit it if I wished to proceed, and expose myself to the risk of failing the very examination I was teaching others to take. Either by bluff or brilliance, I passed. In becoming an examiner I joined a group of energetic and well informed colleagues, and was able to break down further the professional isolation which many GPs feel. The intellectual challenge of constructing discriminating questions and marking them fairly was a formidable stimulus to raise my own standards.

I was surprised and felt very privileged to be elected to Fellowship of the RCGP in the spring of 1981, which I took to be an acknowledgement of my efforts to promote good general practice in my locality. Like the other medical Royal Colleges at the time the RCGP elected its fellows according to rather imprecise criteria which included personal achievement, seniority, and a high profile in medical politics or on the old boys' network. Such methods of election may not be entirely equitable because able but deserving people can be overlooked, and does not reflect the quality of the doctors' actual practice. To overcome this defect the RCGP developed a system called Fellowship by Assessment (FBA), by which members may volunteer for their performance in practice to be peer-assessed according to published rules. Sixty criteria were identified as characterising a good general practitioner, and a process of documentation and practice visits was devised to ensure that candidates achieved them all. Members of the College of five years standing may apply to be assessed, and successful candidates are proposed for fellowship of the college, thus publicly acknowledging the quality of their work. The criteria are very stringent and updated annually, and may take two years or more to achieve. As a fellow myself, though not by this route, I became an assessor, and was privileged to visit many candidates and their practices. I was greatly impressed with standards they achieved, which were far higher than anything I had ever done, and incomparably better than those which used to be accepted as satisfactory twenty five years earlier. I was particularly pleased and proud that one of the earliest doctors to achieve such Fellowship was an eighth generation Moore, my son James, who by now was a GP in Cornwall.

In FBA the College has at last devised a system which describes the essentials of good general practice, and can measure the performance of doctors accordingly. So far two hundred and forty members have been assessed in this way and elected to Fellowship, which is a credit to their dedication and enthusiasm, though this number is less than one percent of all general practitioners in Britain. There is, however, a significant omission from this process of quality control, which is that candidates who have gone to all the trouble and expense of improving their practices to the standard required, receive no reward other than the altruistic satisfaction of doing so and recognition of it by their peers. Yet long ago the College perceived the need to encourage high standards, and in a Policy Statement[21] regretted that ' ... remunerating NHS general practitioners is out of step with the needs of patient care. There is no obvious link between remuneration and performance'. It then proposed a remedy for this deficiency of incentive:-

One option would be for a new and substantial allowance for performance review to be built into the general practitioners' contracts, to be continued throughout their professional lives, provided the results of periodic performance reviews were satisfactory.

The FBA process, which uses published and objective criteria, would form an excellent basis for such an allowance, and could be the long-missing incentive to continual progress and improvement. No such allowance has ever been introduced to general practice, though for years NHS consultants have receive awards for merit on unpublished criteria. Recent changes to the terms of service have set targets for performance, and reward achievement of them financially, but they refer to the organisation of practice rather than the clinical care of individual patients. The deficiencies so clearly described by Collings and Hatfield, and often remarked upon in the fifty years since then, remain uncorrected. Targets intended to achieve government policy are no substitute for the 'incentives which lead to the growth of the physician'.

Time and the generations move on, and in 1992, after thirty-one years in the practice, I decided it was time to reduce my work load although I was not ready for complete retirement which would have opened a gaping financial and occupational hole. I resigned from the practice, to take a part-time job in a new venture which relieved me of clinical stresses while maintaining an interest in my profession. Following one of the periodic government re-organisations of the health service it had been decided that GPs should demonstrate how successful (or unsuccessful) they were by a process of audit, though there was still no financial recognition of those who could demonstrate the highest standards. Ten years earlier I had organised a seminar on audit, but though well attended it had no lasting effect. The new job was to fill my erstwhile colleagues with enthusiasm for demonstrating the quality of their performance, but not only did no one know how to do this, they had neither time to do so themselves nor staff to whom they could delegate the task nor money to pay them. A minority of doctors did respond to the challenge, however, and with support from us in the Shropshire Medical Audit Advisory Group (MAAG) and small grants from the health authority, they were able to demonstrate the quality of some aspects of their work. Like audit groups elsewhere we found little evidence of the high standards we had supposed to exist, and plenty of room for improvement. There were diabetic patients whose treatment could be improved, patients on long term medication who did not have the routine tests they should have had, incorrect procedures in cardiac emergencies, and asthma patients who did not understand their medication .... and plenty more. Here was proof of the prediction by the Royal College of Physicians that the funding of general practice by capitation fee, which rewarded poor work as much as the good and offered no incentive to innovation, really was 'injurious to the public and the profession', however much it had been modified since then.

Ten years after I left it the practice in which I used to be a partner is active and progressive, and at the centre of local developments in the new-style primary care, characteristics which I like to think I played a part in developing. While still having to be responsive to the demands of the sick, there is a strong emphasis on the promotion and maintenance of health. There are clinics to prevent, identify or manage high blood pressure, asthma, diabetes, and heart disease, and for cervical cytology and other screening procedures, many of them run by assistants or nurses. Where there were only three doctors and a part time receptionist there are now five doctor-partners, an associate partner, a registrar in training, and other doctors employed part time. It is a million-pound organisation employing over thirty people, with other health authority staff working in co-operation with them. There are more than 30,000 attendances by patients in the course of a year keeping everyone fully occupied .... but the number of people registered with the practice is still 9,700, the same as when I joined it forty years ago.

In its new form of primary care this part of the medical profession is no longer the cottage industry it once was, but an essential sector of an integrated, even industrialised, health care system. It is still based on the principle from which it arose, namely a long term relationship between one doctor and a number of healthy individuals who may at some time become patients. Yet the profession still suffers from tension, stress and dissatisfaction just as it has done for two hundred years, and long before it was nationalised. Even in the twenty-first century the BMA has issued dire warnings such as its 'Dossier' *Crisis in Care*, and its members have voted to resign from the NHS if their contracts are not soon improved. The Royal College of General Practitioners has led the profession in setting and raising standards, but although it informs negotiations and advises government it is not itself a negotiating body. It has an excellent membership examination, yet it is still possible to be an unsupervised practitioner without having to demonstrate a high degree of competence. It remains the only medical discipline whose practitioners are not required to pass the relevant Royal College examination before entering higher professional training[22,23]. But, to its credit, the College has created the Fellowship by Assessment programme which can openly demonstrate and acknowledge the quality of its practitioners' performance.

Since I entered the profession, the growing complexity of general practice has made it even more difficult to be 'an able general practitioner'. No longer is it acceptable to offer pragmatic solutions or placebos: treatments must be justified by scientific evidence for their effectiveness, and costs contained within tight limits. More than ever, that 'very useful person' must be of demonstrable competence, which justifies an adequate reward and a working environment free of unnecessary stress. Attempts to achieve these ends are being made through the revalidation system of the General Medical Council, the continuing education facilities of universities and colleges, and the enthusiasm of its practitioners. Such efforts are sure to evoke the reactionary responses of alarm as they have always done, because change itself is stressful. The future is always uncertain, and never more so than now when knowledge and expectations are increasing so rapidly.

Looking back on the thirty-two years that took my practice from archaic methods in a mediaeval building to the scientifically sound practice based in purpose-built and well-equipped premises, I am tempted to ask myself whether I would do it again. Yes, I would, but would try to do it better. I would learn to do the job before I started. I would listen, understand and learn more; guess less; resist hassle and haste; and take time to discover whether my results were as good as they should be and make changes where necessary. And, while adopting advances in knowledge and techniques, I would strive to retain the old values of primary, personal and continuing care without letting them degenerate into a 'mere assortment of technical skills' as was feared would happen fifty years ago. HRH The Prince of Wales, when President of the RCGP in 1992, reminded us of the danger[24].

It is sometimes said that the only generalist left in the large general hospital is the patient.

How threatening and inhuman it would be if the individual who is sick had no one who knew him or her first and foremost as a person, and who was able to act as a guide and broker to the specialisms of medicine ...

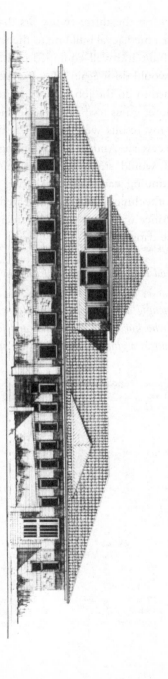

The building constructed for the modern practice.

Abbreviated Genealogy of the Moores and related families

The names of medical practitioners are printed in **bold**

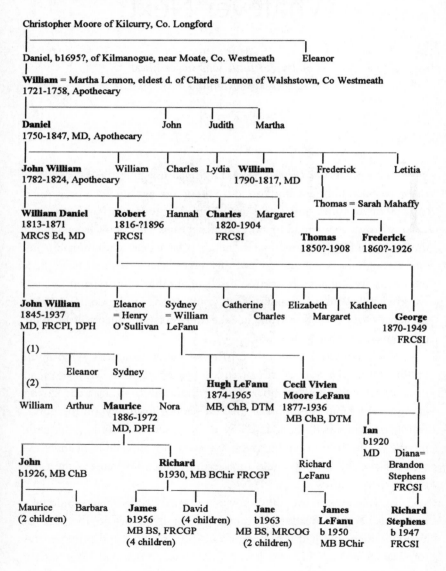

Christopher Moore of Kilcurry, Co. Longford

Daniel, b1695?, of Kilmanogue, near Moate, Co. Westmeath   Eleanor

William = Martha Lennon, eldest d. of Charles Lennon of Walshstown, Co Westmeath
1721-1758, Apothecary

Daniel   John   Judith   Martha
1750-1847, MD, Apothecary

John William   William   Charles   Lydia   **William**   Frederick   Letitia
1782-1824, Apothecary   1790-1817, MD

                                                Thomas = Sarah Mahaffy

William Daniel   **Robert**   Hannah   **Charles**   Margaret
1813-1871   1816-?1896   1820-1904
MRCS Ed, MD   FRCSI   FRCSI   **Thomas**   **Frederick**
                                            1850?-1908   1860?-1926

John William   Eleanor   Sydney   Catherine   Elizabeth   Kathleen
1845-1937   = Henry   = William   Charles   Margaret   **George**
MD, FRCPI, DPH   O'Sullivan   LeFanu   1870-1949
                                                              FRCSI

(1) _____

     Eleanor   Sydney

(2) _____   **Hugh LeFanu**   **Cecil Vivien**
                                           1874-1965   **Moore LeFanu**
William   Arthur   **Maurice**   Nora   MB, ChB, DTM   1877-1936
              1886-1972   MB ChB, DTM
              MD, DPH   **Ian**
                                                                       b1920
                                                                      MD   Diana=

John   **Richard**   Richard   Brandon
b1926, MB ChB   b1930, MB BChir FRCGP   LeFanu   Stephens
                                                                               FRCSI

Maurice   Barbara   **James**   David   **Jane**   **James**   **Richard**
(2 children)   b1956   (4 children)   b1963   **LeFanu**   **Stephens**
                  MB BS, FRCGP   MB BS, MRCOG   b 1950   b 1947
                  (4 children)   (2 children)   MB BChir   FRCSI

CHAPTER TWELVE

Whatever Next?

*The tree of man was never quiet
Then 'twas the Roman, now 'tis I.*
A.E.Housman[1]

I n his poem *On Wenlock Edge,* Housman imagines the trees on that wooded hillside being tossed by the wind, as they have been since Roman times, just as we are troubled now by the same joys and sorrows as warmed or hurt our forebears. This book has sketched the story of a family whose doctor-members have dealt with human troubles throughout two hundred and fifty years. Many of them have died, but seven are still alive to see the dawn of another century, and five are working still. Will generations yet to come choose to be doctors? What challenges will they face from science and society? What will be their problems, and what their rewards?

You are invited to be a fly-on-the-wall at an imaginary symposium on the topic *Whatever Next?*, attended by the medical Moores of all generations. Deceased members were temporarily reincarnated, having glimpsed the rapid evolution of medical science from beyond the grave. All of us, living or dead, were allowed the wisdom of hindsight regarding the events of our own lifetimes[2], but were not allowed to change historical facts, and no one could foresee the future. The time is the early twenty-first century.

As founder of our tradition it was proposed that William should take the chair, but he declined because, having lived before the Age of Enlightenment, he had not mastered modern science, and proposed his son Daniel instead. He was proud that his successor had been such a prominent figure in Dublin's medical heyday, and having come out of one century to contrast it with the next Daniel could surely survey another two hundred years without difficulty.

Daniel was called to chair with acclaim. He welcomed us all to the symposium and invited us to introduce ourselves, which created much excitement and not a little confusion because of the varied styles of dress and speech, and the remarkable family likenesses. Eventually the introductions were completed with the help of name badges hung round our necks like chains of office, an amusing novelty to the older members. After his welcoming remarks Daniel steered the conversation towards a subject in all our minds.... Why had we all been doctors? Was there something in our characters that made us want to be doctors? Could that something be inherited? Who would follow in *our* footsteps?

The members of the family whose remarks are reported are listed below, with their dates. Where names are duplicated the way they are referred to in the text is shown in *italics*.

Moore

William (1721-1758)	Daniel (1750-1847)
John I (1782-1824) *[John I]*	William Daniel (1813-1871)
Charles (1820-1904)	John II (1845-1936) *[Sir John]*
Maurice (1886-1972)	John III (b1927) *[John III]*
Richard (b1930)	James (b1956) *[James M]*
	Jane (b1963)

LeFanu

Hugh (1874-1965)	Cecil (1877-1936)
James (b1950) *[James LeF]*	

William 1

I suppose I must carry the blame, if blame there is. My grandfather's ambition to be a landed gentleman came to nothing, so I was advised to find a decent trade. I had the chance to be an apothecary near home at Ballymahon, which suited me well though I didn't last long!

Daniel

I had no alternative. Orphaned at the age of eight, I was glad to have the shelter of my uncle Clarke and learn the trade with him. My surgical apprenticeship was miserable work in those days, so I was very grateful when he took me into his business.

John I

That business was good for me, too, but like my grandfather I didn't last long.

William Daniel

There wasn't much choice for me either, after you died, father. I was glad to join the business when I was old enough, but we'd have had a thin time if grandfather Daniel hadn't kept the business going. Chemistry fascinated me, but I could see that the apothecary's business was dying, and so I made sure I was a properly qualified medical man.

Sir John

When I was a boy we'd given up the shop, and in those days you started medicine after an Arts degree. I already had a good understanding of science, though it was much more limited then. I was fascinated by meteorology, anyway, so the change wasn't difficult. Maurice, by the time you had to choose how many generations were we?

Maurice

Wait now till I see; six, I think. I was keen on engineering at one time, but when Willy and Arthur decided against medicine I changed my mind because I'd grown used to it with a practice in the house. I was very glad John and Richard made it seven generations, and even more so that there's an eighth in James and Jane.

Some younger people said they had felt an unspoken expectation that they would be doctors, and regretted their lack of independent career advice. Whether through positive decision or lack of alternative, they all felt that in the end medicine had been a good choice.

Daniel

Well then, what is the great attraction of being a doctor?

William Daniel

I enjoyed the intellectual challenge, especially chemistry and how it could be used to make medicines. We were only just beginning to understand it, which was very exciting as it was all so new and different from the classical teaching of the day. We explored new ideas like the real causes of diseases, how they spread, and above all what we can do to help people when they're ill. Our medicines seemed all right at the time, and they were the best we had even if they were rather poisonous. Now, of course, the doctors of our day look like simpletons.

John III

For me the most gratifying part was the trust that patients place in doctors, a kind of extension of the patient's family. Being one of a team of people with different skills widens the opportunities for helping, too, particularly if all its members have the same approach.

Jane

That's true, especially when patients are prepared to confide secrets and private thoughts, because then one can help them tolerate their fears and worries. As doctors we can be part of that process, which isn't the same as curing a disease, but it's the human part that helps patients to get better – 'the bit that's not in the Pharmacopeia'. We use drugs and operations too, of course, but patients need a helping hand to overcome their difficulties. Good communication between doctor and patient gives both an extra healing power.

Daniel

You have the advantage of modern knowledge, Jane. We didn't

understand disease, and couldn't cure it. Customers would read the *Gentleman's Magazine,* come to my shop to buy colchicine for their gout, or tartar emetic for fever, and we would sell it to them. We were there to do what they wanted, though we often pretended it was the other way round. We could advise, but our knowledge was limited, and probably biased by what profit there was in it.

William

Indeed, if you didn't do what the customer wanted he would go somewhere else – though there was little competition in Ballymahon, I'm glad to say!

Maurice

Well that didn't last. Doctors became powerful people, who told their patients what to do. Doctors Orders were strictly obeyed, especially in the Navy.

Jane

Not any more! Patients are the bosses again, and will only take our advice when they understand the reasons behind it, and rightly so. They must choose their own objectives, with our help when necessary, even when it's obvious they need an operation. Consent now has to be properly 'informed', so they must understand what is going on inside and what I'm going to do – though sometimes they don't really want to know.

Sir John

I'm delighted that there's a woman doctor in my family at last, and amazed at the complexity of the operations that you do and the wonderful instruments you use.

Jane

Well, I think women find it easier to talk to a woman about their problems, but some of the older patients, even now, can't believe that *I* am actually going do the operation.

Sir John.

I'm sure you're right, Jane. You may think I'm old-fashioned, and just another stick-in-the-mud Victorian who refused to let women into the profession ....

Richard

Well, none of your daughters read medicine.

Sir John

No, but I didn't stop them. It's wrong to imply that we didn't want women in the profession. You'll recall Miss Sophia Jex-Blake and her campaign for the admission of women to medical degrees in the United Kingdom? Well, when they failed to persuade the authorities in Edinburgh and London to recognise their right to medical education, they came to Ireland. I was one of the Fellows of the College of Physicians who received their delegation, two charming ladies called Miss Pechey and Miss Shove as I remember, and in her book[3] Miss Jex-Blake was kind enough to say they received an 'extremely cordial reception'. The first of the ladies to be examined was actually Eliza Dunbar, and it was I who proposed that her application be accepted, and my friend Dr Grimshaw seconded[4].

Richard

Was it accepted?

Sir John

The voting was equal, but the President's casting vote was in favour, so she took the examination and as she was already MD Zurich, she passed easily.

Jane

So that opened the way for all the others, did it?

Sir John

Not immediately. I'm sorry to say there were still some die-hards in the College who opposed Miss Dunbar's Licence, but they were over-ruled, this time by a majority vote[5].

James M

What about Sophia Jex-Blake, the great campaigner?

Sir John

She came for the next examination, with her friends Miss Atkins and Miss Pechey. I had the pleasure of examining all three of them[6].

John III

And did they pass?

Sir John

Yes, of course, as they were all MDs, too. They were far better than men like Mr Dunne or Mr Corbett, who both failed.

Jane

Well, I'm very grateful to you, and many other women must be too. Half the doctors in Britain and Ireland are women now, so you should be remembered for removing that unfair discrimination. A change for the better, I'm sure.

Daniel

Things are always changing, and it's often hard to know if it really is for the better. We had that long argument with the surgeons who wanted to stop apothecaries treating people and selling them medicines too. Our School for General Practitioners failed, probably because we couldn't see far enough ahead and didn't have the courage of our convictions. Perhaps we should have admitted women!

William Daniel

The Medical Act of 1858 helped, though. The Council of Medical Education wasn't perfect, but it did ensure a proper curriculum. I was pleased to have a hand in that.

Sir John

Yes. It gave us a common identity, but it had its dangers. We could hide behind our status and say 'doctor knows best' even when we didn't. As

Jane said, communication is essential for understanding. If we create barriers we may block that mutual understanding.

John III

I hesitate to criticise my grandfather, but some of the more prominent members of the profession in your day were just about as autocratic as they could be. They thought they were infallible. They say even you seemed pretty autocratic at times!

Sir John

Perhaps I was, John, but we're influenced by the conventions of our own times. I wonder how you and your contemporaries will be seen seventy years after you're dead. Rather antiquated, I expect.

John III

Probably, but if medicine's a single profession, what can doctors do that others can't?

James M

I think a profession's a group of people with a common purpose, a common education and standards of entry, who accept the same ethical principles. And it regulates its own standards of entry and behaviour of its members.

Sir John

I think it's difficult to define a single medical profession, now. In my time there were only physicians and surgeons. Some had particular interests, like the early obstetricians and my friend William Wilde the ophthalmologist. But now there are dozens of specialties, and even sub-specialties. They belong to different professions within a profession, like branches of the same tree.

John III

But how do they differ from other caring professions – midwives, osteopaths, even paramedics now?

Jane

In two ways, I think. First, through the very high criteria for entry, and a curriculum that ensures a common starting point to specialise from – branches of the same tree; and second and perhaps more importantly, in the level of responsibility they are expected to take in matters of life and death.

James M

And a third, which is the privileges they enjoy as a reward for accepting that responsibility, such as the respect of society and an above-average income, though both of those are threatened nowadays. What distinguishes them from others is the title of 'doctor'. 'I'm a doctor' implies that 'you can trust me' – or used to, and that is something we must try to restore.

Daniel

We had three kinds of doctor; physicians and surgeons and apothecaries, an unfortunate and foolish division which we tried to unite. Now you have a single profession, but with so many branches can it be said to have a single purpose, and if so what is it?

With over 650 person-years of experience between us, we debated the purpose of the medical profession. More than a job to earn a living, surely. We thought of several, some affecting the whole community and others only individuals. We were there to promote health and prevent disease, to care for those who were ill and cure them if possible, and when we could not cure we were there to offer support and relief, and in the end to ensure a dignified death. These responsibilities fell on the shoulders of different doctors in various ways, and were not carried by doctors alone. Now that medical care was so complex doctors must belong to teams, and teams within teams, sharing their work with other professionals. Often, but not always, doctors would lead the teams, which could be justified only by their long education and comprehensive understanding of medical science. Science in itself, however, was not enough; compassion, humanity and tolerance were essential too, and these qualities were not exclusive to doctors.

John III

I think we must be wary of too much science, for that may make us too mechanical and materialistic. Medicine's also an Art.

William Daniel

Yes, the science is intriguing, but it's to inform our thinking, not to pull the wool over people's eyes. Our relationship with patients is a human one, so what we offer must be human too.

John III

Could we say that medicine is an art informed by science?

Daniel thought we could all agree to that, and asked us to think about rewards and challenges. Then Ian spoke, for the first time.

Ian

I believe in this generation we've all found medicine a rewarding pro-fession in our various ways, but we should never forget that clinical medicine, that's to say medicine that deals directly with the person, is not dead yet. There'll always be challenges, however much progress we make. For me it was Occupational Medicine, the effects of earning a living on health. How we work, as well as how we live, is very important.

Sir John

Better housing and education have ended the terrible epidemics, and you can deal with pain and infection now better than we could, but there'll always be accidents and diseases however affluent or hygienic people are. The question is, what will these diseases be?

Maurice

In our family we expect to live to our eighties, and (nodding at Daniel) some have nearly reached a hundred, but now everyone expects to live that long – a quarter of their lives in retirement. A lot more clinical work will be with the elderly.

James M

I've never experienced an epidemic, except perhaps influenza. Most of my work now is with arthritis, dementia and degenerative conditions. There's much more terminal care for cancer and heart failure than there used to be, too. Doctors can't do all this themselves, but must co-operate with others professions, care workers in nursing homes and so on.

Jane

I find being in a multi-disciplinary team very satisfying. It helps to bring doctors down from the pedestals (I nearly said pedicles!).

At this point Charles and his great-nephews, Hugh and Cecil LeFanu, who all practised medicine overseas, entered the discussion.

Charles

That's very important – doctors can't be effective alone. We must edu-cate people about disease, especially those with influence. It took years for authorities to do something about the poverty that breeds diseases like TB and typhus. We must prevent poverty, and understand what keeps us healthy and well-nourished, too. You know, a hundred and thirty years after Lind discovered the values of fresh vegetables there were still seamen coming to Belfast in local ships who were dying of scurvy. We're sometimes very slow to learn our lessons.

Hugh LeFanu

You're talking about Europe. In Africa people are so poor they simply can't afford health care. A baby born in Sierra Leone will only live half as long as one in Europe, largely because of infectious disease. As for ageing, you'd be lucky to get to old age in Africa.

Cecil LeFanu

Yes, Hugh, but people do. When you and I were in the Gold Coast there were only a billion people in the whole world. Soon there'll be nearly that many over the age of 65, even in poor countries where the pittance people have won't be nearly enough for proper health care.

Maurice

How much doctors can do depends on the prosperity of their country, and what it can afford to spend on health.

Sir John

What is 'spending on health'? It's not just the cost of hospitals and medicines. How people live affects it. Mortality in the poor is still three times higher than the rich. In lung cancer and suicide, the difference is even more. Social conditions must improve, and that's up to governments to take the lead.

Ian

And working conditions. Industrial disease and accidents still cause too much death and disability, and are a major contribution to stress.

William Daniel

It's curious how diseases vary at different times. At one time scarlet fever wasn't serious, then it became a killer, but now you hardly bother with it, even though you've got that miracle penicillin.

Richard

But we have new epidemics like HIV-AIDS, and less common but deadly things like Lassa fever and Ebola. We have no answers to Multiple Sclerosis or Motor Neurone Disease, nor to many cancers, though we pretend we have. And what we've gained we risk losing by misuse. We've created a whole new kind of pathology from the side effects and interactions.

William Daniel

Oh, but since medicine became a science treatments seem nothing short of miraculous. What do people think are the most important developments of scientific medicine, I wonder ? Obviously there are anaesthesia and antibiotics.

Daniel

James LeFanu, you have written a good deal about that.

James LeF

Well, yes, a bit[7]. First of all there's cortisone and its derivatives, used by every specialty. Over two hundred conditions that were hopeless are now treatable. When it was introduced doctors found they could cure diseases they hardly knew existed. It also turned the pharmaceutical companies into a huge research-cum-manufacturing industry, vital to our economy. Secondly, since the Copenhagen polio epidemic, when tracheostomy and ventilation were used on an unprecedented scale, there's intensive care and life support systems, and more adventurous surgery.

Cecil

All well and good, James, but what about the underdeveloped people of the world? They don't need transplant surgery, they've got enough problems with malnutrition and poverty. Don't you think the advanced nations should share their knowledge and wealth with the developing countries? Cortisone doesn't cure AIDS, nor intensive care prevent drought.

Hugh

I agree. An effective programme for AIDS, malaria and TB would be a good start. You know, those three things cause half of all infectious disease in the world: 300 million cases and 5 million deaths a year[8]. And pure drinking water would be an enormous benefit. Then there's climate change. Don't think you're safe in Europe, because with climate change tropical diseases like malaria will come back to temperate zones, and you're not prepared for it. Even now there are 12,000 cases in European travellers every year, many of them fatal.

Sir John

When speculating about weather, Hugh, a few decades is too short a time to know what's happening. A hundred years ago I said there wasn't the slightest scintilla of evidence of climate change, though I'm prepared to admit that I might have been wrong.

Hugh

Well, so should we all!

Richard

Quite apart from our individual mistakes, think of all the drugs that were withdrawn because they did more harm than good. Thalidomide, Opren, phenylbutazone, even aspirin for children. Medicine gets a bad press for that sort of thing.

Hugh

It's not all bad news, though. Polio will soon be abolished, like small-pox. There used to be three hundred thousand cases a year in the world, but in 2001 there were just a few hundred, and soon there'll be none at all if the WHO programme goes well[9]. That'll save 1.5 billion dollars every year for other health priorities, quite apart from the saving of life and health.

Sir John

Governments will have to fund those programmes, but they won't if they think they'll lose votes by raising taxes. If you *can* get government action, that's fine. I always believed we could eliminate smallpox, despite the resistance to vaccination, but you've still got a problem with the MMR vaccine. You have to have public support for prevention.

James LeF

Well, it depends what you mean by prevention. I sometimes think there's too much of it, and gives do-gooders an excuse to boss people about and tell them their illnesses are their own fault.

Charles

Is it bossy to demand proper housing and clean food and water?

James LeF

No, I'm in favour of that, and immunisation for those that want it. Of course we shouldn't allow pollution, but exposure to a little dirt and a touch of infection from time to time strengthens our immunity to more important diseases, like your 'occasional touch of cholera' Charles. If someone with a high cholesterol wants to smoke himself into an early grave why shouldn't he? So long as they know the risks, people should be free to choose. We don't live in a sterile bubble. Anyway I'm by no means certain that the merchants of doom and gloom are right about cholesterol. Bossiness carried too far, I'd say.

James M

Surely, a family with a hereditary disease has a right to know what the risks are. The human genome project looks promising for inherited diseases.

James LeF

Yes, but they, not the bossy government, should decide what to do about it. As for the so-called genetic revolution, I can't see that getting far. In another 50 years we'll still have the same old problems. You can be pretty sure the promises of miracles are mostly propaganda put out by the scientists to keep their research funds flowing, especially from the pharmaceutical companies. They want effective drugs, of course, but they're commercial organisations whose business is profit, not philanthropy.

Jane

I think you're wrong about that. Safe, effective medicines are essential.

Daniel

And remember, James, you can't see far ahead. Fifty years is a long time.

Charles

What about food, nutrition, and pollution? Surely, that's up to government? You can't choose pure food so long as rogues are allowed to sell rubbish. There's too much food poisoning about still, and even new strains of old germs, BSE and so on.

Sir John

That *is* a proper role for government. I agree with both Jameses, though. The profession has to provide unbiased information and impartial advice, so that people can make proper choices about their problems, but it shouldn't come from people with a vested interest, like manufacturers, or governments trying to save money.

James M

There's definitely too much government control. We're just another service industry now, swept along in a tide of consumerism. There's a lot to
be said for a government-funded medical service, but human values and
medical care are too important to be hostages to political fortunes.

James LeF

When the British Health Service began it was very cost effective, providing more services per million pounds of taxpayers money than any
other, but it's been ruined by political interference and incompetent
management. Politicians disdain the solid middle-class virtues of competence based on practical experience. Government's job is to ensure
a prosperous economy, and let the professions run their own shows.

James M

Yes, but modern medicine is expensive, so those who can't pay need
help which only government can organise. The illness of one is a
cost to all, that's been known since Daniel's day, so it's important that
everyone should be healthy, just as it is that everyone should be
properly educated.

Richard

In a tax-funded system medicine becomes a political football, kicked
about to attract votes, but when more resources are needed the voice
of the professions can't be heard over the clamour for spending on
other things.

Jane

Government controls the number of medical students, and therefore
doctors, and by controlling budgets they have allowed dangerously
inadequate staffing levels, which inevitably leads to stress, and doctors
under stress can't deliver high quality care[10]. It is not just long hours,
broken sleep and a rotten social life; senior doctors don't support juniors
trying to learn skills and responsibility, educational opportunities are
rotten, and the clinical facilities are often grotty and inadequate. No
one can work well like that, and in a prosperous nation it is a disgrace

to expect anyone to do so.

Ian

So young people don't apply for medical schools nowadays because they see it isn't all roses and wine, both in Britain and Ireland. They see unhappy doctors, strikes, mass resignations, and early retirement. Now we can do so much more than we could, shouldn't we be happier, not more miserable?

Maurice

The essence of practice is still the same in the relationship between doctors and patients, and yes, much more can be done now. But who is in charge? It seems to be neither the patient nor the doctor, but the state. He who pays the piper calls the tune, but the state's tune isn't always one that doctors want to dance to.

Daniel

Well thank goodness we were in charge of what we did in our shop, and in the Hall, too, where we tried to set standards. We could never persuade government to do anything sensible either, so that's not the only reason doctors are unhappy now.

Richard.

The BMA had an internet poll recently to discover what made doctors unhappy. Thousands of replies from all over the world blamed four things: overwork, loss of control, underpayment and inadequate support.

Charles

It was ever thus!

James LeF

I agree. Doctors should get on with what they are good at, namely diagnosis and treatment, and because life is stressful they must also be a judicious staff for patients to lean on. We could do that if we could only get an efficient and non-intrusive management system free from political incompetence.

Richard

We're discovering at last that you can't fund universally free health care entirely from taxes. The socialist NHS made proper health care available to those who couldn't afford it before. But times change. Higher disposable incomes are now spent on holidays and luxuries. Subsidies on food and tax relief for housing are being stopped, so why subsidise medical care? Britain is the only developed country where everyone expects to get it at the expense of other people.

Daniel

Charles Lucas tried to do it in my time, at least for those who couldn't pay for it, and it failed. We've never actually had it for everyone in Ireland, though I believe it's available to some people.

Richard

I think those who can afford it should take responsibility for their own costs. Modern insurance systems can organise it, and do so in Ireland and Europe. People insure for other unforeseen expenses, even for bereavement when pets die, and it's better than handing your money over to the government. The Treasury spends our money according to political, not medical priorities. The result is under-funding and lack of resources.

James M

And bossy interference from quangos, with torrents of guidelines and directives, and changes that come from the top down instead of from the people who do the work.

Daniel

So, let's take stock. Nowadays you can prevent and cure many diseases, but old scourges have been replaced by new ones. Poverty and ignorance are still major factors in ill-health, and we've missed the World Health Organisation's target of 'Health for All by the year 2000'. Medicine has become a public and political commodity, instead of a private relationship between patient and doctor. Political control distorts priorities and interferes clinically. And the profession is profoundly unhappy.

William

Apart from the bit about 'Health for All by 2000', it's much the same as any time in the last 250 years!

Charles

It was ever thus!

All

So you said!

Daniel

We were drawn into medicine because of family tradition, yet were satisfied with our lot. Will it be the same in future? How should we advise our children and grandchildren if they are thinking of medicine?

Sir John

There's no nobler profession for those who are moved to do something to help their fellow men ......

Jane

Or women!

Sir John

..... or women, indeed, ... but no one should enter the profession simply because of tradition.

Charles

I'd tell them 'never go into medicine for money or comfort'. You might find neither.

William Daniel

A doctor should want to develop personal relationships of some sort, however interested he – or she – may be in science. Anyone whose main motivation is science can find plenty of other work to do.

Richard

The choice of profession used to be easy, law, medicine, the services
and so on, but now there are hundreds of opportunities, and in some
new graduates earn much more than young doctors ever will. In
England a newly qualified doctor is paid £3000 less than the average
for all graduates.

Maurice

Young people should ask themselves what they are looking for. Is it
prosperity for themselves, or service to others?

Ian

Many youngsters now look to business or engineering. They don't
want to deal with human misery and despair all their lives, and prefer
to leave their problems in the office and have the high life-style that
business salaries can buy.

Richard

Why not archaeology, or natural history, or fine arts? What could be
more fascinating than the beautiful things of history or nature? As for science, the world's running out of food and water, so if you want to be
useful what about agricultural science or geology? Its wrong to close your
options too soon; for medicine you have to choose Leaving Certificate
or A-level subjects when you are still a teenager, and that's too young.

James M

At sixteen it's difficult to foresee the next two years, let alone forty.

Richard

I'd have liked to explore the possibilities of architecture and biology,
and compare them with medicine. If I'd had the opportunity to dis-
cuss the options with someone I might have chosen differently, who
knows? Perhaps I failed my own children in that respect.

James M

Well I certainly don't regret my decision.

William Daniel

For me medicine was already a way of life with interests in both science and humanity, and comfortable rewards. It was hard work, and being involved in the suffering of one's patients was often distressing. But it's different now. The training's long, and the responsibility is tremendous. No one sued us for making mistakes, but now if you get it wrong you're in trouble. You deal with problems all the time, which can be very stressful. I'd have every sympathy with a young person who wanted a more creative and original career.

Daniel

Such as?

William Daniel

Well, science is full of opportunity for new ideas. Horse-less carriages, steam engines, the telegraph, wireless communication.... and those extraordinary computers .... and mobiles, whatever they are.

Charles

And flying machines, electricity, and magnets that can see through people.

Jane

Magnetic resonance imaging is a wonderful advance, but progress is often erratic. The leeches you were so fond of but discarded are now being used again, and people who once said lasers were the answer to everything aren't so sure now.

Sir John

Progress isn't new, you know, and was always difficult. We had to contend with Darwin's new ideas, Pasteur's germ theory, Freud, Roentgen rays...... and a lot of opposition!

Charles

It's always uncertain, too, but that's part of the challenge.

Sir John

The opportunities in medicine are enormous, but it doesn't exclude an interest in arts or science. I was fascinated by meteorology all my life, and a classical education not only helped my medical studies but gave me much pleasure in itself.

James L

I'd go further than that. I think everyone should have a secondary career, such as writing in my case, or research in a special medical niche. We have been forced to concentrate into ever narrower fields, and we need something beyond it to keep a sensible perspective on the world.

Sir John

I suppose specialisation is a necessary evil now because knowledge and techniques are so complex, but I don't like it. I'm sorry to see that 'specialist' is now synonymous with 'consultant', which doesn't necessarily mean 'good doctor'. Sir Heneage Ogilvie said[11] 'the term specialist implies neither praise nor blame, but simply limitation'. He thought consultants were often 'wise guys', only technicians who could do complicated tricks

Jane

As one who is already a specialist and looking forward to being a consultant I'd dispute that. A field may be limited, but the knowledge and techniques in it are so complex they should only be used by those who are wise and skilled enough to do so safely. Ethical implications are greater than ever, too, and that's a big challenge to our wisdom.

James M

Without specialisation and technology we couldn't use all the knowledge we now have. A final year medical student probably knows more now than a doctor ever did a century ago, but I suspect it's harder to use knowledge well. Specialism isn't just learning more about less, it needs the wisdom to use it in the best possible way.

Sir John

Jane, I'm sure you will always be wise, however specialised your work may be, and I'm very glad to hear of your success. And James, there's something else which Ogilvie said which has been forgotten for fifty years, that general practitioners should be rewarded for the *quality* of their work, rather than the *quantity* as measured by the number of patients on a list.

James M

If his advice had been heeded where might we be now? The self-esteem of GPs might not have declined as it did.

Ian

Quality is what counts, and not just technically. I agree with my fellow-Irishman James McCormick, that personal care is threatened by guide-lines, directives, duty rotas, teams and so on[12]. We mustn't let the personal doctor be killed by control, or vanish in the delusion that good medicine is only a collection of technical processes.

John III

As a family, do we have a rather blinkered view of medicine? You don't have to be a doctor to be effective, even in health, because, for instance, those who create employment relieve poverty, which promotes health. Teachers, artists, actors and writers create cultures that stimulate intellectual and psychological health. You could argue that architects and builders contribute to health by creating pleasant environments for living. Health educators, health economists and family planning people all have their part to play. You only *need* to be a doctor if you want to diagnose and treat the sick.

Ian

Not even that. My two daughters contemplated medicine but didn't go through with it. One's a clinical psychologist and the other's an alternative practitioner, and they both work with people who have problems. In some ways it is an advantage not to be a doctor without the baggage of the profession's mistakes or the public's prejudice.

Daniel

Such as arguing whether medicine is a trade or a profession! If doctors were less concerned with their image and more with what they're doing perhaps they wouldn't be so unhappy. And the public should accept that service to humanity inevitably has a price. But that's as may be. I come back to my question. How should we advise our descendants about a career in medicine?

Sir John

Look about you carefully. If you find something else, consider it seriously. If medicine is still what you want you'll find it's very rewarding.

James LeF

If you want intellectual excitement, medicine has so many aspects you'll probably find something worthwhile, though there's less variety now because of technical specialisation.

Jane

Don't go in to medicine for the protection of the white coat. It's easy to think that doctors are superior creatures in some way, even immune to human failings, especially if you come from a medical tradition. On the other hand don't be so humble that your job dominates your life. *You* must run your career; don't let *it* run you. If you can do that, you'll be all right.

Richard

I'm not so sure. Yes, you must be in charge of your own career, but that's not so easy now. In the old days a doctor could expect a good income, respect from society and a fair degree of job security. There used to be an implied contract of trust between us and our patients, as individuals and as a profession. We agreed to work hard in the early years knowing we'd gain that respect, and probably achieve the good income later. We enjoyed the autonomy, which the public accepted because, though fallible, we were conscientious and caring. But now people expect medical miracles, so we have to be available at all times, work in teams like mass-production lines, and deliver care under pressure of time and lack of resources. We have to conform to scientific evidence, according to prescribed guidelines. Worse still we have to be accountable, so that people know who to blame when things go wrong[13,14].

James LeF

I agree. There's a view that medicine is like the electronics industry, with ever-new products, but it can't be. There's a fine line between caring and support on the one hand and meddlesome, dangerous interference on the other.

Daniel

Medicine's place in society is ever-changing. We had the challenge of forging the shape of the profession, of education. Others battled with apathy about housing, hygiene, notification of disease, and so on. In the twentieth century people struggled with medical care at public expense, and we all had the problem of accepting change, and reluctance to throw away our cherished beliefs.

William Daniel

Medicine has done well as a science, but what we used to think was true has often been shown to be false, and that will go on happening. Humanity's a frail and mysterious thing, and people respond as humans, not machines. Science must inform, not dictate, show the fallacies of charlatans, and prove the value of new discoveries. But it's not infallible, and you have to move on as knowledge develops.

Sir John

And never forget that your science is of no value if it is unacceptable to ordinary people, for they will reject it.

Richard

In the past it was tacitly accepted that 'doctor knows best', but the modern public is well informed and educated. They look for scientific certainty everywhere, but do so in vain because we're not omnipotent and can never be absolutely sure. We need a new approach which ensures that patients know our abilities yet understand our limitations, accept that illness and pain are part of life. We must restore trust, so that doctors can use their knowledge for the benefit of their patients. The future's uncertain, and sure to be different, but if we're wise we can restore the satisfaction of a demanding job well done.

James M

There have been healers in every civilisation, and they'll be needed more than ever as medicine becomes more complicated. The ancient Greeks had doctors, and so does Star Trek! For me, being a doctor certainly beats working for a living.

Richard

Yes James, but only if we get rid of what the *BMJ* calls the 'bogus contract' where people expect a solution to every problem, and doctors are unhappy because they can't meet expectations.

James M

Agreed, but it's up to us to create that new and better contract. Where there's research there'll be progress, certainly, but just as our forebears struggled with the problems of their own time, so must we face ours. Practising scientifically valid medicine with affordable humane priorities is the challenge for the next generation. I'd say 'Go for it'.

All agreed that medicine was an excellent but demanding career for the next generation so long as they can resist the seductive glamour of technical procedures that conflict with our frail humanity.

Suddenly there was a knock at the door. 'Come in' called Daniel, and the door opened to reveal two slim and elegant girls, bearing an uncanny resemblance to us all, for they were Richard's grand-daughters.

"I'm Anna" said one. "And I'm Lizzie" said the other. "We're the next generation".

Daniel

Come along in, ... and welcome! Perhaps you heard what we've been talking about. Do *you* have an answer to my question? Will young people still want to be doctors as medicine gets more demanding?

Anna

It looks difficult, but very interesting. There's a lot to learn, the rewards are small at first and slow to come, but this overcrowded world needs competent and compassionate doctors as much as ever.

Lizzie

It's a career with plenty to stimulate the mind, and its values are human rather than material. I'm keen to have a try. There's plenty to do and I, for one, want to do it.

Sir John

Did you look at the other side, at the cares, the worries, and the burdens? Are you sure you can do it?

Anna

If Eliza Dunbar and Sophia Jex-Blake did it, so can we. As you said yourself, we're ruled by the conventions of our times, which form our expectations. I have just begun the modern and progressive course at Manchester, and am enjoying it enormously.

Lizzie

It's up to us to meet the needs of the future.

Daniel

Well said! Anna and Lizzie, you're a credit to the family. We've known the past and the present, but the future is yours. Work hard, use your knowledge with compassion*, and you'll do well, we have no doubt.

---

* *Cum Scientia Caritas;* motto of the Royal College of General Practitioners.

Earlier medical communications.

references

REFERENCES TO CHAPTER ONE

1. Moore J W, quoting Rutting T, *Chronological History of the weather and seasons,* Dublin Journal of Medical Science, vol 126, 1908, p254
2. Mrs Elizabeth Bowlby, personal communication
3. Maurice A U and Maurice T, *The Marlborough Doctors: six generations of one family's medical practice since 1792.* 1995, Alan Sutton Publishing, Stroud, Gloucestershire
4. Mrs B S M Arnott, personal communication
5. Dr Keri Thomas, personal communication
6. Anonymous. Dublin Journal of Medical Science vol 2 1839, p24
7. Anonymous monograph, *Photographs of Eminent Medical Men, with brief analytical notes of their works.* London, John Churchill and Sons, undated
8. Meenan F O C, *The Georgian Squares of Dublin and their doctors,* Irish Journal of Medical Science, 6th Series, 484, April 1966, pp149-54
9. Breathnach C S, *John William Moore,* Irish Journal of Medical Science, vol 152, 1983, p69
10. Obituary, *Sir John Moore,* British Medical Journal, October 23, 1937 p831-2
11. Leading article, *Medical Press and Circular,* 7 April 1875
12. Mr Brandon Stephens, personal communication
13. Charlton J and Murphy M, *The Health of Adult Britain Vol 1.* Office of National Statistics, 1997, p84
14. Lyons J B, *A Pride of Professors; The Professors of Medicine at the Royal College of Surgeons in Ireland 1813-1985,* Dublin, A & A Farmar, 1999, p181
15. Pyke-Lees W, *The Centenary of the General Medical Council, 1858-1958; The History of the Present Work of the Council.* General Medical Council, 1958
16. Mr Richard Le Fanu, personal communication
17. Grimwade F C, *War History of the 4th Battalion, the London Regiment 1914-1919.*
18. Obituary, *Sir William Osler,* contribution by J W Moore, British Medical Journal, Jan 10 1920, p68
19. Minutes of the GMC, 1920

REFERENCES TO CHAPTER TWO

1 Shaw Mason W, *A Statistical or Parochial Survey of Ireland,* 1819, Dublin, The Faulkener Press

2 Major R H, *Classic Descriptions of Disease,* Blackwell Scientific Publications 3rd Edition 1948, p55

3 Haslam F, *From Hogarth to Rowlandson: medicine in art in 18th century Britain.* Liverpool University Press 1996, p29

4 Quoted in *'Medical Practitioner' or 'Doctor',* British Medical Journal, 31 Mar 1906, p757

5 Porter R, *The Greatest Benefit to Mankind; a medical history of humanity from antiquity to the present.* Fontana Press 1998, p313

6 Major RH, op. cit. p193

7 Major, op. cit. p195

8 Major, op. cit. p196

9 Porter, op.cit. p266

10 Loudon I, *Medical Care and the General Practitioner, 1750-1850.* Oxford University Press. 1986, p25

11 William Shakespeare, *Romeo and Juliet.* Act V scene 1

12 Haslam, op. cit. p116

13 Moore J W, quoting Rutting T, *Chronological History of the weather and seasons,* Dublin Journal of Medical Science, vol 126, 1908, p254,

14 Foster R F, in *The Oxford Illustrated History of Ireland.* R F Foster Ed, Oxford University Press 1989, p170

15 Donovan D, *Observations on the diseases to which the famine of last year gave origin.* Dublin Medical Press, 1 March 1848, p179

16 Graham Rev. J, in *A Statistical Account or Parochial Survey of Ireland,* Shaw Mason. op.cit.

17 Baxter, Luke, *From Stone to Page; ancestral records of Moydow, County Longford.* Moydow Cemeteries Committee in association with Longford Historical Society 1999.

18 Charlton J and Murphy M, Eds. *The Health of Adult Britain 1841-1994 Vol 1.* Office for National Statistics 1998, p20

19 Logan J, *Folk Medicine.* Journal of the Irish Medical Association. Vol 41, 1957, p125

20 Logan J, *Making the Cure.* Dublin, The Talbot Press, 1972, p22

21 MacNamara D, *Do-it-yourself Medicine in County Clare during the first half of the nineteenth century.* Journal of the Irish Medical Association. vol 52, 1963, p120-4

22 Logan J, op.cit.

23 Fleetwood J. *The History of Medicine in Ireland,* Dublin, The Skellig Press, 2nd Ed 1983, p62

24 Pechey J, Ed. *The Whole Works of that Excellent Practical Physician Thomas Sydenham,* Tenth Edition, London 1734

25 Fleetwood, op.cit. p87

REFERENCES TO CHAPTER THREE

1 Moore W D, *History of Pharmacy in Ireland*, Dublin Quarterly Journal of Medical Science, vol vi, 1846, p64-102

2 Dublin Directories for relevant years

3 McCullough N, *Dublin, an Urban History,* Dublin, Anne Street Press, 1989 pp51 & 45

4 McWalter J C, *A History of the Worshipful Company of Apothecaries of the City of Dublin,* Dublin, E. Ponsonby Ltd, 1916, p17

5 Cameron, Sir Charles, *History of the Royal College of Surgeons in Ireland*, Fannin & Co, 1886, p134-5

6 McWalter, op. cit., p19

7 Fleetwood J F, *Thomas Davis Lecture,* Radio Eirean

8 McWalter, op.cit., p23

9 Moore W D, *History of Pharmacy in Ireland,* op. cit., p64-102

10 Ibid

11 McWalter op. cit.

12 Ibid

13 Loudon I, *Medical Care and the General Practitioner, 1750-1850.* Oxford, The Clarendon Press, 1986, p22

14 McWalter op. cit., p38

15 Cameron, Sir Charles, op. cit., p135

16 Moore W D, op. cit., *History* p100

17 Minute Books of the Apothecaries Hall, unpublished

18 Foster R F, *The Oxford Illustrated History of Ireland,* Oxford University Press, 1989, pp182-3

19 Minute Books of the Apothecaries' Hall
20 Minute Books of the Apothecaries' Hall
21 McWalter, op. cit., p130
22 Minute Books of the Apothecaries' Hall
23 McWalter, op. cit., p130
24 McWalter, op. cit., p141–2

REFERENCES TO CHAPTER FOUR

1   *Twiss's Life of Lord Chancellor Eldon*, quoted in Dublin Medical Press 12 April 1846, p189

2   Lyons J B, *A Pride of Professors*, Dublin, A&A Farmar, 1999, p1

3   Anonymous, *Medical Education*, Article V, Westminster and Foreign Quarterly Review, July 1858, p120

4   *Household Words*, Quoted in Dublin Medical Press, 17 Sept 1856

5   Loudon I, *Medical Care and the General Practitioner, 1750-1850*, Oxford, The Clarendon Press, 1986, p167

6   Editorial, *The Lancet*. 1 1831, p867–8

7   Editorial, *The Lancet*, 1 1830, p539–40

8   Editorial, *The Lancet*, 2 1853, p553–4

9   Ibid

10 McWalter J C, *A History of the Worshipful Company of Apothecaries of the City of Dublin*, Dublin, E Ponsonby Ltd 1915, p143

11 Fleetwood J, *The History of Medicine in Ireland*, Dublin, The Skellig Press, 2nd edition 1983, p92

12 Cameron, Sir Charles, *History of the Royal College of Surgeons in Ireland*, Dublin, Fannin & Co, 1886, p134

13 Editorial, The Lancet, 1, Feb 13 1830

14 Editorial, The Lancet, 2, May 7 1836

15 Fleetwood, op.cit. p93

16 McWalter, op. cit. p102

17 Ellis, Sir John, *The London Hospital Medical College, 1785-1985; the story of England's first Medical School*. London, The London Hospital Medical Club, 1986, p1

18 Howie J, in *General Practice under the National Health Service 1948-1997*. Eds Loudon I, Horder J and Webster C, Oxford, The Clarendon Press,1998, p151

19 McWalter op. cit. p151

20 Ibid, p150

21 Ibid, p157

22 Ibid, p91

23 Cameron, op. cit. p189

24 McWalter, op. cit. p156

25 Cameron, op. cit. p189

26 Cameron, op. cit. p190

27 Dublin Medical Press, vol vi, 1839, p41

28 *Public Notice,* Dublin Medical Press, vol vi, 1839

29 *Medical Congress,* Dublin Medical Press, vol vi, 1839, p369

30 Cameron, op. cit. p193

31 *King's and Queens's College of Physicians,* Dublin Medical Press, vol vi, 1839 p319

32 Dublin Medical Press, vol vi, 1839 p315

33 Letter, R Travers Blackley, Dublin Medical Press, vol vi, 1839 p139-40

34 Letter, Verax, Dublin Medical Press, vol vi, 1839, p118

35 Dublin Medical Press, vol vi, 1839, p297-8

36 'BETA', Letter, Dublin Medical Press, vol vi, 1839, 248-9

37 Maunsell H, Letter, Dublin Medical Press, vol vi, 1839, p184

38 Donovan M, Letter, Dublin Medical Press, vol vi, 1839, p302

39 Donovan M, Letter, Dublin Medical Press, vol vi, 1839 p315

40 Donovan M, Dublin Medical Press, vol vii, 1839, p103

41 Doyle E. *Dublin's School of Medicine.* Journal of the Irish Medical Association, 1959,45, p103

42 Cameron op. cit. p538

43 Cameron op. cit. p238

REFERENCES TO CHAPTER FIVE

1 Moore W D, *Observations on the Latent Period of Scarlatina; with Illustrative Cases.* Dublin Journal of Medical Science, vol xii, 1851, p302

2 Moore W D, *An Outline of the History of Pharmacy in Ireland.* Dublin Quarterly Journal of Medical Science, vol vi 1848, 64-102

3 Duncan A, *Medical Commentaries for the Year 1788*

4 *Memorial of Daniel Moore,* Dublin Journal of Medical Science, vol vii, 1847 p291-3

5   McWalter J C, *History of the Worshipful Company of Apothecaries of the City of Dublin*, Dublin, E Ponsonby, 1916, p117

6   McWalter, op. cit. p47

7   Minute Books, Apothecaries' Hall of Dublin, unpublished

8   Moore W D, *Observations* op. cit.

9   Graves R J, *London Medical and Surgical Journal*, 1835, vol vii. p516-7

10 Moore W D, op. cit.

11 Moore J W, *Eruptive and Continued Fevers*, Dublin, Fannin & Co, 1892, p160

12 Pickles W, *Epidemiology in Country Practice*, John Wright & Sons, Bristol, 1939, Facsimile Edition, Royal College of General Practitioners, 1984

13 Kennedy H, *Some Observations of Fever*, Dublin Journal of Medical Science, vol xiii, 1838, p107-11

14 Wall T, *A Case of circumscribed false Aneurism of the Brachial Artery, caused by Puncture in Bloodletting, and cured by Operation*. Dublin Journal of Medical Science, vol x, 1836, p411

15 Babbington J, *Remarks on epidemic Typhous Fever in the County Donegal*, Dublin Journal of Medical Science, vol x, 1836, p404-10

16 Major R H, *Classic Descriptions of Disease*, Oxford, Blackwell Scientific Publications, 3rd Edition 1945, p420

17 Ibid, p563

18 Ibid, p68

19 Porter R, *The Greatest Benefit to Mankind; a medical history of humanity from antiquity to the present*. London, Fontana Press, 1999, p225

20 Moore W D, *Statistical View of the comparative Frequency in which the principal Medicines used during the last sixty Years have been prescribed in Dublin*, Dublin Journal of Medical Science, vol x, 1836, pp24-32

21 William Shakespeare, *The Merry Wives of Windsor*, Act 3 scene 1

22 Lucas E W, *Book of Prescriptions*, 10th edition, London, J&A Churchill, 1915, p279

23 McCallum R I, *Antimony in Medical History*, Durham, The Pentland Press, 1999

24 Lucas, op.cit. p167

25 Wellcome Institute for Medical History, *Daybook of Robert Craik*

26 Graves R J, *On the use of Tartar Emetic in Cases of Delirium occurring in Typhus Fever*, Dublin Journal of Medical Science, vol ix, 1836, p449-66

27 Graves R J, ibid

28 Moore W D, *On the Coagulability of Human Milk*, Dublin Journal of Medical Science, vol vii, 1849 p275

29 Moore W D, *Experiments on sugar in the urine of the foetus*, Dublin Journal of Medical Science, vol xx, 1855, p88

30 Moore W D, *An alvine concretion consisting of cholesterine*, Dublin Journal of Medical Science, vol vii, 1853, p246-8

31 Moore W D, *The Spontaneous Cure of a Rectal Tumour in a Child*, Dublin Journal of Medical Science, vol xi, 1851, p223

32 Moore W D, op. cit. *Statistical View*, Dublin Journal of Medical Science, vol x, 1836, pp24-32

33 Moore W D, *On the Urine of the Crocodile*, Dublin Quarterly Journal of Medical Science, vol xi, 1851, p479

34 Anonymous monograph, *Photographs of Eminent Medical Men, William Daniel Moore, MD Dub., MRIA*, London, John Churchill and Son, undated

35 Bernadette Cunningham, Librarian, Royal Irish Academy, Personal communication

36 *Memorial of Daniel Moore*, Dublin Journal of Medical Science, vol vii, 1847, p291-3

REFERENCES TO CHAPTER SIX

1 Cork Street Fever Hospital, Medical Report, 1882, p17

2 Stokes W, *Researches on the State of the Heart and the Use of Wine in Typhus Fever*. Dublin Journal of Medical Science, vol xv, 1839 p1

3 Fleetwood J, *The History of Medicine in Ireland*, Dublin, The Skellig Press, 2nd Ed 1988 p136

4 Cork Street Fever Hospital, Medical Report, 1883/4, p1

5 Pechey J, Ed., *The Whole Works of that Excellent Practical Physician Dr Thomas Sydenham*, 10th edition, London, 1734 p164-5

6 Moore W D, *Observations on the Latent Period of Scarlatina; with Illustrative Cases*, Dublin Journal of Medical Science, vol xii, 1851, p302

7 Ibid, p315

8 Anstill T, *Cases of Scarlatina*. Provincial Medical and Surgical Journal, vol i, 27 March 1841, pp417-8

9 Moore W D, *Observations*, op.cit., p310

10   Porter R, Ed., *The Cambridge Illustrated History of Medicine,* Cambridge University Press, 1996, p229

11   Loudon I, *The Tragedy of Childbed Fever,* Oxford University Press, 2000, p101

12   Moore C F, *Dublin Obstetrical Reports,* Dublin Quarterly Journal of Medical Science, vol 48, 1869, p353

13   Moore J W, *Is it desirable that there should be a System of Compulsory Notification of Infectious Disease?* Dublin Journal of Medical Science, vol 77, 1884, p482

14   Moore J W, *Report to the Academy of Medicine in Ireland,* Dublin Journal of Medical Science, vol 77, 1884, p365

15   Charlton J and Murphy M, Eds., *The Health of Adult Britain 1841 – 1994,* vol 1, London, Office for National Statistics, p32

16   Moore C F, op. cit., p354

17   Editorial (tables) *Relation of puerperal fever to Zymotic Poisons. The Lancet,* ii, July 20 1872, p84

18   Charlton J and Murphy M, op.cit., table 4.1, p32

19   Cork Street Fever Hospital Report, 1878/9, p9

20   Fleetwood, op. cit., p140

21   Tuomy M, quoted by Moore CF in *Reports of Dublin Obstetrical Society,* Dublin Journal of Medical Science, vol 48, 1869, p350

22   Cork Street Fever Hospital Report, 1883-4

23   Moore J W, *Meteorology, Practical and Applied.* London, F J Rebman, 1894, p379

24   Donovan D, Dublin Medical Press, vol 29, 1 Mar 1848, p130

25   Moore J W, *Continued and Eruptive Fevers,* Dublin, Fannin & Co, 1892, p279

26   Lombard H C, *Observations suggested by a Comparison of postmortem appearances produced by Typhous Fever in Dublin, Paris and Geneva.* Dublin Journal of Medical Science, vol x, 1836 p17

27   Cheyne J, *Medical Report of the Hardwicke Fever Hospital, 1817,* Dublin Hospital Reports and Communications, vol i, 1817

28   Fleetwood, op. cit., p103

29   Law R, *Observations on fever,* Dublin Journal of Medical Science, vol xii, 1838, p187

30   Stokes W, *Researches on the State of the Heart.* op.cit

31   Fleetwood, op. cit., p193

32 Cusack J and Stokes W, *On the Mortality of Medical Practitioners from Fever in Ireland*, Dublin Quarterly Journal of Medical Science, vol 4, 1847, p134–145

33 Mateer W, *Statistics on Fever, with General Observations on its Nature, Causes and Treatment* Dublin Journal of Medical Science, vol x, 1836, p32

34 Moore J W, *Eruptive and Continued Fevers* p251

35 Cusack J and Stokes W, op. cit.

36 Macnamara D, *Doolin Memorial Lecture 1966,* Journal of the Irish Medical Association, vol 59, 1966, 312, p101

37 Fleetwood, op. cit., p124

38 Erinensis, The Lancet, 1826, p720

39 Macnamara D, op.cit., p103

40 Moore J W, *Epidemiology in Ireland, Address to the Dublin Congress of the Royal Institute of Public Health, 1928,* Irish Journal of Medical Science, October 1928 p8

41 Donovan D, *Observations on the Diseases to which the Famine of the last year gave origin; and on the morbid effects of deficiency of food.* Dublin Medical Press, Vol xix, March 1848 p130-2

42 Moore J W, *Fevers,* op.cit. p305

43 Stokes W, *Researches on the State of the Heart.* op. cit.

44 Donovan D, op. cit., p131

45 Mateer W, op. cit., p45

46 Cheyne J, op. cit., p12 & 24

47 Stokes W, *Researches on the state of the Heart.* op. cit., p4

48 Ibid, p65

49 Moore J W, *Cases under the care of J.W.Moore.* Dublin Journal of Medical Science, 60, 1875, p277

50 Cork Street Fever Hospital Report, 1883/4, p20

51 Ibid, p22

52 Keane F, *Typhus fever.* Irish Journal of Medical Science, 1930, 515-8

REFERENCES TO CHAPTER SEVEN

1 Underwood E A, *The centenary of British Public Health,* British Medical Journal, 8 May 1948, p890

2 Kiple K F, in *The Cambridge Illustrated History of Medicine*, Ed. Porter R, Cambridge University Press 1996, p41

3   Moore J W, *Sanitary Organisation in Ireland in its Medical Aspect,* Dublin Journal of Medical Science, vol 79, 1885, p200

4   The Lancet, 1, 1832, p182

5   The Lancet, 1, 1832, p205

6   McCoy S, *Notes on Malignant Cholera, as it appeared in Dublin.* Dublin Journal of Medical Science, vol iii, 1833, p357

7   Ibid.

8   Tufnell, *Surgical Society of Ireland.* Dublin Medical Press, Mar 18 1846, p161-8

9   Letter, Dublin Medical Press, Oct 18, 1848

10 Letter, Donovan M, Dublin Medical Press, Oct 18, 1848, p249

11 Phelan D, letter, Dublin Medical Press, 17 Aug 1866, p256

12 McCoy, op. cit.

13 Moore C F, *A sketch of the recent outbreak of Cholera at Finglas.* Dublin Quarterly Journal of Medical Science, vol 18, 1854, p330

14 Ibid.

15 Ibid.

16 Ibid.

17 Ibid.

18 Ibid.

19 *Medical Association of the College of Physicians, Ireland.* Medical Press and Circular, April 17 1867

20 Ibid.

21 Moore C F, op. cit. p340

22 Tufnell, op. cit.

23 McCoy, op. cit.

24 Ibid.

25 Latta T, *Saline venous Injections in cases of malignant Cholera carried out while in the vapour Bath.* The Lancet, 1, 1832, p173 & p208

26 *Special report on the treatment of cholera by venous injections.* Medical Press and Circular, 31 Oct 1866

27 *Transfusion of Blood in Malignant Cholera.* The Lancet, 1, 1832, p202-3

28 The Lancet, 1, 1832, p176

29 The Lancet, 1 1832, p178

30 MacCormac H, Medical Press and Circular, 12 August 1866

31 Griffith, G. de G, *Treatment of cholera by chloroform inhalation,* Medical Press and Circular, 12 Aug 1866

32 *The Times,* quoted in Dublin Medical Press, 25 Oct 1848

33 Cecil and Loeb Eds, *Textbook of Medicine,* Saunders, 1963 p254

34 Moore J W, *Epidemiology in Ireland: past and present.* Irish Journal of Medical Science 1928, p626–40

35 Ibid.

36 Moore J W, *Eruptive and Continued Fevers,* Dublin, Fannin & Co 1892

37 Cork Street Fever Hospital Report, 1878/9, p19

38 Gatenby P, *Dublin's Meath Hospital,* Town House, Dublin, 1996, p34

39 Rolleston J D, *The Smallpox Pandemic of 1870-74.* Proceedings of Royal Society of Medicine, vol 27, 1933, p11

40 Notice, *Ireland; Smallpox and Vaccination.* British Medical Journal, 30 March 1872

41 Moore J W, *Fevers.* op. cit. p106

42 Ibid. p108

43 Ibid. p108

44 Porter R, *The Greatest Benefit to Mankind; Medical History of Humanity from Antiquity to the Present.* London, Fontana Press 1999 p486

45 Oliffe J F, *Reflections on the Treatment of Variola,* The Lancet, i, 1840/1, p672-9

46 Moore J W *Fevers,* op.cit. p113-4

47 Moore J W, *A case of Smallpox and its Lessons,* Dublin Journal of Medical Science, vol 98, 1894, p490

48 Collie A, *On the Treatment of Smallpox.* The Lancet, 30 Sep 1871, p461

REFERENCES TO CHAPTER EIGHT

1 *The Lancet,* Quaestor, 1855

2 Charlton J, and Murphy M, Eds, *The Health of Adult Britain 1841 – 1994,* vol 1, London, Office for National Statistics, p158

3 *The Medical Circular,* June 20 1860, p424

4 Leading article, *Pestilential State of the Thames,* British Medical Journal, July 3rd 1858, p535

5 Ibid.

6 Leading article, *The Centenary of Public Health,* British Medical Journal, May 8 1948, p886

7 Porter R, *The Greatest Benefit to Mankind; a medical history humanity from antiquity to the present.* Fontana Press, 1998, p402

8   The Medical Press and Circular, Dec 13 1871, p529

9   The Lancet, January 1875, letters pp73, 110, 149

10 Farr W, *Density or proximity of population; its advantages and disadvantages*. The Practitioner, Aug 1879, p76

11 Langmuir A D, *William Farr: founder of modern concepts of surveillance*. Journal of Epidemiology, vol 5 No1, p13,

12 Moore C F, *A glance at preventive medicine in 1769 and 1874*. Dublin Journal of Medical Science, vol 58, 1874, p61–68

13 Leading Article, *The Centenary of Public Health*, British Medical Journal, 8 May 1948, p886

14 Moore C F, *Reports of the Dublin Obstetrical Society*, Dublin Journal of Medical Science, vol 58, 1869, p354

15 Loudon I, *The Tragedy of Childbed Fever*, Oxford University Press, 2000, p195

16 Moore C F, *Domestic Scavenging*, Medical Press and Circular, 3 Mar 1880, p164

17 Grimshaw T and Moore J W, *A case of Pythogenic pneumonia*. Dublin Journal of Medical Science, May 1875

18 Leading Article, *Dublin Sanitation*, The Medical Press and Circular, 7 July 1880, p9–10

19 Leading Article, *The Dublin Death Rate*, The Medical Press and Circular, 14 July 1880, p35

20 Moore J W, *Epidemiology in Ireland; past and present*. Irish Journal of Medical Science, October 1928, p626

21 Moore J W, *Sanitary Organisation in Ireland in its Medical Aspect, (Address to sub-section of State Medicine in the Academy of Medicine in Ireland, Feb 5 1885)* Dublin Journal of Medical Science, March 1885.

22 Falkiner N M, *Evolution of the Diploma in Public Health*. Irish Journal of Medical Science, 5th series, 1924, p318

23 Dublin University Almanack for MDCCCLXXII (1872)

24 Ibid.

25 *The Irish Times,* October 23 2000, p22

26 Moore J W, *Meteorology, Practical and Applied*. London, F J Rebman 11, Adam Street, Strand, 1894

27 Moore J W, *Notes on Mean Temperature in its Relations to Disease and Mortality with special reference to the City of Dublin*. Dublin Quarterly Journal of Medical Science, August 1869, p107

28 Guy W. *An Attempt to determine the influence of the Seasons and Weather on Sickness and Mortality.* Journal of the Statistical Society, May 1843, p133

29 Guy W, *On Temperature and its Relation to Mortality: an Illustration of the Application of the Numerical Method to the Discovery of the Truth.* Journal of the Statistical Society, June 1881, p235

30 Grimshaw T W, and Moore J W, op. cit.

31 Cameron C A, *Observations on the entry of Air into Main Sewers.* British Medical Journal, 18 Sept 1880, p476

32 Grimshaw and Moore, op. cit. p19

33 Porter R, *The Greatest Benefit to Mankind,* Fontana Press, 1999, 433

34 Moore J W, *The Microcosm of Disease, an address introductory to the session 1879-80 of the Meath Hospital.* Dublin, John Falconer, 53 Upper Sackville-st 1879

35 Moore J W, *The Influenza epidemic of 1889-90, as observed in Dublin.* Dublin Journal of Medical Science, April 1890, p3

36 Hardy A, *The Epidemic Streets. Infectious Disease and the Rise of Preventive Medicine 1856-1900,* Oxford, The Clarendon Press, 1993

37 Moore J W, *Medical Report from Cork Street Fever Hospital,1879.* Dublin, John Falconer, 53 Upper Sackville-st

38 Ibid.

39 Grimshaw T W, *Remarks on the Prevalence and Distribution of Fever in Dublin,* Dublin 1872, Fannin & Co

REFERENCES TO CHAPTER NINE

1 Leading articles, *Our preventable mortality,* British Medical Journal, 1858, 2 Oct, p826, & 6 Nov, p931

2 Leading article, The Lancet 1, 2 Feb 1865, p129

3 Leading article, The Lancet 2, 5 Dec 1874, p807

4 *Report of BMA Annual Meeting,* British Medical Journal, Sep 18 1880, p471

5 Report, *Scarlatina in milk,* British Medical Journal, Jan 17 1880, p107

6 Moore J W, *An Outbreak of Disease traceable to the Drinking of Impure Water.* Dublin Journal of Medical Science, vol 73, 1882, p131

7 *Report of BMA Annual Meeting,* British Medical Journal, 18 Sep 1880, p471

8 Moore J W, *Oyster Fever,* The Practitioner, vol ix, 1899, p251

9 Moore J W, *Notes on Mean Temperature in its Relations to Disease and Mortality with special reference to the City of Dublin*, Dublin Quarterly Journal of Medical Science, Aug 1869, p107

10 Leading article, *Registration of Infectious Disease*, British Medical Journal, 28 Feb 1880

11 *Report of Committee on Registration of Disease*, British Medical Journal, 12 Aug 1876, p211

12 *Report of committee on registration of disease British Medical Journal*, 16 Aug 1879, p257

13 Moore J W, *Remarks on the compulsory notification and registration of infectious diseases*, British Medical Journal, 31 Jan 1880, p158-60, and Dublin Journal of Medical Science, vol 69, 1880, p96

14 Ransome A, *On the need of combined medical observation.* British Medical Journal, Oct 5 1864, p405

15 Cameron C, *Notification of Infectious Diseases in Dublin.* The Lancet, 1, 1881, p34

16 Editorial, *The Association and the notification of Infectious Disease*, British Medical Journal, 31 Jan 1880, p172

17 Quinlan F J B, letter, British Medical Journal, Mar 6 1880, p384

18 Report, *Parliamentary Bills Committee,* British Medical Journal, 22 Nov 1879, p830

19 Leading article, *Registration of Disease,* British Medical Journal, 8 Feb 1879, p197

20 Crossley C R, letter, Medical Times and Gazette, 7 June 1879, p631

21 Hutton R E, letter, British Medical Journal, 14 June 1879, p914

22 Bond F T, letter, British Medical Journal, 28 Feb 1880, p346

23 Report, *The notification of infectious cases,* British Medical Journal, June 5 1880, p861

24 Anonymous letter, British Medical Journal, June 19 1880, p952,

25 Report, *The Registration of Infectious Disease at Nottingham*, British Medical Journal, 19 June 1889, p953

26 Littlejohn H D, letter, *Medical Times and Gazette*, 13 Nov 1880, p575

27 Report, *The notification of infectious disease,* British Medical Journal, 20 Nov 1880, p825

28 Report, *Registration of disease,* British Medical Journal, 27 Nov 1880, p854

29 Report, *Notification of Infectious disease in Ireland,* The Lancet, 12 March 1881 p434

30   Moore J W, *Is it desirable that there should be a System of Notification of Infectious Disease?*, Dublin Journal of Medical Science, vol 72, 1881, p482

31   Moore J W, *The Present and Future of State Medicine. Introductory Address to the Subsection of the Royal Academy of Medicine in Ireland*, Dublin Journal of Medical Science, vol 72, 1887, p482

32   *The Times*, 18 Sep 1889

33   Charlton J and Murphy M, Eds, *The Health of Adult Britain 1841 – 1994*, London, Office for National Statistics, vol 1, p34

34   *The Times*, Letter, 10 August 1889 (a)

35   *The Times*, Letter, 10 August 1889 (b)

36   Warburton J, *The History of the City of Dublin.* Vol 2, p709 J. Whitelaw and R. Walsh, W. Bulmer and Co, Cleveland-row, St James's, London, 1818

37   Moore J W, *How are we to deal, by isolation or otherwise, with convalescents from acute infective disease, so as to prevent the spread of disease?* Dublin Journal of Medical Science, vol 68, 1879, p189

38   Moore J W, *Homes for Convalescents from acute Infective Diseases.* Dublin Journal of Medical Science, vol 68, 1879, p189

39   Moore J W, *The Infectious Hospitals (Dublin) scheme*, Dublin Journal of Medical Science, vol 100, 1895, p486

40   Cameron, Sir Charles, *On the Isolation of Fever Patients*, Dublin Journal of Medical Science, vol 100, p500

41   Moore, Sir John, *Notification of Tuberculosis in Ireland: its failure and the reasons therefore.* Dublin Journal of Medical Science, vol 137, 1914, p331

42   Moore J W, *Sanitary Organisation in Ireland in its Medical Aspect*, Dublin Journal of Medical Science, vol 79, 1885, p197

43   Ibid.

44   Moore, Sir John, *Hindrances to Public Health Work in Ireland*, Dublin Journal of Medical Science, vol 11, 1921, p56

REFERENCES TO CHAPTER TEN

1   World Health Authority, Definition of Health. http://www.who.int

2   *Notes on Current Topics*, The Medical Press, 30 May 1900, p566

3   Report, *Birthday Honours*, British Medical Journal, 26 May 1900, p1309

4   Doolin W, *Admission of Sir John William Moore as Honorary Fellow of the Royal Academy of Medicine in Ireland*, Irish Journal of Medical Science, 1935, p133

5   Moore J W, *Tuberculosis in Ireland*, The Practitioner, 1915 p312

6   Moore J W, in *The Therapeutics of Open Air*, British Medical Journal, 13 Oct 1900, p1096

7   Gatenby P, *Dublin's Meath Hospital,* Dublin, Town House, 1996, p104

8   McKeown T, *The Role of Medicine; Dream, Mirage or Nemesis?* Oxford, Basil Blackwell, 1979

9   Charlton J and Murphy M, Eds, *The Health of Adult Britain 1841 – 1994*, London, Office for National Statistics, vol 1, p20

10 World Health Authority, *Declaration of Alma-Ata, 1978,* http://www. who.int/hpr/docs/almaata.html

11 Leading article, *The National Insurance Act,* The Medical Press, 29 Nov 1911, p568

12 Leading Article, *The National Insurance Bill,* The Medical Press, 17 May 1911

13 Supplement to The Medical Press and Circular, Dec 20 1911, pii

14 Notice, *Resolutions and recommendation of the Royal College of Physicians of London relating to the National Insurance Bill,* The Medical Press, July 26, 1911, p103

15 Digby A, *The Evolution of British General Practice 1850-1948*, Oxford University Press, 1999, p305

16 DOCTOR Magazine, 29 Mar 2001

17 Collings J S, *General Practice in England Today,* The Lancet, 25 Mar 1950, pp555-585

18 Hatfield S J, *A Field Survey of General Practice 1951-2*, British Medical Journal, 26 Sep 1953, pp683-706

19 Horder J P, *Physicians and Family Doctors: a new relationship.* Journal of the Royal College of General Practitioners, 1977, 27, pp391-397

20 LeFanu J, *The Rise and Fall of Modern Medicine.* Little, Brown and Co, London 1999

21 Loudon I, *The tragedy of Childbed Fever,* Oxford University Press, 2000, p208

22 Colebrook L and Kenny M, *Treatment of Human Puerperal Infections, and of experimental infections in mice, with Prontosil,* The Lancet, 6 June 1936, p1283

23 Masters D, *Miracle Drug; the inner history of penicillin.* Eyre and Spottiswoode, London 1946

24 Moore, Sir John, *Some Recent Clinical Records,* Irish Journal of Medical Science, 1922-3, p507-14

25 *Parliamentary Intelligence, (Cost of Insulin)*, The Lancet, 4 Aug 1923, p261

26 Leading article, *Cortisone in the treatment of rheumatism.* British Medical Journal, 7 May 1949, p812

27 Abercrombie G F, *December Fog in London and the Emergency Bed Service*, The Lancet, 31 Jan 1953, p234

28 Charlton and Murphy, op. cit. p194

29 Editorial, *Health costs due to outdoor air pollution by traffic*, The Lancet, 2000, 356, 782-3

30 Kunzli N et al, *Public-health impact of outdoor and traffic related air pollution: a European assessment*, The Lancet, 2000, 356, 795-801

31 Yamey G, *Study shows growing inequalities in health in Britain.* British Medical Journal, 319, 1999, 1453

32 Charlton and Murphy, op. cit. p167

33 Balarajan R, Yuen P and Machin D, *Inequalities in Health: changes in RHAs in the past decade,* British Medical Journal, 294, 1987, 1561

34 West RR and Lowe CR, *Mortality from Ischaemic Heart Disease – Inter-town variation and its association with climate in England and Wales,* International Journal of Epidemiology, vol 5, No 2, p195

35 Law M R and Morris K J, *Why is mortality higher in poorer areas and in more northern areas of England and Wales?* Journal of Epidemiology and Community Health, 1998; 52, 344-52

36 Cancer Trends in England and Wales 1950-1999. National Statistics Internet summary 27.2. 2001

37 Charlton and Murphy, op. cit., vol 1, p96

38 Pereira Gray D, *Feeling at Home, The James Mackenzie Lecture 1977,* Journal of the Royal College of General Practitioners, 1978, 28, 6-17

39 World Health Authority Internet Site, op.cit.

40 WHO Fact Sheet No 154, May 1998

41 WHO Fact Sheet No107, March 2000

42 WHO Fact sheet No 94, October 1998

43 WHO Fact Sheet No 97, 1998

44 British Thoracic Society, Press release, Dec 1999

45 British Thoracic Society, Press release, Feb 2001

46 WHO Fact sheet No 94, October 1998

47 Gro Harlem Bruntland, Speech at New Delhi, India, 6 January 2000, Office of the Director-General of WHO

48 Moore J, *Women's views of the risks and benefits of diagnostic laparoscopy in the investigation of chronic pelvic pain. A thesis submitted for the degree of Master of Science, to the University of Oxford,* Dec 1999, unpublished

49 Moore M S, MD Thesis, Dublin Journal of Medical Science, 1911

50 LeFanu J, op.cit.

51 Andrews S, *Hirudo medicinalis: the medical leech.* Journal of Audiovisual Media in Medicine, Vol 24, No 3, pp126–131

52 Thearle J M, *Leeches in Medicine.* Australia and New Zealand Journal of Surgery, 1998, 68, 292-295

53 Moore J W, *Medical Education and Examination in 1887.* Dublin Journal of Medical Science, vol 85, 1888, p36–46

REFERENCES TO CHAPTER ELEVEN

1 Leading article, *The General Practitioner,* The Dublin Medical Press, July 11 1855, p25

2 Rose F M, *General Practice and Special Practice,* British Medical Journal, Supplement, 27 Oct 1951, p173

3 William Shakespeare, *As You Like It,* Act 2, scene 7

4 Leading article, *The GP at the Crossroads,* British Medical Journal, 25 March 1950, p709

5 Batten L W, *The Essence of General Practice,* The Lancet, 25 Aug 1956, p366

6 Review of General Practice II, *Snapshots of Today,* British Medical Journal, Supplement, 3 Nov 1951, p189

7 Hunt J H, *A College of General Practice,* British Medical Journal, Supplement, 27 Oct 1951, p175

8 Irvine D, *1984: The quiet revolution? The William Pickles Lecture, 1975.* Journal of the Royal College of General Practitioners, 1975, 25, 399-407

9 Petchey R, Williams J and Baker M, *Ending up a GP: a qualitative study of junior doctors' perceptions of general practice as a career.* Family Practice, 1997, Vol 14, No 3, 194-8

10 Lewis M, *Personal View. Should we accept all comers?* British Medical Journal, 1999, 318, 407

11 Loudon I, *The concept of the Family Doctor,* Bulletin of Medical History, 1984, 58, 347-362

12   Loudon I, *The Origin of the General Practitioner. The James Mackenzie Lecture.* Journal of the Royal College of General Practitioners, 1983, 33, p13-18

13   National Association of General Practitioners. *Report of Provisional Committee; National Association of General Practitioners, 3rd Report of Deputation to the Home Secretary, Sir James Graham,* The Lancet, 1 Feb 1845

14   McConaghey R M S, *Proposals to found a Royal College of General Practitioners in the nineteenth century,* Journal of the Royal College of General Practitioners, 1972, 22, 775

15   Leading article, *The General Practitioner,* The Medical Press, 11 July 1855, p25,

16   *Current Topics,* The Medical Press, May 11, 1910, p483

17   MacFeat G, *The Family Doctor,* British Medical Journal, Supplement, 7 July 1951, p1

18   Report, *College of General Practice; more evidence collected.* British Medical Journal, Supplement, 15 Dec 1951, p262

19   Fry J, Lord Hunt of Fawley and Pinsent R J F H, Eds., *A History of the Royal College of General Practitioners,* MTP Press Ltd, 1983

20   Working Party Report, *The Future General Practitioner,* British Medical Journal, for the Royal College of General Practitioners, 1977

21   Royal College of General Practitioners, *Policy Statement 2, 1983,* p9

22   Lewis M, op. cit.

23   Pereira Gray D, *Ten questions about quality,* British Journal of General Practice, Feb 1999, 157 (Back Pages)

24   HRH The Prince of Wales, as President of the RCGP. *The inaugural John Hunt Lecture,* 11 June 1992. Royal College of General Practitioners.

REFERENCES TO CHAPTER TWELVE

1   Housman A E, *On Wenlock Edge,* from *A Shropshire Lad.* The Collected Poems of A.E.Housman, London, Jonathan Cape, 1939, (paperback edition 1967)

2   The remarks attributed to deceased members are based on the author's understanding of their published writings, or his personal knowledge and memory. In the case of the LeFanu brothers they are based on information supplied by Mr Richard LeFanu. Those attributed to living members have been interpreted by the author from contributions made by them at his

request, unless otherwise noted. Any errors in representing their views are entirely the fault of the author

3 Jex-Blake S, *Medical Women; a thesis and a history.* Edinburgh, Oliphant, Anderson and Ferrier, 1886

4 King's and Queen's College of Physicians in Ireland, Minutes 1877, p282

5 Ibid, p298

6 Ibid, p351

7 Le Fanu J, *The Rise and Fall of Modern Medicine.* Little, Brown and Co, London 1999

8 WHO Fact sheet

9 WHO Press release, 16 April 2002

10 Leading article, *Hours, sleep teamwork and stress,* British Medical Journal, 1998, 317, 1335

11 Ogilvie, Sir Heneage, *Whither Medicine?,* The Lancet, 25 Oct 1952, p820

12 McCormick J, *Death of the personal doctor,* The Lancet, 1996, 348; 667–8

13 Smith R, Editorial, *Why are doctors so unhappy?* British Medical Journal, 2001,322, 1073

14 Edwards E, Kornacki MJ and Silversin J, *Unhappy doctors: what are the causes and what can be done?*